70.00

GUIDE TO MICROBIOLOGICAL CONTROL IN PHARMACEUTICALS

ELLIS HORWOOD SERIES IN PHARMACEUTICAL TECHNOLOGY

Editor: Professor M. H. RUBINSTEIN, School of Health Sciences, Liverpool Polytechnic

* In preparation

GUIDE TO MICROBIOLOGICAL CONTROL IN PHARMACEUTICALS

Editors

S. P. DENYER
Department of Pharmaceutical Sciences, University of Nottingham

R. M. BAIRD
formerly NETRHA Pharmaceutical Microbiology Laboratory
St Bartholomew's Hospital, London

ELLIS HORWOOD
NEW YORK LONDON TORONTO SYDNEY TOKYO SINGAPORE

First published in 1990 by
ELLIS HORWOOD LIMITED
Market Cross House, Cooper Street,
Chichester, West Sussex, PO19 1EB, England

A division of
Simon & Schuster International Group
A Paramount Communications Company

Typeset in Times by Ellis Horwood Limited
Printed and bound in Great Britain
by Hartnolls, Bodmin, Cornwall

British Library Cataloguing in Publication Data

Guide to microbiological control in pharmaceuticals
1. Pharmaceutical products. Contamination by
microorganisms
I. Denyer, S. P. II. Baird, R. M.
615.1
ISBN 0–13–372822–6

Library of Congress Cataloging-in-Publication Data

Guide to microbiological control in pharmaceuticals / editors,
S. P. Denyer, R. M. Baird
p. cm. — (Ellis Horwood series in pharmaceutical
technology)
ISBN 0–13–372822–6
1. Drugs — Microbiology. 2. Microbial contamination —
Prevention. 3. Pharmaceutical technology — Quality control.
I. Denyer, S. P. II. Baird, R. M. III. Series: Ellis Horwood
books in biological sciences. Series in pharmaceutical
technology.
[DNLM: 1. Drug Contamination — prevention & control.
2. Drugs — standards. 3. Microbiological Techniques.
4. Pharmaceutical Aids. QV 820 G9461]
RS199.M53G85   1990
615'.19–dc20
DNLM/DLC for Library of Congress   90–4916
                                                      CIP

Table of contents

Preface

In the past, consideration of microbiological problems and their means of control occurred only late in pharmaceutical product design; this has led to inevitable compromises in product quality at all stages of development, manufacture and use. Increasingly sophisticated drug delivery systems are likely to compound further the problems of microbiological integrity, and this coupled with the hardening of regulatory attitudes and increasing consumer awareness means that microbiological problems will assume a new importance. Our current level of understanding does allow us to address many of these problems in advance and thereby to design suitable strategies for their control; to be successful such strategies must be introduced at the earliest stage of product conception. Recent advances in technology, particularly in clean room design and manufacturing equipment, have provided the means to limit product challenge during manufacture to a minimum. In order to exploit these opportunities to the full, a clear appreciation of all aspects of pharmaceutical microbiology is required. Unfortunately relevant information is often concealed within the literature of several disciplines including those of the engineering, food, cosmetic and toiletry industries; in this text we have sought to draw this together in a single volume considering both practical and theoretical aspects.

In recognition of the diverse disciplines involved in pharmaceutical production, a brief introduction to microbiology is presented for the non-microbiologist. We have then brought together those principal aspects of microbiology which are relevant to the pre-formulation, formulation, manufacturing and licence application stages of pharmaceutical production. While attention has been largely focused on the industrial situation much is also of direct relevance to the hospital manufacturing pharmacist. Additionally we anticipate that this guide will have a wider appeal: scientists from other disciplines frequently have to address similar microbiological problems.

Inevitably in a text such as this there are areas of common ground between individual chapters. Where these exist we have attempted to direct the reader's attention through extensive cross-referencing, but without compromising the integrity of individual chapters. Finally, the universal nature of microbiological problems is reflected in the international contributions presented, and whilst necessarily limited in its size and scope, we hope the text has international appeal.

ACKNOWLEDGEMENTS

The editors would like to record their grateful appreciation to the many contributors who found time in their busy schedules to provide the chapters on which this book is built, and to Mrs J. Woodhouse for her much valued secretarial assistance throughout its preparation. Our thanks and gratitude go also to our families, whose support and encouragement greatly assisted us in the book's final construction; without their patient understanding no publication would have emerged.

S. P. Denyer
R. M. Baird

1

Introduction to microbiology

W. B. Hugo†
Formerly Reader in Pharmaceutical Microbiology, Department of Pharmaceutical Sciences, Nottingham University, Nottingham NG7 2RD, UK

† Present address: 618 Wollaton Road, Nottingham NG8 2AA, UK

1   INTRODUCTION

Certain manufactured goods, of which foodstuffs, cosmetics and pharmaceutical products are the prime examples, can be contaminated with micro-organisms during manufacture; this contamination can, at the best, cause spoilage and consequent rejection of the contaminated material and, at the worst, harm or even bring death to the consumer. The culprits are usually bacteria or fungi. At one time, these micro-organisms were both grouped together in the one class of fungi, where bacteria were called fission fungi. We now know that bacteria and fungi differ fundamentally in subcellular anatomy and biologists now assign them to separate groups.

Of contaminants, fungi or moulds will be familiar to all as, often coloured, growth on jams, discarded bread and fruit and even on the leather of boots stored wet in a garden shed. Bacterial contamination may manifest itself as colonies on foodstuffs but is generally not as visually familiar as moulds. A red bacterium, however, later to be named *Chromobacterium prodigiosum* and now *Serratia marcescens*, growing on bread gave rise to many reports of miracles or portents dating back from the third century BC. The amateur wine maker will also be familiar with the ravages wreaked by bacterial contamination of his product.

2   THE GENERAL STRUCTURE OF A BACTERIAL AND FUNGAL CELL

Bacteria are unicellular and can exist as a discrete entity. In the fungi, whereas yeasts are unicellular organisms typically 10 μm in diameter, almost all, if not all, the contaminant moulds grow as filaments or hyphae which may be cross-walled (septate) or as a continuous tube (coenocytic). Both bacterial and fungal cells possess a cell wall which is a rigid structure but with differing chemical constitutions. Here any formal anatomical similarity ends.

2.1   The bacterial cell

Bacteria are small, generally being between 0.75 and 4 μm in length. They are characteristically shaped, and those responsible for spoilage come from groups which are either short cylinders with rounded ends (bacilli) or spherical (cocci). Fig. 1 shows the main features. On, or towards, the outside there is a rigid cell wall which confers the characteristic shape. Chemically this is a complex polymer of sugars, amino sugars and amino acids. Within that lies a non-rigid structure known as the cytoplasmic membrane. This consists of a raft of phospholipid molecules, which are fatty material containing a phosphate group. In this raft float protein molecules which have structural or enzymic functions (Fig. 2). The rest of the cell is known as the cytoplasm. It consists of a viscous fluid in which there is embedded (a) the nucleus, made up of nucleic acids and responsible for directing enzymic and structural protein synthesis and thus controlling the basic characters of the cell, and (b) ribosomes, which are the site of the nucleic acid-directed protein synthesis. In addition, enzymes and substances (often in polymeric form) are found in the cytoplasm; the latter act as reserves for essential materials.

Bacterial cells occur in two structural types known as Gram-positive and Gram-negative Figs 1A and 1B respectively), and no one reading a book on bacteriology

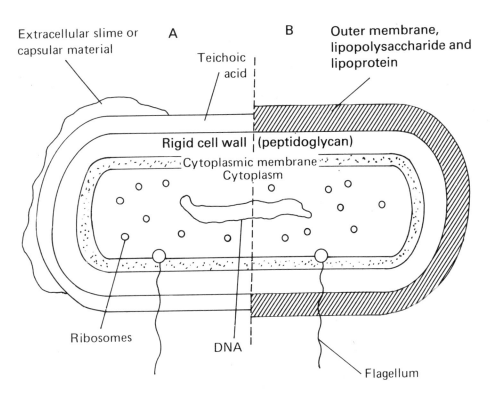

Fig. 1 — Diagram of the main features of the bacterial cell. A, Gram-positive cell; B, Gram-negative cell.

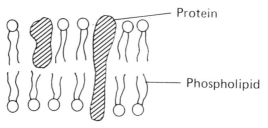

Fig. 2 — Phospholipid bilayer with inserted protein molecules: the structure of many biological cytoplasmic membranes.

will fail to find these terms. The terms positive and negative refer to a staining reaction and the word Gram refers to the discoverer of the method — Christian Gram. A glance at the simplified diagram (Fig. 1) will show that Gram-negative cells have an additional structure, the outer membrane, outside the rigid cell wall; this is lacking in Gram-positive cells. This outer membrane confers the differential staining property and in many cases contains toxic material responsible, if ingested or injected, for disease and elevated temperature (pyrogen). It may also contribute to the resistance of some Gram-negative bacteria towards certain antibacterial agents.

2.2   The fungal cell
Whether unicellular (yeasts) or filamentous with or without cross-walls (moulds), both types of spoilage fungi have a rigid cell wall of cellulose and another polymeric material called chitin, chemically related to the shells of crustaceans. Within this rigid wall lies the cell membrane consisting of phospholipids and proteins. In addition, and here is a fundamental difference from bacteria, the fungal membrane contains sterols. Typical sterols found in fungal membranes are ergosterol and zymosterol.

Lying within this membrane is the cytoplasm. This contains the nuclear material surrounded, unlike bacteria, by a pore-containing nuclear membrane. It directs protein synthesis as in the bacterial cell. Also within the cytoplasm are found the ribosomes, as before, sites of the directed protein synthesis. These ribosomes differ in size and structure from those in bacterial cells.

2.3   Prokaryote and eukaryote
This very brief outline of the structure of a bacterial and fungal cell has drawn attention to fundamental differences between these cell types. These differences, detected by the techniques of subcellular biology, have enabled biologists to suggest a fundamental division in the living world. Bacteria were named prokaryotic organisms or prokaryotes, a name derived from their unenclosed nucleus, and fungi (and, in fact, all other living plants and animals) were called eukaryotic or eukaryotes; they possessed a nuclear membrane. Some of these differences have been summarized in Table 1.

2.4   The bacterial and fungal spore
It is in the spore, which although a word common to both bacterial and fungal morphology, that the largest difference in function between the two groups can be

Table 1 — Some differences between bacterial (prokaryotic) cells and fungal (eukaryotic) cells

Feature	Prokaryote	Eukaryote
Nucleus	One	More than one
Chromosome; nuclear membrane	Absent	Present
Flagella	Simple	Complex
Rigid cell wall	Peptidoglycan	Cellulose, chitin and other polymers
Cytoplasmic membrane	Generally do not contain sterols	Contains sterols
Ribosome	70S[a]	80S[a]
Oxidative phosphorylation	In cytoplasmic membrane	In mitochondria
Mitochondria	Absent	Present

[a]S is a measure of ribosome size (calculated from sedimentation in a centrifuge); 80S ribosomes are larger than 70S.

seen. In brief, bacterial spore formation, which is limited to two genera important in contamination, constitute a survival package which is formed under adverse conditions and from which, when conditions are again suitable, vegetative bacteria arise. Fungal spores, however, are part of the normal life cycle of these organisms.

2.4.1 Bacterial spores

Spore, or endospore, formation in bacilli and clostridia (the two spore-forming bacterial genera of most significance in contamination) is a complicated biochemical and morphological process but the end result is a structure (Fig. 3) which is

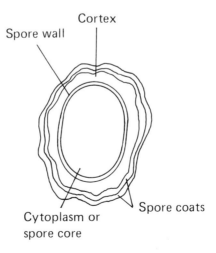

Fig. 3 — Cross-section of a bacterial spore.

significantly more resistant to adverse conditions, e.g. heat, chemicals, desiccation and radiation, than the vegetative cell. In fact, it is the heat resistance of spores which dictates the time/temperature relationships of sterilization processes (see Chapter 7) and disinfection regimens.

Whatever the factor committing bacteria to sporulation the stages in the process appear to be the same for all spore-forming bacteria.

An asymmetric cross-wall develops in the bacterial cell and the nuclear material appears in the smaller compartment called the forespore. This becomes the spore protoplast which then forms the cortical membrane, followed by the cortex and spore coats. With the formation of the cortex and spore coats is seen (a) onset of radiation resistance, and (b) onset of resistance to heat and chemicals.

Parallel with the emergence of resistance, complex biochemical changes occur which include synthesis of spore-specific proteins, cysteine-rich structures and dipicolinic acid and an incorporation of calcium. At the commencement of cortex formation the cells appear more refractile when viewed under the microscope.

Finally the original cell (mother cell as it is called) lyses and the mature spore is released. This is shown diagrammatically in Fig. 4. The site and position of spores in

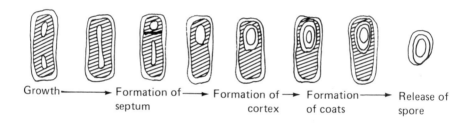

Growth ⟶ Formation of septum ⟶ Formation of cortex ⟶ Formation of coats ⟶ Release of spore

Fig. 4 — Changes occurring during spore formation.

relation to the mother cell varies from species to species of bacteria. Some are terminal to give a drumstick-like appearance, others are median, while others are subterminal; the developing spore may be larger than or equal in size to the original mother cell.

The reverse process to spore formation is termed germination. Some divide the process and call it germination and outgrowth.

Germination may be initiated by a general improvement in the nutritional environment with a more favourable ambient temperature. It may also be triggered by the presence of a specific chemical such as glucose or L-alanine or by sublethal heating (i.e. at 60°C for 60 min). Germination is accompanied by (a) loss of heat resistance and resistance to chemicals, (b) a loss of refractivity (under the microscope), and (c) a release of dipicolinic acid into the surrounding medium. Finally the vegetative cell so formed grows out from the spore — the outgrowth phenomenon (Fig. 5).

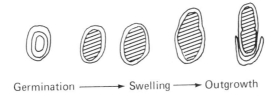

Germination ⟶ Swelling ⟶ Outgrowth

Fig. 5 — Stages of spore germination and outgrowth.

The biochemistry of bacterial spore formation and re-germination and the mechanism of resistance has been the subject of intensive study and publication. For a comprehensive account see Russell (1982).

2.4.2 Fungal spores

Two types of fungal spore are produced, some originating asexually (arthrospores, chlamydospores, conidiospores and sporangiospores) and some sexually (ascospores, basidiospores and zygospores). These are often coloured, furthermore they are resistant to environmental stress and may be carried on air currents in the environment, hence giving rise to further contamination when they alight in favourable situations and germinate. The microscopic structure of fungal fruiting (spore-bearing) bodies is an aid to identification (Fig. 6).

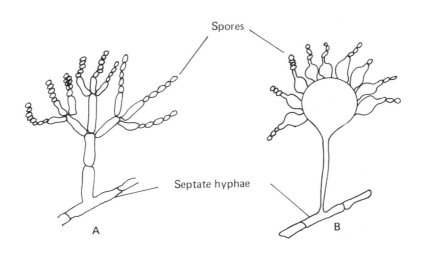

Fig. 6 — Fungal conidiophores bearing asexual reproductive spores of *Penicillium* spp. (A) and *Aspergillus* spp. (B).

3. BACTERIAL AND FUNGAL GROWTH

It is important to realize from the outset that a large number of bacteria and fungi, including many of those associated with contamination, can grow in what may appear to be nutritionally very simple systems and often at quite low temperatures. Cold is not lethal, although growth is slowed at low temperatures. The notion that bacteria and to a lesser extent moulds require a rich and often exotic nutritional environment and careful and controlled incubation at 37°C (bacteria) or 25°C (moulds) arose because of the dominance of medical bacteriology and mycology where such conditions were almost invariably mandatory.

Process water is an acceptable culture medium for many bacteria and to a lesser extent moulds and can be a dangerous commodity in the pharmaceutical, food and cosmetic industries unless carefully handled (see Chapters 2 and 3). The causal organism of Legionnaire's disease grows in water-cooled heat-exchangers (Anon. 1989).

There is, however, for each bacterial and fungal species a set of conditions which are necessary for optimum growth, and if correctly balanced will give maximum yields. It should be realized, however, that while laboratory studies often seek to optimize growth, in the case of contamination conditions may not be optimal but nevertheless may allow growth to proceed, giving rise to spoilage.

3.1   Requirements for growth

These can be divided conceptually into two categories: first, the range of substrates, the consumables needed; and second, the nature of the environment, i.e. temperature, pH, osmotic pressure.

3.1.1   Consumables

It would perhaps be salutary and illustrative of the point made in the opening paragraph of this section to quote a formula which will support the growth of many bacterial and fungal contaminants. It consists of an aqueous solution containing (g/l): $(NH_4)_2HPO_4$, 0.6; KH_2PO_4, 0.4; glucose, 10.0. Growth will be slow and can be enhanced by the presence of trace elements (in addition to those present in the laboratory reagents) and carbohydrates, fats, proteinaceous material, amino acids, sugars, and vitamins such as nicotinic acid, riboflavine and thiamine.

3.1.2   Environmental factors

3.1.2.1   Water

The presence of water is essential and dry products or intrinsically anhydrous material are not liable to spoilage. The drying of foods to preserve them has been exploited by man from very early in history.

The requirement of a micro-organism (bacterial or fungal) for water can be quantified by determining a factor which measures available water in a system and is called its water activity. If the water vapour pressure (P) of the system — a solution or moist semi-solid — is measured and compared with that of pure water under the same conditions (P_0) then

$$\text{water activity} = a_w = \frac{P}{P_0} \tag{1}$$

When culture media are adjusted by means of solutes to known values of a_w it is possible to determine, in general terms, the ability of various groups of organisms to grow at these values (Table 2). The use of syrups, strong solutions of (usually) sucrose, where the water activity is low, has proved valuable in preservation (Cory 1975).

Table 2 — Limiting water activity (a_w) values for a range of micro-organisms

Organism	Limiting a_w for growth
Bacteria in general	0.95–0.92
Micrococci, lactobacilli	0.90
Staphylococcus aureus	0.86
Halophilic bacteria	0.75
Yeasts	0.94–0.88
Moulds	0.93–0.70
Osmophilic yeasts	0.73

3.1.2.2   Gaseous nutrients
Some micro-organisms grow in the absence of oxygen and are termed anaerobic; most, however, require oxygen and are called aerobic. Some bacteria possess the facility to grow in either the absence or presence of oxygen and are termed facultative organisms. In general terms this means that the exclusion of oxygen (air) may not prevent some spoilage organisms from growing.

3.1.2.3   pH
There is an optimum pH range over which micro-organisms can grow (Fig. 7(A)). In particular, bacteria grow best at pH 7.4–7.6 but many moulds can tolerate more acid conditions, pH 5–6. Some micro-organisms are surprisingly tolerant of hostile pH environments and contamination can occur in products where pH is outside the optimum growth value although the growth may be slower.

3.1.2.4   Temperature
As with pH there is an optimum temperature range. Low temperatures will slow growth and raising temperatures will increase growth rate. As the temperature rises above optimum, however, growth is inhibited and micro-organisms are killed, a phenomenon exploited in heat sterilization (see Chapter 7). The effect of temperature on growth is shown in Fig. 7(B).

It is very important to realize that whereas higher temperatures are lethal as

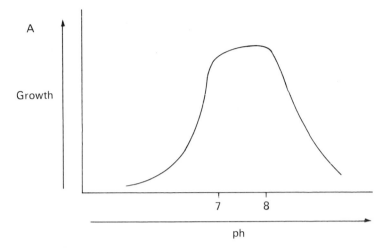

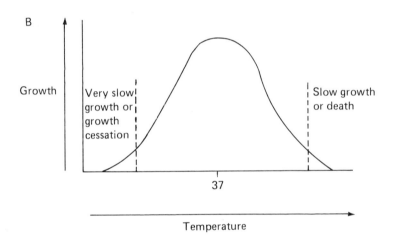

Fig. 7 — Effect of pH (A) and temperature (B) on bacterial growth.

pointed out above, low temperatures are not, and very slow growth may in certain cases occur in refrigerators and even deep-freeze cabinets. Although most human pathogenic bacteria, those of interest in medicine, grow best at the temperature of the human body (37°C), surveys (Skinner 1968) have shown a wide variety of optimum temperature ranges to exist for bacteria. Thus to summarize, bacteria are usually grouped as follows:

(a) Psychrophilic bacteria or psychrophiles; grow best at 15–20°C, can grow at 0–5°C and do not grow above 30°C.

(b) Mesophilic bacteria or mesophiles; grow best at 25–40°C; do not grow above 45°C or below 5°C.

(c) Thermophilic bacteria or thermophiles; grow best at 55°C; some will grow at 80°C; little growth occurs below 25°C.

Many fungi grow best over temperature ranges of 15–25°C, although they can grow at refrigeration temperatures and human pathogens will, of course, grow well at 37°C.

3.2 Measurement of microbial growth

Bacterial and yeast growth under the differing environmental conditions outlined above may be put on a numerical basis by carrying out counts or by other methods of quantifying growth.

(a) *Total counts*. The microbial cells are placed on a counting chamber slide which is engraved with squares of known area and a cover-slip is supported over the grid to give sections of known volume. By counting cells in these sections a calculation can be made of the total cell count. This method cannot distinguish between live and dead cells. It is similar to the haemocytometric method of counting red cells in a sample of blood.

(b) *Viable counts*. Micro-organism-containing material, diluted if necessary, is placed in a solid culture medium and the organisms allowed to grow into visible colonies. The count represents the number of colony-forming units (c.f.u.'s) in the (diluted) sample. The actual count in the original sample is obtained by multiplying the c.f.u.'s by the dilution factor.

(c) *Spectrophotometric method*. A suspension of bacteria or yeasts scatters light. If light is passed through a suspension it is possible to obtain a measure of the cell numbers present by referring to calibration curves in which optical densities are compared to either total or viable counts.

(d) *Total biomass determinations*. In the laboratory situation, microbial growth can be followed by wet or dry weight determinations on samples removed from suspension, or by chemical determination of microbial components, e.g. protein content. These approaches find greatest value in measuring growth of filamentous fungi, as these organisms do not form discrete units as do bacterial or yeast cells.

3.3 The pattern of growth

When bacteria enter a new environment, either deliberately in experimental situations or as a contaminant, the relationship of bacterial growth against time shows a very characteristic pattern (Fig. 8).

At first there is no apparent growth and this is called the lag phase. During this phase it is thought that bacteria are adapting to their environment. Bacterial numbers remain constant and equal to the inoculum number although a few may die. After this period of lag and adaptation, growth proceeds quickly and, in highly favourable circumstances, bacterial cell numbers may double in 20–40 minutes. Here, the relationship between the log of bacterial numbers and time is linear; this phase of growth is called the logarithmic (log) or exponential phase. If nutrients are limited, or are not renewed, growth eventually ceases due to food exhaustion and possible accumulation of inhibitory waste products. Again there is a period when

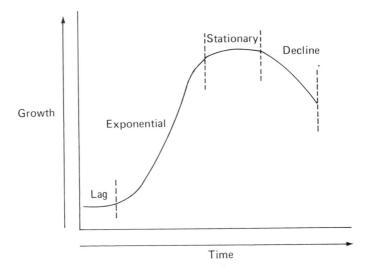

Fig. 8 — Phases of microbial growth.

bacterial numbers do not change. This period is called the stationary phase. Finally numbers of viable organisms are found to fall. This is thought to be due to an exacerbation of the forces which induce to stationary phase. This part of the growth curve is spoken of as the phase of decline or, sometimes, the death phase.

Fungal growth follows a similar pattern. For filamentous fungi, the increase of total cell dry weight is usually used as a measurement of growth.

It should be remembered that fungal hyphae will make their way through their substrate, environment or a contaminated product. These hyphae, when they reach the surface of the material in which they are growing, will form fruiting bodies which are often coloured and which give rise to the familiar visual sign of mould or fungal growth. It is from these aerial bodies that spores can be disseminated to colonize fresh areas (see section 2.4.2).

Over their growth phase, and following changes in their environment, micro-organisms exhibit considerable plasticity which may influence significantly their adaptability and sensitivity to antimicrobial effects.

3.4 Bacterial reproduction

Bacteria grow best if all the conditions — water, nutrients, temperature, pH and osmotic pressure — are optimal. Growth will be inhibited if any of these factors vary from the maximum or if growth inhibitors are present. The process of preservation depends on using suitable growth inhibitors.

Bacteria reproduce by what is called binary fission, i.e. one cell becomes two, two become four, four become eight, and so on. This reproductive pattern does not involve the exchange of genetic material and each cell is a copy or clone of the parent. It is possible to calculate the mean time for the bacterial cells in a culture to duplicate by the pattern of binary fission. If the bacterial numbers at the start are N_0 and, after a given time, t, are determined to be N, then the mean generation time, MGT, is given by the formula

$$MGT = \frac{t \times 0.301}{\log N - \log N_0} \qquad (2)$$

It is possible now to quantify the various factors affecting growth by calculating the MGT for each parameter being investigated.

3.4.1 Genetic exchange

Up to 1928 binary fission was thought to be the only method by which bacteria were able to reproduce genetic information but since that date three methods of reproduction involving genetic exchange have been identified. In 1928, before the role of DNA and the genetic code were elucidated, genetic exchange was found to occur in a culture of an organism called *Diplococcus pneumoniae*; this process was called transformation. In 1946, an active transfer of genetic material via special appendages was discovered and called conjugation. Finally, in 1952, it was discovered that bacterial viruses, known as bacteriophages, could promote genetic exchange; this process was called transduction. These techniques of genetic exchange are responsible for much of the development and emergence of antibiotic-resistant micro-organisms in clinical practice.

However, from the point of view of growth of contaminants binary fission can be considered the method of bacterial reproduction.

3.5 Fungal reproduction

Most filamentous fungi reproduce by both asexual and sexual processes. The most common method of asexual reproduction is by means of spores (see section 2.4.2), contained in sac-like structures called sporangia or borne on hyphal offshoots known as conidiophores (see Fig. 6). Fragmented hyphae may also play a role in propagation. Sexual reproduction requires the union of two compatible nuclei, brought about by the successful elaboration of, and contact between, specialized sex organ structures (gametangia).

Yeast cells commonly reproduce by budding, where a small outgrowth (daughter cell) arises from the parent and, following mitosis, continues to grow until it separates from the parent cell. Occasionally, yeast cells may also reproduce by binary fission as described earlier for bacteria (section 3.4).

3.6 Chemical inhibition and destruction of micro-organisms

Microbial growth can be inhibited by adverse conditions other than a shift from the optimum growth environment. Thus chemical preservatives, and sterilization processes, for example heat, reactive gas or irradiation, can also affect growth and survival, and are exploited in the pharmaceutical, food, environmental and medical fields (see Chapters 7, 8, 10 and 11). Table 3 indicates the regions in the microbial cell which may be the target for growth inhibitory or lethal action. The majority of mechanism of action studies have been performed on bacterial systems.

Table 3 — The site of action of selected chemical and physical antimicrobial agents.

Antimicrobial agent	Possible target(s)
Alcohols	Cytoplasmic membrane permeability
Anilides	Cytoplasmic membrane permeability
Bronopol	Enzymes with thiol groups
Chlorhexidine	Cytoplasmic membrane permeability; general cytoplasm coagulation
Chlorine, chlorine releasers	Bacterial cell wall structure; enzyme thiol groups; amino groups of proteins
Ethylene oxide	Enzyme thiol groups; amino and other groups of proteins
Formaldehyde, formaldehyde releasers	Bacterial cell wall (low concentrations); amino and thiol groups
Glutaraldehyde	Bacterial cell wall; thiol, amino and other reactive groups; general cytoplasm coagulation
Heat: dry	Oxidation
moist	Enzyme denaturation and cytoplasm coagulation
Hydrogen peroxide	Enzyme thiol groups
Irradiation	DNA
Mercury(II) salts, organic mercurials	Bacterial cell wall (low concentrations); enzyme thiol groups; general cytoplasm coagulation
Parabens (p-hydroxybenzoic acid esters)	Cytoplasmic membrane permeability; DNA and RNA synthesis
Phenols, halogenated phenols	Bacterial cell wall (low concentrations); cytoplasmic membrane permeability
Quaternary ammonium compounds	Cytoplasmic membrane permeability
Sorbic acid, other lipophilic weak acids	Cytoplasmic membrane permeability
Sulphur dioxide, sulphites	Enzymes with thiol groups; amino groups of proteins

The difference in the structures of the Gram-negative and Gram-positive bacteria, insofar that the former have an outer membrane (Fig. 1), has an interesting bearing on the resistance of these two groups to biocides. As a general rule, Gram-negative bacteria often show a greater resistance to biocides (antiseptics, disinfectants and preservatives) than do the Gram-positive cells and this is thought to be due to the protective nature of the Gram-negative outer membrane, which acts as an exclusion barrier to biocidal agents. In much the same manner, the bacterial spore is considered to be more resistant than its corresponding vegetative cell through the presence of its spore coats (section 2.4.1).

4   METABOLIC ACTIVITY

Bacteria and fungi possess a remarkable ability to metabolize a very wide range of substances. This metabolic versatility is of paramount importance to microbial survival in and subsequent spoilage of contaminated products. Spoilage is dealt with in detail in Chapter 2. Many of the metabolic pathways are similar to those found in higher animals; some generalized metabolic reactions of bacteria and fungi are given in Fig. 9. These reactions are catalysed by enzymes.

Carbohydrate metabolism

$+C_6H_{10}O_5+n + nH_2O \rightarrow nC_6H_{12}O_6$ hydrolysis

$C_6H_{12}O_6 \rightarrow 2CH_3 \cdot CH_2OH + 2CO_2$ anaerobic respiration

$C_6H_{12}O_6 + 6O_2 \rightarrow 6CO_2 + 6H_2O$ aerobic respiration

Fat metabolism

$$
\begin{array}{ll}
CH_2OOC(CH_2)_n \cdot CH_3 & \qquad\qquad CH_2 \cdot OH \\
| & \qquad\qquad | \\
CHOOC(CH_2)_n \cdot CH_3 \quad +3H_2O \rightarrow & \quad CH \cdot OH \quad + \quad 3CH_3(CH_2)_n \cdot COOH \\
| & \qquad\qquad | \\
CH_2OOC(CH_2)_n \cdot CH_3 & \qquad\qquad CH_2 \cdot OH \qquad\qquad lipolysis
\end{array}
$$

Protein and amino acid metabolism

$+NH \cdot CHR \cdot CO+_n + nH_2O \rightarrow nNH_2 \cdot CHR.COOH$ proteolysis

$NH_2 \cdot CHR \cdot COOH \rightarrow NH_2 \cdot CH_2R + CO_2$ decarboxylation

Fig. 9 — Some examples of generalized metabolic reactions of bacteria and fungi.

4.1 Carbohydrates

Starches and celluloses are converted to glucose, which is then metabolized to substances such as organic acids, aldehydes or alcohols or, in the presence of adequate levels of oxygen, to carbon dioxide and water. The Embden–Meyerhof and Krebs cycles are two well-documented cycles in which living organisms metabolize carbohydrate. Some of the by-products of carbohydrate metabolism during spoilage may acidify or taint the product.

4.2 Fats

These will be converted to glycerol and fatty acids. The latter acidify and taint products containing fatty material when contaminated with lipolytic (fat-splitting) organisms.

4.3 Proteins and amino acids

Proteins may be cleaved to amino acids and these are then decarboxylated to yield evil-smelling amines which will also tend to alkalinize the mixture. Some of the very bad odours of contaminated products are due to this sequence of reactions.

4.4 Preservatives

The antimicrobial agents included to preserve products are not immune from metabolic attack and if their concentration falls, due to instability in storage for instance, they may be metabolized, especially if bacteria of the genus *Pseudomonas* form the contaminating organism (see Chapter 2).

5 PRINCIPLES OF MICROBIAL IDENTIFICATION

Although bacteria are small, when growing in aggregate (colonies) they are readily visible and as such are seen if contaminating solid material or growing on solidified culture media. Similarly, moulds just visible with the naked eye are readily seen if growing in colonies, especially if pigmented spores are present.

Direct observations may be made with the microscope and experts will quickly be able to tell whether bacteria are present as rods or spheres, and if moulds are being examined a good idea of the nature of the mould (fungus) will be obtained from the characteristic shape of hyphae and spore-bearing structures. Ultimate identification, often not necessary in contamination studies, falls within the ambit of the specialist mycologist. With bacteria the performance of special staining techniques, especially the Gram stain, before microscopic examination will enable bacteria to be assigned Gram-positive or Gram-negative.

The metabolic ability of micro-organisms can be exploited in identification. Special culture conditions are devised by which bacteria, and to a lesser extent fungi, can be distinguished by the variance in their reponse to these conditions. In particular, the differing ability of micro-organisms to handle carbohydrates (sugars), i.e. their ability to metabolize them via the Embden–Meyerhof or Krebs cycle pathways, can be used in their identification.

In recent years, newer rapid methods of identification involving specialist immunological techniques, monoclonal antibodies and bioluminescence have been exploited.

5.1 Selective and diagnostic culture media

In the foregoing account it was revealed that (a) bacterial growth may be inhibited by adverse conditions including the presence of toxic chemicals, and (b) that bacteria, by virtue of their biochemical activities, can effect chemical transformations. Both these factors are exploited in the construction of selective and diagnostic media and examples of both approaches will be given here.

Whole texts have been devoted to culture media, and Cowan and Steel's text (see section 8) contains some relevant sections. In addition, the catalogues of media manufacturers such as the Oxoid and Difco companies are very informative.

(a) *Selective media.* These exploit the selective toxicity of added ingredients as well as containing agents which aid further identification. A good example of this type of medium is MacConkey agar. This medium was described in 1905 and evolved to detect organisms in drinking water which might be of faecal origin. It was also designed to distinguish bacteria which could, and could not, ferment lactose. The latter property might indicate the presence of salmonellae: danger-ous intestinal pathogens which could cause, amongst other things, outbreaks of food poisoning. The medium consisted of a nutrient base with the addition of bile salts, lactose and a red dye called neutral red. The bile salts were included to suppress organisms other than those of gut origin, it being argued that bacteria from the gut could survive in the presence of bile.

Those organisms which could ferment lactose acidified the medium and this acidification caused a precipitation of red dye on the colony, which then appeared red. Organisms such as the dangerous salmonellae did not ferment lactose and the colonies remained translucent.

(b) *Diagnostic media.* Bacteria vary in their ability to metabolize a large variety of carbohydrates, typically sugars, but also certain alcohols and glycosides. Diag-nostic schemes for bacteria were thus evolved, based on differential metabolic behaviour on a range of these substances. It was then necessary to differentiate between those organisms which could utilize the various substrates as shown by their conversion to acid products with the possible production of gas.

The routine method used consisted of a container with a growth medium incorporating the substrate concerned and a dye pH indicator; bromocresol purple has been widely used. To detect gas production a very small inverted test tube (Durham tube) was included in the medium and manipulated to ensure it was full of that medium. Any gas produced would collect in the tube and could be easily seen. Current developments in biochemical tests for identification still utilize these basic principles, while presenting the media in more convenient and miniaturized forms.

An excellent colour atlas of micro-organisms (Olds 1975) and their behaviour on selective and diagnostic media has been published.

6. PATHOGENICITY

Historically, micro-organisms have been grouped into pathogenic or non-pathogenic types, according to their ability to cause disease. In recent years increasing interest has also been shown in the so-called opportunist pathogens, capable of causing disease when given the opportunity to do so. These include the free-living Gram-negative bacteria such as pseudomonads and members of the Enterobacteriaceae, for example *Klebsiella* and *Serratia* spp., all of which have simple nutritional requirements, so enabling them to survive in some unlikely environments, including disinfectant and antiseptic solutions. Opportunist pathogens pose a particular threat to certain groups of patients at risk, especially neonates, the elderly and those compromised by trauma, burns or immunosuppressant therapy.

True pathogens, such as *Clostridium tetani* and *Salmonella* spp., rarely occur in pharmaceutical products but inevitably cause serious problems when present. On the other hand opportunist pathogens are much more common contaminants in these products, particularly in aqueous preparations where total viable counts may well exceed 10^6 c.f.u./ml. For a more detailed discussion of this topic, the reader is referred to Chapter 2 and Gilbert (1987).

7   GENERAL PROPERTIES OF SELECTED MICRO-ORGANISMS

The foregoing sections in this chapter have treated the subject of microbiology in a general way, and little mention has been made of specific micro-organisms. The summary below considers some of the micro-organisms of particular interest in the field of pharmaceutical microbiology. It includes not only common spoilage and/or challenge organisms but also some organisms considered to be hazardous if present in pharmaceutical products.

7.1   Gram-negative organisms

7.1.1   *Pseudomonas aeruginosa*

This organism has acquired some notoriety as a contaminant of pharmaceutical products, especially eye preparations (because of its ocular pathogenicity), and above all because of its peculiar resistance to biocides, many of which it is able to metabolize. Widely distributed in the environment, it is a free-living opportunist pathogen and can cause particular problems in susceptible groups of patients, especially neonates, the elderly and the immunocomprised. It is a Gram-negative, flagellated rod-shaped organism which does not form spores. It is aerobic. It does not ferment carbohydrates and thus will not produce gaseous products when growing in the presence of carbohydrates. Under appropriate conditions of growth it may produce a blue or green fluorescent pigment. *Ps. aeruginosa* grows readily on standard laboratory media, but will grow even in distilled water provided *trace* amounts of organic matter are present. As a mesophile, *Ps. aeruginosa* will grow over a temperature range from 20°C to 42°C, with optimal growth occurring at 37°C.

7.1.2 Escherichia coli
This too is a Gram-negative, motile, non-sporing rod typically of dimensions 1 μm × 4 μm and is a member of the Enterobacteriaceae. It differs from *Ps. aeruginosa* in being able to also grow anaerobically. When it grows on carbohydrate it does so by fermentation producing gaseous products. Media with only a single carbon source are sufficient for promoting *E. coli* growth. It can grow at low temperatures and also at temperatures as high as 40°C. Optimal growth occurs at 37°C. It forms part of the gut flora of man; its presence in products is therefore indicative of faecal contamination and gross defects in hygiene.

7.1.3 Salmonellae
These are a large group of Gram-negative rods, closely related to *E. coli*, and may be present in the faecal material of animals or of human carriers of salmonellae. *Sal. typimurium* and *Sal. enteritidis* are both causes of poisoning, and if present in oral pharmaceutical products or foods can give rise to nausea, vomiting and diarrhoea through endotoxin release.

7.1.4 Klebsiella
A member of the Enterobacteriaceae, this genus is represented by *Klebsiella pneumoniae* (but sometimes called *K. aerogenes*) a short (1–2 μm long by 0.5–0.8 μm wide), Gram-negative, non-motile rod, frequently encapsulated with carbohydrate material. The *Klebsiella* are aerobic and usually ferment carobydrates with the production of acid and gas. The optimum temperature for growth is 37°C with limits of 12°C and 43°C. The natural habitat for this genus is the bowel and respiratory tract of humans and animals, and in the environment they are found in soil and water. *Klebsiella* may be a cause of bacteraemia or urinary and respiratory tract infection in humans, especially in hospitalized and immunocompromised patients, and *K. pneumoniae* is responsible for a variety of diseases in animals.

7.1.5 Serratia
Also a member of the Enterobacteriaceae, the genus *Serratia* consists of short (0.5–1.0 μm), motile, Gram-negative rods. They are typically found in soil and water. Generally the optimum temperature for growth is between 30°C and 37°C, but some strains will show growth at temperatures as low as 1°C. Certain strains produce a red pigment (prodigiosin), the production of which is oxygen-dependent and

encouraged at sub-optimal growth temperatures. *Ser. marcescens* may cause bacter-aemia and localized infections in the urinary and respiratory tracts and in wounds; most infections occur in hospitalized patients.

7.2 Gram-positive organisms

7.2.1 Staphylococcus aureus
This is a Gram-positive spherical organism of approximately 1 μm diameter. It is non-motile and does not form spores. It is able to grow aerobically and anaerobically and will grow readily in a chemically defined medium containing glucose, essential salts, selected amino acids, thiamine and nicotinic acid (Davis *et al.* 1980; Jassim *et al.* 1989). It is relatively resistant to antimicrobial preservatives such as phenol, can remain alive at temperatures as cold as 4°C and as warm as 60°C, and will grow in media containing up to 10% sodium chloride.

It, and the closely related *Staph. epidermidis*, if present in pharmaceutical products may indicate contamination from a human source, for example from the hands, skin or hair. *Staph. aureus* is a common cause of boils, middle ear infection, pneumonias and osteomyelitis. It can proliferate in foods secreting an exotoxin which can give rise to food poisoning.

7.2.2 Bacillus cereus *and* Bacillus subtilis
These are Gram-positive, spore-forming, rod-shaped organisms, usually motile. *B. cereus* can grow anaerobically while *B. subtilis* cannot. These organisms, if present in pharmaceutical products, are indicative of dust contamination. Therefore, any structural alterations to buildings or uncontrolled sweeping may give rise to these contaminants appearing in pharmaceutical products. *B. cereus* can cause intestinal poisoning.

7.2.3 Clostridia
The clostridia are Gram-positive, rod-shaped bacteria which produce spores. They are strict anaerobes, although a few species will tolerate the presence of oxygen; most will ferment carbohydrates. They are found widely distributed in nature, in the soil and alimentary tract of man and animals. *Clostridium perfringens* (*welchi*), *Cl. tetani* and *Cl. botulinum* are pathogens causing gas-gangrene wound infection, tetanus and botulism food poisoning, respectively. Owing to their ubiquitous presence in the environment clostridia, and in particular clostridial spores, can be found as contaminants in pharmaceutical products.

7.3 Fungi

7.3.1 Aspergillus niger
This organism grows only in the filamentous (mycelial) form and is familiar to most people as a white, turning to black, disc of growth on jams and other exposed foodstuffs. Colonies grow over a wide temperature range, up to 50°C, although optimal temperature for growth is at 24°C. Under the microscope the characteristic fruiting bodies (Fig. 6), which when formed are responsible for the colour change from white to black, may be seen.

Spores of *Aspergillus* are commonly present in air and can infest and germinate in pharmaceutical and cosmetic products causing discoloration and spoilage. They are generally not as resistant to antimicrobial agents as are bacterial spores. Some *Aspergillus* strains produce characteristic poisons, the aflatoxins.

7.3.2 Candida albicans
This is a pathogenic yeast, causing oral and vaginal thrush. It readily grows on conventional mycological media at room temperature (optimal growth at 25°C) or at 37°C. It is dimorphic, growing first as yeast cells, but with ageing will form chlamydospores, which are more difficult to destroy. There are no temperature tolerance differences between the two forms. Viewed microscopically, it appears to possess septate hyphae, known as pseudo-mycelia, amongst the yeast-like cells. It is unpigmented and colonies have a creamy-white appearance.

7.3.3 Zygosaccharomyces rouxii
This is another species of yeast which has the property of being able to grow in liquids and gels of high osmotic pressure. It is non-pathogenic but can cause spoilage if it infests pharmaceutical and toilet products.

8 REFERENCES
Anon (1989) Report of the expert advisory committee on biocides, HMSO, London.
Corry, J. E. L. (1975) The water relationships and heat resistance of micro-organisms. *Prog. Ind. Microbiol.* **17** 73–108.
Davis, B. D., Dulbecco, R., Eisen, H. N. and Ginsberg, H. S. (1980) *Microbiology*, 3rd edn. Harper and Row, Hagerstown, MD.
Gilbert, P. (1987) Principles of microbial pathogenicity and epidemiology. In: Hugo, W. B. and Russell, A. D. (eds), *Pharmaceutical microbiology*, 4th edn. Blackwell Scientific Publications, Oxford, pp, 83–97.
Jassim, S., Salt, W. G. and Stretton, R. J. (1989) *In vitro* studies of haemolysis by some staphylococci grown in chemically defined media. *J. Appl. Bacteriol.* **67** 511–520.
Olds, R. J. (1975) *A colour atlas of microbiology*. Wolfe Publishing, London.
Russell, A. D. (1982) *The destruction of bacterial spores*. Academic Press, London.
Skinner, F. A. (1968) The limits of bacterial existence. *Proc. R. Soc. B* **171** 77–89.

9 FURTHER READING
The following texts provide comprehensive accounts of general microbiology and bacteriology, identification methods and biochemistry.

Bergey's manual of systematic bacteriology, 9th edn (1984) Williams and Wilkins, Ancaster, Ontario.
Cowan, S. T. (1974) *Cowan and Steel's manual for the identification of medical bacteria*, 2nd edn. Cambridge University Press, Cambridge.
Hugo, W. B. and Russell, A. D. (1987) *Pharmaceutical microbiology*, 4th edn. Blackwell Scientific Publications, Oxford.
Stryer, L. (1988) *Biochemistry*, 3rd edn. W. H. Freeman, San Francisco.
Wilson, Sir G. S. and Miles, Sir A. (1983–1984) *Topley and Wilson's principles of bacteriology and immunity*, 7th edn, vols 1–4. Edward Arnold, London. (8th edition in preparation).

2

Microbial contamination: spoilage and hazard

S. F. Bloomfield
King's College London, Chelsea Department of Pharmacy, Manresa Road,
London, SW3 6LX, UK

1. INTRODUCTION

Any pharmaceutical product, whether manufactured in the hospital or industrial environment, has the potential to be contaminated with micro-organisms which may include bacteria, yeasts or moulds. Microbial contamination may originate from the raw materials or may be introduced during manufacture. Products may also become contaminated during storage and use.

Microbial contamination in pharmaceutical products represents a potential hazard for two reasons. First, it may cause product spoilage; the metabolic versatility of micro-organisms is such that any formulation ingredient from simple sugars to complex aromatic molecules may undergo chemical modification in the presence of a suitable organism. Spoilage will not only affect therapeutic properties but may also discourage patient compliance. Second, product contamination represents a health hazard to the patient, although the extent of the hazard will vary from product to product and patient to patient, depending on the types and numbers of organisms present, the route of adminstration and the resistance of the patient to infection.

The most logical approach to minimizing the microbial hazard would be to specify that all products are manufactured as sterile products in single-dose packs. Although products introduced into sterile areas of the body, or those coming into contact with the eye or products applied to broken skin and mucous membrane, are manufactured in a sterile form, sterility is deemed neither appropriate nor commercially viable for oral or other topical products at the present time. Thus an acceptable level of microbial quality assurance needs to be established for such products.

However, in attempting to set suitable microbial limits or standards, we are faced with the problem that, because of the multiple and varied factors involved, we cannot define precisely what level and types of contamination represent a hazard and what is safe — nor are we ever likely to. Thus by limiting microbial contamination we are merely reducing the risks of infection and spoilage to a level dictated by our current knowledge and the financial resources available.

In this chapter, current knowledge of microbial contamination of pharmaceutical products and the associated hazards are reviewed. Earlier reviews on this subject are given by Smart and Spooner (1972), Beveridge (1975, 1987), Baird (1988) and Spooner (1988).

2 CONTAMINATION OF PHARMACEUTICAL PRODUCTS

During the 1960s, mainly due to concern over the growing number of reported outbreaks of infection attributed to contaminated pharmaceuticals and cosmetics, a number of studies were initiated to assess the extent of the problem and to make recommendations. In the UK two studies were initiated, one by the Public Health Laboratory Service (PHLS) to investigate hospital medicaments, and the other by the Pharmaceutical Society (PSGB) to study both products and raw materials (Anon. 1971a, 1971b). The object of these studies was to assess the general microbial quality of manufactured products and to identify the sources of product contamination. Extensive investigations were also undertaken in other European countries (most notably Sweden) and the USA. The overall results of these studies are summarized in Table 1. Of the 6700 samples examined, about 27% were found to

Table 1 — Survey of microbial quality of pharmaceuticals, toiletries and cosmetics

Reference		Type of product	Number investigated	Number contaminated
Baker	(1959)	Toiletries	5	2 (40%)
Kallings et al.	(1966)	Pharmaceuticals	134	91 (68%)
Ulrich	(1968)	Pharmaceuticals	696	535 (76%)
Hirsch et al.	(1969)	Pharmaceuticals	57	47 (82%)
Wolven and Levenstein	(1969)	Cosmetics	250	61 (24%)
Dunnigan and Evans	(1970)	Cosmetics	169	33 (20%)
Anon.	(1971a)	Pharmaceuticals	1220	390 (31%)
Beveridge and Hope	(1971)	Pharmaceuticals	138	58 (42%)
Robinson	(1971)	Pharmaceuticals	279	85 (30%)
Wolven and Levenstein	(1972)	Cosmetics	228	8 (3%)
Ahearn et al.	(1973)	Cosmetics	200	3 (2%)
Baird et al.	(1976)	Pharmaceuticals	499	46 (9%)
Awad	(1977)	Pharmaceuticals	911	109 (13%)
Awad	(1977)	Pharmaceuticals	247	79 (32%)
Awad	(1977)	Pharmaceuticals	110	31 (28%)
Awad	(1977)	Pharmaceuticals	1462	184 (13%)
Baird	(1977)	Cosmetics	147	48 (32%)
Wallhaeusser	(1978)	Pharmaceuticals	17	12 (70%)
Total			6764	1814 (27%)

contain detectable contamination, although contamination rates varied from 2% to 82% according to product type. Contamination levels for individual samples ranged from less than ten organisms per sample up to 10^5–10^6 organisms per gram or per millilitre. Typical results from the PHLS survey (Table 2) showed that, although the

Table 2 — Contamination rates for manufactured pharmaceutical products (PHLS survey, Anon. 1971a)

Product type	Total percentage contaminated	Percentage contaminated with $>10^5$ g^{-1} or ml^{-1}
Aqueous	35%	22%
Gels	34%	15%
Oily	26%	10%
Dry	33%	7%
Spirits	3%	3%
Total	32%	18%

overall contamination rate was similar for aqueous, gel, oily and dry products, the frequency of heavy contamination was related to water availability in the product.

For the 6000 or more samples where isolates were identified, the majority were found to be Gram-positive bacilli and micrococci; these organisms are generally regarded as non-pathogenic. Yeasts and moulds were also commonly found, mainly in creams and ointments. Of the species regarded as potentially pathogenic (Table 3) *Pseudomonas aeruginosa* and other pseudomonads were most frequently isolated. Other reported contaminants included species of *Alcaligenes, Flavobacterium, Acinetobacter, Achromobacter, Serratia* and *Citrobacter*.

Table 3 — Contaminants isolated from 6068 pharmaceutical, cosmetic and toiletry products during surveys carried out from 1959 to 1979[a]

Contaminant	No. isolates
Ps. aeruginosa	46
other pseudomonads	36
E. coli	6
Staphylococcus aureus	2
Salmonella spp.	Nil
Enterobacter spp.	5
Klebsiella spp.	6
Proteus spp.	1

[a]As described in Table 1.

3   SOURCES OF MICROBIAL CONTAMINATION IN PHARMACEUTICAL PRODUCTS

In order to optimize methods for controlling microbial contamination of pharmaceuticals, it is necessary to understand the sources and routes from which contamination may originate. Microbial contamination from raw materials will invariably be transferred to the product, whilst further contamination may be introduced from the manufacturing equipment and environment, from the process operators and from packaging materials.

In general dry powders of synthetic origin used as raw materials in pharmaceuticals yield low bacterial counts, the organisms present being mainly aerobic spore-bearers. In contrast, dry powders of natural origin may be heavily contaminated, often with Gram-positive spore-formers and moulds, but on occasions also with coliforms and Gram-negative species (Westwood and Pin Lim 1971; Anon. 1971a, 1971b). By far the most common source of spoilage or pathogenic species is water or unpreserved stock solutions; for example, solutions such as peppermint water may become heavily contaminated with Gram-negative organisms if not properly prepared or if incorrectly stored. Typical Gram-negative water-borne species which may grow, even in distilled water, include *Acinetobacter, Achromobacter, Enterobacter, Flavobacterium* and *Pseudomonas*; species of enteric origin such as *Escherichia coli* and *Salmonella*, although not free-living, may survive for substantial periods in polluted water. Microbial contamination of raw materials including water is discussed in more detail in Chapter 3.

Contamination arising from manufactuiring and filling plant which comes into direct contact with the product must also be carefully controlled. Growth of contaminants, most particularly Gram-negative bacteria, readily occurs in dead spaces (joints and valves, etc.) where water and product residues accumulate; once established this contamination can be very persistent and difficult to eliminate.

Although contamination from the manufacturing environment is considered less important, since it is not in direct contact with the product, there is clear evidence that transfer can occur where control is not properly implemented. In a study of a hospital manufacturing unit (Baird *et al.* 1976), *Ps. aeruginosa* was isolated from products manufactured in the pharmacy. Isolation of the same strain of this organism from environmental sites within the pharmacy indicated that this was the source of contamination in many products. When strict environmental control procedures were implemented, the product isolation rate for *Ps. aeruginosa* fell to 2–3%.

Environmental contaminants of dry surfaces such as floors and walls comprise mainly Gram-positive rods, cocci and fungal spores. Gram-negative bacteria are more susceptible to the lethal effects of drying, but small numbers may persist on dry surfaces for substantial periods (Scott and Bloomfield 1990). In wet areas such as sinks and drains, particularly where stagnant water accumulates, typical water-borne species such as *Pseudomonas* and *Acinetobacter* can readily survive and grow. Airborne contamination is mainly associated with dust and skin scales and is again mostly mould and bacterial spores and skin cocci. The reader is referred to Chapter 3 for a more detailed discussion of environmental contamination.

Contamination from process operators must be considered as a significant hazard. During normal activity, loss of skin scales by shedding is about 10^4 per minute; a large proportion of these skin scales will be contaminated with species of the normal skin flora. These are mainly non-pathogenic micrococci, diphtheroids and staphylococci but may also include *Staphylococcus aureus* as part of the normal skin flora. Other organisms (e.g. *Salmonella* and *E. coli*), which are not part of the resident flora, may also be carried transiently on the skin surface where poor hygienic practices exist amongst operators; potentially these could be shed into the product via skin scales or direct contact. Control of manufacturing contamination is further discussed in Chapters 3, 4 and 5.

Product containers and closures must be bacteriologically clean. They should be adequately designed and constructed to protect the product. This is of particular importance with sterile fluids. Felts *et al.* (1972) reported contamination of intravenous fluids with species of *Erwinia, Enterobacter* and *Pseudomonas*. It was subsequently found that the space between the infusion bottle cap and neck had become contaminated when bottles were spray-cooled with tap water following sterilization. In another reported incident (Phillips *et al.* 1972), contamination of infusion fluids was traced to spray-cooling water contaminated with *Ps. thomasii* gaining ingress to infusion bottles. Further experiments demonstrated that small amounts of water became trapped above the rubber bung and in the screw threads of the bottle necks (Coles and Tredree 1972). Robertson (1970) reported contamination of glucose saline infusion with *Trichoderma* and *Penicillium* spp. caused by use of cracked infusion bottles. Similar problems were also reported by Sack (1970) and Daisy *et al.* (1979).

In addition to contamination arising from raw materials and during manufacture, products may become contaminated during storage and use. Types and levels of 'in-use' contamination are almost impossible to predict and only limited published data are availabe. Topical products, especially those packed in pots, are at particular risk; Baird *et al.* (1979a) carried out a study of 'in-use' contamination of topical medicaments used for treatment of pressure sores. In samples taken from two hospitals, 20–25% were found to be contaminated with *Ps. aeruginosa* (counts ranging from 10^2 to 10^6 c.f.u. g^{-1}) and 21–59% with *Staph. aureus* (counts ranging from 10^2 to 10^4 c.f.u. g^{-1}). In a third hospital these organisms were not isolated from any products. On further investigation it was found that in the former hospitals nurses removed creams from containers with their bare hands, whilst in the third hospital medicaments were removed from pots with spatulae and applied with gloved hands. Introduction of this procedure combined with the use of products packed in tubes caused isolation rates to fall to 0.4% and 5% for *Ps. aeruginosa* and *Staph. aureus*, respectively. In a similar study of topical medicaments used by patients in a skin diseases hospital, it was found that 73% of 41 samples of emulsifying ointment were contaminated with *Ps. aeruginosa*, with counts ranging from 10^4 to 10^6 c.f.u. g^{-1} (Baird *et al.* 1980). *Proteus* spp. and *Staph. aureus* were also isolated from some samples. Savin (1967) reported a study of 194 pots of creams and ointments of which six were found to contain skin flora and three contained coliforms which were not present in samples from the pharmacy.

In-use contamination of ophthalmic ointments was studied by comparing open and unused tubes. Only one out of 24 unused tubes was contaminated, whilst 18 of the 50 used tubes contained organisms which include *Staph. epidermidis*, *Staph. aureus* and fungi (Lehrfeld and Donnelly 1948).

Contamination of oral medicaments in use in the hospital environment was studied by Baird and Petrie (1981). Of 445 products sampled, 25.6% were found to be contaminated, mainly with aerobic Gram-positive rods, although Gram-positive cocci and Gram-negative rods were found in 2.9% and 3.1% of samples, respectively. Most of the Gram-negative isolates were identified as *Pseudomonas* spp. but in this survey *Ps. aeruginosa* was not found. Viable counts varied between 10^2 and more than 10^6 c.f.u. ml^{-1}. A survey of microbial contamination of pharmaceutical products in the home was reported by Baird *et al.* (1979b). Viable organisms were recovered from 14% of 1977 samples examined. One problem encountered in these two latter surveys was the lack of information on microbial quality of samples at the time of issue but it was generally concluded that medicines used in the home were less vulnerable to contamination than those used in hospitals.

Whereas contamination of sterile products during manufacture is now rarely a problem, contamination of intravenous fluids and apparatus during clinical use is still known to occur. From a literature survey (1971–1983), Denyer (1984) concluded that 'in-use' contamination of intravenous fluids from bottled containers and collapsible plastic containers was of the order of 4.3% and 2.6%, respectively, although in general the organisms were present in low numbers.

In evaluating the results of 'in-use' surveys of microbial contamination, it must be borne in mind that contamination levels in used products reflect not only the bioburden introduced by the patient but also the survival characteristics of the contaminant in the product.

4 FACTORS WHICH AFFECT SURVIVAL AND GROWTH OF ORGANISMS IN PRODUCTS

The microbial quality of pharmaceuticals is determined not only by the types and levels of organisms introduced during manufacture, storage and use, but also by their subsequent behaviour within the product. Whereas small numbers of organisms introduced into a product during manufacture or use may be of little consequence to the patient, where these organisms undergo subsequent multiplication within the product the infection hazard will be significantly increased. Guyne (1973) and Felts *et al.* (1972) demonstrated that when small numbers of species such as *E. coli, Ps. aeruginosa, Klebsiella pneumoniae, Staph. aureus* and *Staph. epidermidis* were introduced into intravenous solutions of saline, Ringer–lactate and 5% dextrose, Gram-negative bacilli increased in population over 24 hours whereas Gram-positive cocci remained stationary or died off. In all cases of growth, bacterial counts of 10^6 c.f.u. ml^{-1} were recorded although the solutions showed no visible turbidity.

Many physicochemical factors can affect the fate of micro-organisms entering a product; in practice many products are self-preserving such that residual contamination is reduced to undetectably low levels during storage.

As micro-organisms have an absolute requirement for water, water activity and water availability have a profound effect on survival and growth. Although dry products are less susceptible than aqueous products, contamination and spoilage of solid dosage forms has been reported in the literature on a number of occasions (Kallings *et al.* 1966; Lang *et al.* 1967; Komarmy *et al.* 1967; Eikhoff 1967; Beveridge 1975). Factors affecting survival and growth of microbial contaminataion in solid oral dosage forms has been studied by Blair (1989).

Since micro-organisms grow optimally at neutral or near neutral pH formulations which are acid or alkaline in character are obviously less prone to spoilage. Other factors to be considered are nutrient availability, osmotic pressure, surface tension, oxygen and nutrient availability (see Chapter 1). The potential for exploitation of the self-preserving properties of pharmaceutical formulations is illustrated by the results of the PHLS survey (Anon. 1971a); in general, it was found that low microbial counts were associated with products of low water availability, low pH and high sucrose content.

5 MICROBIAL SPOILAGE OF PHARMACEUTICAL PRODUCTS

The ability of micro-organisms to produce degradative spoilage in products depends on their ability to synthesize appropriate enzymes. The fact that pharmaceuticals, cosmetics, foods and other products are so much at risk stems from the fact that micro-organisms are extremely versatile and adaptive in their ability to synthesize degradative enzymes. It should be noted, however, that within the whole range of organisms (bacteria, yeasts and moulds) degradative ability varies considerably such that certain species are frequently involved, others only rarely so. Degradative half-lives for individual formulation constituents can vary from a few hours up to several months or even years depending on the nature of the molecule, the product environment, the numbers and types of organisms present and whether initially produced metabolites support further growth.

Low-molecular-weight substrates such as sugars, amino acids, organic acids and glycerol are broken down by primary catabolic pathways (see Chapter 1). The enzymes for these pathways are constitutive in a wide range of organisms. Most compounds of pharmaceutical interest are, however, high-molecular-weight or aromatic molecules and are more resistant to degradation such that the enzymes responsible are produced by a smaller range of organisms.

Breakdown of proteins, polysaccharides and lipids is brought about by proteinases and peptidases, polysaccharidases and lipases, respectively (see Chapter 1). Many of these enzymes have low substrate specificity and will attack a wide range of compounds within the group. Polysaccharidases capable of hydrolysing starch, agar and cellulose are produced by a range of organisms including *Bacillus, Pseudomonas* and *Clostridium*. Production of α-amylase is particularly prevelant in *Bacillus* spp. These species, together with *Aspergillus* and *Penicillium* spp., are the most common source of proteinase and peptidase enzymes causing breakdown of compounds such as gelatin. Production of lipase is less widely distributed and occurs most commonly amongst moulds — hence the reason that spoilage of creams and emulsions is generally due to mould growth.

The ability of certain organisms to degrade aromatic compounds and long-chain hydrocarbons is remarkable since these types of molecules are stable to attack by many chemically active agents. This property is, however, restricted to a limited group of bacteria, the most notable being the pseudomonads and related Gram-negative species, and some fungi. The capacity to degrade aromatic compounds is due to the synthesis of oxygenase enzymes which catalyse direct incorporation of oxygen into the substrate molecule. For aromatic molecules, introduction of hydroxyl groups, catalysed by oxygenase enzymes, affects the stable resonance of the benzene ring, thus making it more susceptible to attack by further oxygenase enzymes which catalyse ring opening. The ring fission products are then further metabolized, producing intermediates of the tricarboxylic cycle which are in turn metabolized via that cycle. The probable pathway for degradation of acetylsalicylic acid by *Acinetobacter lwoffii*, as elucidated by Grant *et al.* (1970), is illustrated in Fig. 1.

Product spoilage arising from enzymatic degradation can manifest itself in a number of ways. Breakdown of the active ingredient will cause a loss of potency. Alternatively degradation of formulation components may occur which may be associated with inefficient dosage delivery and reduced bioavailability. Observable formulation breakdown, such as production of pigments and noxious odours, will make the product unacceptable to the patient. Microbial activity in the product can also result in production of potentially harmful toxins or the degradation of preservatives allowing growth of other contaminant species.

5.1 Breakdown of active ingredients

Laboratory experiments demonstrate the range of therapeutic agents which may be degraded by microbial enzymes. Degradation of antibiotics, particularly the degradation of penicillin by β-lactamase, has been extensively studied, as reviewed by Franklin and Snow (1989). Microbial enzymes which degrade chloramphenicol have been known since 1949 (Smith and Worrel 1949) Laboratory studies of microbial degradation of compounds such as aspirin, phenacetin and paracetamol (Grant 1970,

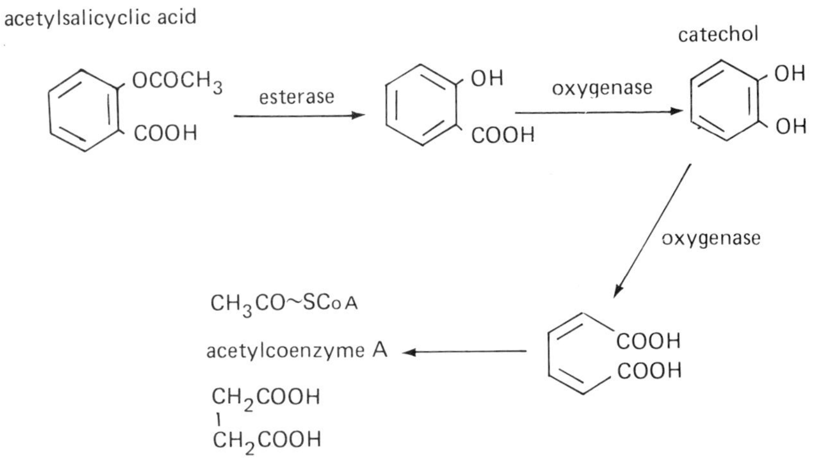

Fig. 1 — Probable pathway for breakdown of acetylsalicylic acid by *Acinetobacter lwoffii*.

1971; Grant and Wilson 1973; Hart and Orr 1974), alkaloids (Bucherer 1965; Grant 1973; Kedzia *et al*. 1961), thalidomide (Mitvedt and Lindstedt 1970) and steroid esters (Cox and Sewell 1968; Brookes *et al*. 1982) have been reported in the literature. In some cases the degradative pathways have been elucidated. Reports of microbial transformations of biologically active molecules in formulated products have been recently reviewed by Denyer (1988) as shown in Table 4.

Table 4 — Microbial transformations of biologically active compounds in formulated products

Product	Transformation	Organisms	Reference
Syrup of Tolu	Cinnamic acid→ toluene-like product	*Penicillium* spp.	Wills (1958)
Atropine eye-drops	Loss of atropine	*Corynebacterium* spp. *Pseudomonas* spp.	Kedzia *et al*. (1961), Beveridge (1975)
Belladonna and ipecacuanha paediatric mixture BPC	Loss of atropine	Mixed flora	Beveridge (1975)
Aspirin mixture	Aspirin hydrolysis	—	Beveridge (unpublished)
Paracetamol mixture	Paracetamol degradation	—	Beveridge (unpublished)
Aspirin and codeine tablets BP	Aspirin hydrolysis	—	Denyer (unpublished)
Prednisolone tablets	Localized steroid transformation	*Aspergillus* spp.	Beveridge (1987, and unpublished)
Hydrocortisone cream	Hydrocortisone androst-4-ene-11-ol-3: 17 dione	*Cladosporium herbarum*	Cox and Sewell (1968)
Rose-hip preparation	Destruction of vitamin C	Anaerobic bacteria	Beveridge (unpublished)

Reprinted with permission of Elsevier Applied Science from Denyer (1988).

5.2   Production of toxins

Some species of micro-organisms are capable of releasing toxic metabolites which may render the product dangerous to the patient. Probably the most important of these in relation to pharmaceutical products are pyrogens. These are mainly lipopolysaccharide components of Gram-negative bacterial cell walls which can cause acute febrile reactions if introduced directly into the bloodstream. These toxins are heat-stable and may be present even when viable organisms are no longer detectable. They are, however, only poorly adsorbed via the gastrointestinal tract and are therefore of little importance in oral preparations.

Bacterial toxins which are associated with acute food-poisoning outbreaks have not been reported in pharmaceuticals, although the presence of toxin-producing *Bacillus cereus* (Arribas *et al.* 1988) and aflatoxin-producing *Aspergillus flavus* (Hikoto *et al.* 1978) has been detected. It has been shown experimentally that pharmaceutical starches can support the formation of mycotoxins when artificially inoculated with toxigenic strains of *Aspergillus* (Fernandez and Genis 1979). Toxin production in pharmaceuticals has been further discussed by Wallhaeusser (1977).

5.3   General formulation breakdown

Spoilage is usually observed as the result of a general breakdown of the formulation. Complex formulations are particularly prone to this type of spoilage, which may involve phenomena such as cracking or creaming of emulsions, viscosity changes, or separation of suspended material. Practical observations of formulation breakdown, as reviewed by Denyer (1988), are shown in Table 5. These changes will not only make the product aesthetically unacceptable but can also affect dosage delivery through separation of suspended particles or an emulsified oily phase, or the alteration of drug release characteristics from surface-damaged tablets. Physico-chemical changes may in turn be the effect of many different degradative events within the product.

5.3.1   Degradation of surfactants

Many of the surfactants used in pharmaceutical emulsions are subject to microbial degradation, particularly the non-ionic surfactants. Ability to degrade surfactant molecules is again limited to a small range of organisms, particularly the pseudo-monads. Susceptibility to biodegradation depends on the chemical structure, biodegradability decreasing as the length of the hydrocarbon chain and the degree of chain branching increases. Formulations containing anionic surfactants are normally quite well protected because of the alkaline nature of the formulation. Nevertheless alkyl and alkylbenzene sulphate and sulphonate esters can be hydrolysed to the corresponding alcohol, which is then converted to a fatty acid. ω-Oxidation of the terminal methyl group is then followed by β-oxidation of the hydrocarbon chain and fission of aromatic rings.

Many non-ionic surfactants are found to be biodegradable; although degradation pathways may not have been elucidated, these generally involve hydrolytic and oxidative pathways. Biodegradation of surfactants has been reviewed by Swisher (1987).

Table 5 — Products suffering observable degradative changes following microbial contamination

Type of product	Examples	Observed change	Spoilage organisms	Reference
Solutions and mixtures	Simple aqueous solutions	Turbidity	Algae, moulds, bacteria, yeasts	Smart and Spooner (1972)
	Concentrated dill water	Visible growth	*Penicillium roqueforti*	Parker and Barnes (1967)
	Indigestion mixtures	Colour change (white to black)	Sulphate reducers	Spooner (1988)
	Magnesium hydroxide antacids	Ammoniacal odours	Coliforms	Robinson (1971)
Suspending/ thickening agents	Carboxymethyl-cellulose gels/ lubricants	Loss of viscosity	*Trichoderma* spp.	Beveridge (1975)
	Starch, tragacanth, acacia mucilages	Loss of viscosity	—	Beveridge (1975)
	Tragacanth mucilage	Fermentation (alcohol and gas)	Yeasts	Denyer (unpublished)
Syrups	Syrup BP	Fermentation	Osmotolerant yeasts	Westwood and Pin-Lim (1971)
	Syrup-containing cough remedies	Microbial deposits	Osmotolerant moulds	Smart and Spooner (1972)
Emulsions	Oil–water olive oil emulsions	Separation of phases, discolo-ration, unplea-sant taste and smell	*Trichoderma viride*, *Ps. aeruginosa*, *Asp. flavus*, *Asp. niger*.	Beveridge (1975)
Creams	Calamine	Visible growth	Mould	Smart and Spooner (1972)
	Cosmetic	Visible surface growth	*Penicillium* spp.	Parker and Barnes (1967)
Tablets	Aspirin and codeine BP	Surface discoloration and acetic acid smell	—	Denyer (unpublished)
	Nitrazepam	Discoloration, strange smell	Mould	Anon (1983)
	Prednisolone	Surface discoloration	*Aspergillus* spp.	Beveridge (unpublished)
	Sugar-coated tablets	Disintegration and 'pitting' of coating	*Penicillium* spp. *Aspergillus* spp.	Parker and Barnes (1967)

Reprinted with permission of Elsevier Applied Science from Denyer (1988).

5.3.2 Degradation of thickening and suspending agents

A wide variety of materials are used in pharmaceuticals for this purpose, many of which are biodegradable by extracellular enzymes. Degradation of these polymeric molecules yields monomers such as sugars which serve as substrates for growth and further spoilage effects. Starch, acacia, sodium carboxymethylcelluloses and dextran are all biodegradable. Agar is resistant to attack although agar-degrading organisms do exist. Polyethylene glycols except those of high molecular weight are degraded, although polymers used in packaging are generally resistant. Gelatin is hydrolysed by a wide range of commonly occurring micro-organisms.

5.3.3   Utilization of humectants and co-solvents
Glycerol and sorbitol support microbial growth at low concentrations. At low concentrations alcohol can serve as a substrate for growth.

5.3.4   Degradation of sweetening, flavouring and colouring agents
Sugars and other sweetening agents can act as substrates for microbial attack, particularly by the osmophilic yeasts. Oral suspensions or emulsions containing sugars are liable to fermentation with production of gas and acid which may be sufficient to alter the stability of the formulation. Stock solutions of flavouring and colouring agents, and even simple salt solutions such as potassium citrate and calcium gluconate, will support growth of nutritionally non-exacting bacteria and yeasts.

5.3.5   Degradation of oils and emulsions
Micro-organisms do not grow in a non-aqueous environment, but in an emulsified system they may grow in the aqueous phase producing lipolytic enzymes which attack the triglyceride oil component at the oil–water interface liberating glycerol and fatty acids. Fatty acids may be further metabolized by β-oxidation of the alkyl chain with the production of ketones. Glycerol is a utilizable substrate for many organisms. Some insight into spoilage of emulsified systems has been gained from studies of the breakdown of engineering cutting oils (Guyne and Bennett 1959).

Ointments and oils are less prone to attack but spoilage many occur where these products contain traces of condensed water or are stored in a humid atmosphere. Spoilage of arachis oil and liquid paraffin has been reported (Rivers and Walters 1966).

5.4   Geneal decrease in acceptability of the product
Changes in product formulation may not only affect therapeutic potency but may also make the product unacceptable to the patient. In addition, other changes involving microbial degradation with the production of metabolic waste materials may make the product aesthetically unacceptable. Examples of such compounds include hydrogen sulphide, amines, ketones, fatty acids, alcohols or ammonia, which impart a noxious odour or unpleasant taste to the product. Products may become discoloured by various microbial pigments; organisms most frequently implicated are the pseudomonads, which produce pigments varying from blue to brown.

The most obvious sign of spoilage is visible growth either as colonies or a pellicle on the surface of a product. Alternatively polymerization of sugar or surfactant molecules in syrups or shampoos produces a viscous slimy mass within the product, whilst aggregation of material can produce sediment in a liquid product or a gritty texture in a cream.

5.5   Degradation of preservatives
Although antimicrobial agents are used in pharmaceutical products to prevent spoilage, many commonly used preservatives are themselves degraded by micro-organisms, most notably the pseudomonads but also species of *Acinetobacter*, *Moraxella* and *Nocardia*. Preservatives known to be susceptible to degradation include chlorhexidine, cetrimide, phenolics, phenylethyl alcohol, benzoic acid,

benzalkonium chloride and the *p*-hydroxybenzoates (Beveridge and Hugo 1964a, 1964b; Hugo and Foster 1964; Beveridge and Tall 1969; Beveridge and Hart 1970; Grant 1970; Hart 1970; Kido *et al.* 1988).

6 INFECTION HAZARDS FROM MICROBIAL CONTAMINATION OF PHARMACEUTICALS

Experience has shown that products may show no sensory evidence of contamination but may still contain a growing microbial population. In the normal healthy adult this represents little problem unless the organism is a primary pathogen; but if the user is immunocompromised in any way, or the product is introduced into a normally sterile area of the body or applied to damaged skin, mucous membrane or the eye, infection may occur. The clinical significance of micro-organisms in pharmaceuticals was reviewed by Parker (1972) and Ringertz and Ringertz (1982). Overall the infection risk depends on four factors.

6.1 Type of organism

Of the organisms which have been isolated from pharmaceutical products, *Salmonella* is the only one which must be regarded as a primary pathogen, i.e. an organism which produces disease even when unintentionally administered. The majority of primary pathogens do not survive well outside the human or animal body. By contrast, organisms regarded as potential or conditional pathogens have been quite frequently reported as contaminants of pharmaceuticals. These are not generally harmful to the normal healthy adult, but readily become infectious where resistance mechanisms are impaired. Such opportunist pathogens include pseudomonads and enterobacteria and species of *Flavobacterium* and *Staphylococcus*.

Of the Enterobacteriaceae it is the free-living species (*Enterobacter, Klebsiella, Serratia*) which most usually occur in pharmaceuticals; although they may cause disease these species are not usually found as part of the normal body flora. By contrast, species such as *E. coli, Proteus* spp. and perhaps also some species of *Klebsiella* are commonly found as part of the normal body flora; although harmless in the bowel, they readily cause disease if transferred to other areas. These organisms have only a limited ability to survive outside the body and are less frequently found as contaminants of pharmaceuticals.

Ps. aeruginosa is a free-living organism. Although it is present as part of the normal bowel flora in only about 4–6% of the normal population, it will readily cause infection of wounds or burns. *Pseudomonas cepacia* is another free-living species which has caused infection on a number of occasions (Levey and Guinness 1981; Berkelman *et al.* 1984). *Flavobacterium meningosepticum* is a pigmented water-borne species which can cause severe generalized sepsis in infants (Parker 1972). Up to 30% of the population may be either persistent or intermittent carriers of *Staph. aureus* (Armstrong-Esther and Smith 1976); although this organism does not thrive outside the body, it is quite resistant to drying and can persist in products for substantial periods of time.

Other species most frequently implicated in opportunistic nosocomial infections include *Acinetobacter anitratus*, *Staph. epidermidis*, and *Streptococcus pyogenes*. However, none of these organisms have yet been definitely implicated in outbreaks due to contaminated pharmaceuticals.

6.2   Infective dose

Observations recorded in the literature indicate that the 'infective dose' of an organism may vary considerably and may depend on several factors. Administered orally, quite large doses may be required; experiments with healthy adults suggest that the infective dose of *Salmonella* or *E. coli* may be as high as 10^6–10^7 organisms or as low as 10^2–10^3, depending on the species involved (McCullough and Eisele 1951; Ferguson and June 1952). Outbreaks involving chocolate and Cheddar cheese suggest that the infective dose for *Salmonella* may be as few as 50–100 organisms, and less than ten organisms, respectively (Gill *et al.* 1983; Greenwood and Hooper 1983; D'Aoust 1985). In very small children the infective dose for *Salmonella* may be as low as 200. Buck and Cooke (1969) found that ingestion of at least 10^6 *Ps. aeruginosa* may be necessary for intestinal colonization of normal persons.

As far as topical preparations are concerned, experiments with healthy volunteers showed that an inoculum up to 10^6 *Staph. aureus* may be required to produce pus, but as little as 10^2 may be sufficient where the skin is traumatized or occluded (Marples 1976). According to Crompton *et al.* (1962), intraocular injection of as few as 60 cells of *Ps. aeruginosa* was sufficient to cause infection in rabbits. Even relatively trivial abrasions of the eye can substantially increase the risk of infection.

6.3   Host resistance to infection

Although in most situations the normal healthy adult has adequate resistance to infection, pharmaceutical products are frequently administered to people whose body defences to infection are impaired. This situation may arise in patients with pre-existing disease such as leukaemia or diabetes. It may also be associated with immunosuppressive drug therapy which may include steroid treatment or chemotherapy. Impaired local resistance is associated with surgical and accident wounds, burns and pressure sores. It is also frequently associated with insertion of catheters or other surgical devices. Geriatric patients and babies, particularly during the first few days of life, show increased susceptibility to infection.

6.4   Route of administration

Infection risks associated with a contaminated pharmaceutical will depend largely on its intended use. In general, the risk of infection will be much reduced for a drug given orally or applied to intact skin compared with a formulation used for treatment of abraded skin or mucous membrane, or a damaged eye.

For products which are introduced into normally sterile areas of the body, the potential risks are considerable. A recent review of microbial contamination of intravenous fluids during use (Denyer 1984) suggests that the small numbers of mainly non-pathogenic organisms are generally well tolerated and that infection is a rare occurrence.

Although, as reviewed earlier in this chapter, some controlled studies with healthy adult volunteers have been used to assess infection risks, most of our knowledge regarding the clinical significance of contamination in medicinal products comes from published reports of infection outbreaks from use of such products. These are reviewed in the following sections.

6.4.1 Oral medicines

The literature contains several reports of outbreaks of *Salmonella* infection resulting from contaminated oral products. In 1966 an outbreak of infection in 202 patients in Sweden was subsequently traced to thyroid tablets which were found to contain *Salmonella bareilly, Salmonella munchen* and other faecal organisms in excess of 10^6 c.f.u. g^{-1} (Kallings *et al.* 1966; Kallings 1973). In 1967 a number of cases of gastro-intestinal tract infection in the USA were traced to carmine capsules contaminated with *Salmonella cubana* (Lang *et al.* 1967; Komarmy *et al.* 1967; Eikhoff 1967). Infection from *Salmonella agona* associated with contaminated pancreatin was reported in two children (Glencross 1972). *Salmonella shwarzengrund* and *Salmonella eimsbuttel* were also found in batches of pancreatin causing infection in two children with cystic fibrosis (Rowe and Hall 1975).

Shooter *et al.* (1969) reported bowel colonization (although not infection) of a number of hospital patients following inadvertent administration of peppermint water containing 10^6 c.f.u. ml^{-1} *Ps. aeruginosa*.

More recently an outbreak of septicaemia caused by use of a thymol mouthwash contaminated with *Ps. aeruginosa* was recorded (Stephenson *et al.* 1984). Millership *et al.* (1986) also reported colonization of patients from communal ward use of mouthwashes and feeds which were heavily contaminated with coliforms.

6.4.2 Topical administration

Although intact skin presents an efficient barrier against infection, for damaged skin the infection risks are substantially increased. Multidose containers, particularly those used by more than one person, are prone to contamination, especially in the hospital situation, and there are reports of infection outbreaks from the application of such products.

One of the earliest reports was a fatal outbreak of *Clostridium tetani* infection in babies caused by contaminated talcum power (Tremewen 1946; Hills 1946). In 1966, Noble and Savin reported a number of cases of skin lesions which were traced to betamethasone cream contaminated with *Ps. aeruginosa* (Morse *et al.* 1967). McCormack and Kunin (1966) attributed an outbreak of umbilical sepsis to *Serratia marcescens* in the saline solution used to moisten the cord stump. In 1967, hand cream contaminated with *K. pneumoniae* was implicated in an outbreak of septi-caemia in an intensive therapy unit (Morse *et al.* 1967). Bassett *et al.* (1970) isolated *Pseudomonas multivorans* from infected operation wounds in nine hospital patients; the source of infection was subsequently traced to a diluted chlorhexidine–cetrimide disinfectant found to be contaminated with 10^6 pseudomonads per millilitre. Coloni-zation and infection with *Ps. aeruginosa* arising from use of contaminated deter-gents, disinfectants and topical medicaments including zinc-based barrier creams and emulsifying ointment were also reported by Victorin (1967), Cooke *et al.* (1970), Baird and Shooter (1976), and Baird *et al.* (1979a, 1980). More recently, Salveson and Bergen (1981) reported contamination from a range of organisms in a chlorhexi-dine hand cream used to prevent infection in catheterized patients; use of the contaminated cream was associated with urinary tract infection in a number of these patients. Clinical infection following application of an iodophor antiseptic solution contaminated with *Ps. aeruginosa* and *Ps. cepacia* has also been reported by Parrot *et al.* (1982) and Berkelman *et al.* (1984).

6.4.3 Respiratory infections
Nosocomial respiratory tract infections involving Gram-negative bacteria have been reported quite frequently and in some instances this has been traced to nebulizers and humidifiers used in inhalation therapy (Favero *et al.* 1971; Pierce and Sanford 1973; Petersen *et al.* 1978). In two instances, aerosol solutions contaminated with *Klebsiella* spp. and *Ser. marcescens* (Sanders *et al.* 1970) have been implicated as the cause of pulmonary infection. An outbreak of respiratory infection was also traced to endotracheal tubes lubricated with contaminated lignocaine jelly (Kallings *et al.* 1966).

6.4.4 Disinfectants
Although disinfectants are used to kill micro-organisms, some Gram-negative species, most notably the pseudomonads, can acquire resistance and grow in disinfectant solutions, utilizing the antimicrobial agent as a carbon source. Investigations associated with the use of contaminated disinfectants have been reviewed by Bloomfield (1988). Of the 42 incidents investigated, 24 were reported to be associated with, or implicated in, colonization of patients or outbreaks of infection. The majority of reports related to phenolics, quaternary ammonium or chlorhexidine formulations. The contaminants were mainly pseudomonads, particularly *Ps. aeruginosa* and *Ps. cepacia*. Other Gram-negative species included *Alcaligenes faecalis*, *Enterobacter cloacae*, *Enterobacter agglomerans*, *E. coli*, *Ser. marcescens* and *F. meningosepticum*. Gram-positive isolates were not recorded in this review but were reported in a recent study of hospital-prepared disinfectants (Nkibiasala *et al.* 1989).

6.4.5 Ophthalmic preparations
Although sterility has been a pharmacopoeial requirement for ophthalmic drops and lotions since 1966, there are a number of reports in the literature, particularly prior to 1966, of infections resulting from the use of contaminated eye preparations. The organism of major concern was again *Ps. aeruginosa*, which produces corneal ulceration and can cause blindness.

In 1952, Theodore and Feinstein published a paper indicating strong correlation between *Pseudomonas* infections in clinical practice and use of contaminated eye preparations. Allen (1959) estimated that in the USA at least 200 people each year were suffering loss of eyesight from use of contaminated eye-drops. Crompton *et al.* (1964) reported evidence of eye infections from use of eye-drops contaminated with a species of *Aerobacter*. Ringertz and Ernerfeldt (1965) and Kallings *et al.* (1966) reported *Ps. aeruginosa* infections arising from contaminated batches of neomycin and cortisone eye ointments, respectively. Ayliffe *et al.* (1966) reported infections causing blindness from the use of saline contaminated with *Ps. aeruginosa* during intraocular operations. Most recently a number of cases of keratitis were traced to eye-drops contaminated with *Ser. marcescens* although the organisms appeared to have originated from the dropper caps (Templeton *et al.* 1982).

A number of serious infections from the use of contaminated eye cosmetics have also been reported (Wilson *et al.* 1971; Ahearn *et al.* 1973; Wilson *et al.* 1975; Wilson and Ahearn 1977; Reid and Wood 1979). Infecting organisms included not only bacterial species but also various yeasts and fungi such as *Candida albicans*, *Fusarium* and *Penicillium* spp.

6.4.6 Irrigating fluids and dialysis fluids
The literature contains several reports of urinary tract infections caused by contaminated irrigating fluids (Last *et al.* 1966; Mitchell and Hayward 1966). An outbreak of *Pseudomonas* infection from a contaminated urinary catheter kit was traced to the germicidal cleansing solution which was contaminated with 10^3 bacteria per millilitre (Hardy *et al.* 1970).

Haemodialysis represents a particular problem. Favero *et al.* (1974) reported two cases of septicaemia from dialysis fluid contaminated with *Ps. aeruginosa*. Curtis *et al.* (1967) described an outbreak of bacteraemia due to *Bacillus cereus* contamination of the dialysis fluid.

6.4.7 Injections
Undoubtedly the most serious infection outbreaks are those associated with contaminated injection fluids where bacteraemic shock and in some cases death of the patient may result. In 1970, Robertson reported two cases of infection arising from use of glucose–saline solution contaminated with *Trichoderma* and *Penicillium* spp. A number of cases of sepsis following the administration of fluids was reported by Felts *et al.* (1972). Species of *Erwinia*, *Ent. cloacae* and *Ps. stutzeri* were isolated from the fluids. Phillips *et al.* (1972) reported an outbreak of infection involving 40 hospital patients following administration of influsions contaminated with *Ps. thomasii*. The most notorious outbreak in the UK resulted in the death of six hospital patients following the administration of contaminated dextrose solution (Meers *et al.* 1973). The contents of 155 bottles of the suspect batch were examined, of which approximately one-third were cloudy. *K. aerogenes*, *Ent. cloacae*, *Erwina herbicola*, *Ps. thomasii*, coryneforms and other species of Enterobacteriaceae were isolated from the fluids. Lapage *et al.* (1973) identified 80 baterial strains, chiefly enterobacteria, pseudomonads and coryneforms associated with two outbreaks of infection from contaminated intravenous fluids.

7 OVERVIEW
Substantial improvements in the microbial quality of manufactured pharmaceutical products have been seen in the last twenty or so years. This can be illustrated by comparing the results of the 1971 PHLS survey (Anon. 1971a) with the results of a more recent survey of hospital-manufactured products carried out over the period 1975–1983 by Baird (1985). Whereas the PHLS survey indicated that 2.7% of 1220 product samples were contaminated with *Ps. aeruginosa* and 15% with other Gram-negative rods, the more recent survey (13 000 samples) showed only two isolates of *Ps. aeruginosa*, with only 0.24% of samples containing Gram-negative rods. Despite

these improvements, however, there is no room for complacency since outbreaks of infection continue to be reported from time to time (Baird *et al.* 1980; Salveson and Bergen 1981; Stephenson *et al.* 1984; Millership *et al.* 1986).

8   REFERENCES

Ahearn, D. G., Wilson, C. A., Julian, A. J., Reinhardt, D. J. and Ajello, G. (1973) Microbial growth in eye cosmetics: contamination during use. In: *Developments in industrial microbiology*, Vol. **15**. Plenum Press, New York, pp. 211–219.

Allen, H. F. (1959) Aseptic technique in ophthalmology. *Trans. Am. Ophthalmol. Soc.* **57** 377–472.

Anon. (1971a) Microbial contamination of medicines administered to hospital patients. *Pharm. J.* **207** 96–99.

Anon. (1971b) Microbial contamination in pharmaceuticals for oral and topical use. *Pharm. J.* **207** 400–402.

Anon. (1983) *Pharm. J.* **230** 300.

Armstrong-Esther, C. A. and Smith, J. E. (1976) Carriage patterns of *Staphylococcus aureus* in a healthy non-hospital population of adults and children. *Ann. Human Biol.* **3** 221–227.

Arribas, M. L. G., Plaza, C. J., de la Rosa, M. C. and Mosso, M. A. (1988) Characterisation of *Bacillus cereus* strains isolated from drugs and evaluation of their toxins. *J. App. Bacteriol.* **64** 257–264.

Awad, Z. A. (1977) In use contamination of pharmaceutical products and their possible role in hospital cross infection. PhD thesis, University of London.

Ayliffe, G. A. J., Barry, D. R., Lowbury, E. J. I., Roper-Hall, M. J. and Walker, W. M. (1966) Postoperative infection with *Pseudomonas aeruginosa* in an eye hospital. *Lancet* **i** 1113–1117.

Baird, R. M. (1977) Microbial contamination of cosmetic products. *J. Soc. Cosmet. Chem.* **28** 17–20.

Baird, R. M. (1985) Microbial contamination of pharmaceutical products made in a hospital pharmacy: a nine year survey. *Pharm. J.* **231** 54–55.

Baird, R. M. (1988) Microbial contamination of manufactured products: official and unofficial limits. In: Bloomfield, S. F., Baird, R. M., Leak, R. E. and Leach, R. (eds) *Microbial quality assurance in pharmaceuticals, cosmetics and toiletries.* Ellis Horwood, Chichester, pp. 61–76.

Baird, R. M. and Petrie, P. S. (1981) A study of microbiological contamination of oral medicaments. *Pharm. J.* **226** 10–11.

Baird, R. M. and Shooter, R. A. (1976) *Pseudomonas aeruginosa* infections associated with use of contaminated medicaments. *Br. Med. J.* **2** 349–350.

Baird, R. M., Brown, W. R. L. and Shooter, R. A. (1976) *Pseudomonas aeruginosa* in hospital pharmacies. *Br. Med. J.* **i** 511–512.

Baird, R. M., Sturgiss, M., Awad, Z. A. and Shooter, R. A. (1979a) Microbial contamination of topical medicaments used in the treatment and prevention of pressure sores. *J. Hyg. Camb.* **83** 445–450.

Baird, R. M., Crowden, C. A., O'Farrell, S. M. and Shooter, R. A. (1979b) Microbial contamination of pharmaceutical products in the home. *J. Hyg. Camb.* **83** 277–283.

Baird, R. M., Awad, Z. A. and Shooter, R. A. (1980) Contaminated medicaments in use in a hospital for diseases of the skin. *J. Hyg. Camb.* **84** 103–108.

Baker, J. H. (1959) That unwanted cosmetic ingredient: bacteria. *J. Soc. Cosmet. Chem.* **10** 133–143.

Bassett, D. C. J., Stokes, K. J and Thomas, W. R. G. (1970) Wound infection due to *Pseudomonas multivorans:* a water-borne contaminant of disinfectant solutions. *Lancet* **i** 1188–1191.

Berkelman, R. L., Anderson, R. L., Davis, B. J., Highsmith, A. K., Petersen, N. J., Bono, W. W., Cook, E. H., Mackel, M. S., Favero, M. S. and Martone, W. J. (1984) Intrinsic bacterial contamination of a commercial iodophor solution. *Appl. Environ. Microbiol.* **47** 752–756.

Beveridge, E. G. (1975) The microbial spoilage of pharmaceutical products. In: Lovelock, D. W. and Gilbert, R. J. (eds), *Microbial aspects of the deterioration of materials.* Academic Press, London, pp. 213–235.

Beveridge, E. G. (1987) Microbial spoilage and preservation of pharmaceutical products. In: Hugo, W. B. and Russell, A. D. (eds), *Pharmaceutical Microbiology,* 4th edn. Blackwell Scientific, Oxford, pp. 360–380.

Beveridge, E. G. and Hart, A. (1970) The utilization for growth and the degradation of *p*-hydroxybenzoate esters by bacteria. *Int. Biodet. Bull.* **6** 9–25.

Beveridge, E. G. and Hope, I. A. (1971) Microbial content of pharmaceutical solutions. *Pharm. J.* **207** 102–103.

Beveridge, E. G. and Hugo, W. B. (1964a) The resistance of gallic acid and its alkyl esters to attack by bacteria able to degrade aromatic ring structures. *J. App. Bacteriol.* **27** 304–311.

Beveridge, E. G. and Hugo, W. B. (1964b) The metabolism of gallic acid by *Pseudomonas convexa* X.i. *J. Appl. Bacteriol.* **27** 448–459.

Beveridge, E. G. and Tall, D. (1969) The metabolic availability of phenol analogues to bacterium NCIB 8250. *J. App. Bacteriol.* **32** 304–311.

Blair, T. A. (1989) Some factors influencing the survival of microbial contamination in solid oral dosage forms. PhD Thesis, University of London.

Bloomfield, S. F. (1988) Biodeterioration and disinfectants. In : Houghton, P. R., Smith, R. N. and Egins, H. O. W. (eds), *Biodeterioration,* Vol. 7. Elsevier Applied Science, London, pp. 135–145.

Brookes, F. L., Hugo, W. B. and Denyer, S. P. (1982) Transformation of betamethasone 17-valerate by skin microflora. *J. Pharm. Pharmacol.* **34** 61P.

Bucherer, H. (1965) Microbial degradation of toxicants. IV. Microbial degradation of phenyl acetate, strychnine, brucine, vomicine and tubocurarine. *Zentbl. Bakt. Parasitkde. Abt. II* **119** 232–238.

Buck, A. C. and Cooke, E. M. (1969) The fate of ingested *Pseudomonas aeruginosa* in normal persons. *J. Med. Microbiol.* **2** 521–525.

Coles, J. and Tredree, R. L. (1972) Contamination of autoclaved fluids with cooling water. *Pharm. J.* **207** 193–195.

Cooke, E. M., Shooter, R. A., O'Farrell, S. M. and Martin, D. R. (1970) Faecal carriage of *Pseudomonas aeruginosa* by newborn babies. *Lancet* **ii** 1045–1046.

Cox, P. H. and Sewell, B. A. (1968) The metabolism of steroids by *Cladosporium herbarum. J. Soc. Cosmet. Chem.* **19** 461–467.

Crompton, D. O., Anderson, K. F. and Kennare, M. A. (1962) Experimental infection of the rabbit anterior chamber. *Trans. Ophthalmol. Soc. Aust.* **22** 81.

Crompton, D. O., Murchland, J. B. and Anderson, K. F. (1964) Sterility of eye drops: a rare ocular pathogen. *Lancet* **i** 1391.

Curtis, J. R., Wing, A. J. and Coleman, J. C. (1967) *Bacillus cereus* bacteraemia: a complication of intermittent dialysis. *Lancet* **i** 136–138.

Daisy, J. A., Abrutyn, E. A. and MacGregor, R. R. (1979) Inadvertent administratin of intravenous fluids contaminated with fungus. *Ann. Intern. Med.* **91** 563–565.

D'Aoust, J. Y. (1985) Infective dose of *Salmonella typhimurium* in Cheddar cheese: brief report. *Am. J. Epidemiol.* **122** 717–720.

Denyer, S. P. (1984) Microbial contamination of intravenous fluids during use. *Br. J. Pharm. Practice* **6** 122–126.

Denyer, S. P. (1988) Clinical consequences of microbial action on medicines. In: Houghton, D. R., Smith, R. N. and Egins, H. O. W. (eds), *Biodeterioration, Vol. 7.* Elsevier Applied Science, London, pp. 146–151.

Dunnigan, A. P. and Evans, J. R. (1970) Report of a special survey: microbiological contamination of topical drugs and cosmetics. *Toilet Goods Assoc. J. Cosmet.* **2** 39–41.

Eikhoff, T. C. (1967) Nosocomial salmonellosis due to carmine. *Ann. Intern. Med.* **66** 813–814.

Favero, M. S., Carson, L. A., Bond, W. W. and Peterson, N. J. (1971) *Pseudomonas aeruginosa:* growth in distilled water from hospitals. *Science* **173** 836–838.

Favero, M. S., Peterson, N. J., Boyer, K. M., Carson, L. A. and Bond, W. W. (1974) Microbial contamination of renal dialysis systems and associated health risks. *Am. Soc. Artif. Int. Organs* **20** 175–183.

Felts, S. K., Schaffner, W., Melly, M. A. and Koenig, M. G. (1972) Sepsis caused by contaminated intravenous fluids: epidemiologic, clinical and laboratory investigation of an outbreak in one hospital. *Ann. Intern. Med.* **77** 881–890.

Ferguson, W. W. and June, R. C. (1952) Experiments on feeding adult voluteers with *Escherichia coli* 111, B4, a coliform organism associated with infant diarrhoea. *Am. J. Hyg.* **55** 155–169.

Fernandez, G. S. and Genis, M. J. (1979) The formation of aflatoxins in different types of starches for pharmaceutical use. *Pharm. Acta Helv.* **54** 78–81.

Franklin, T. J. and Snow, G. A. (1989) in collaboration with Barrett-Bee, K. J. and Nolan, R. D., *Biochemistry of antimicrobial action.* Chapman and Hall, London.

Gill, O. N., Barlett, C. L. R., Sockett, P. N. and Vaile, M. S. B. (1983) Outbreak of *Salmonella napoli* infection caused by contaminated chocolate bars. *Lancet* **i** 574–575.

Glencross, E. J. G. (1972) Pancreatin as a source of hospital-acquired Salmonellosis. *Br. Med. J.* **2** 376–378.

Grant, D. J. W. (1970) The oxidative degradation of benzoate and catechol by *Klebsiella aerogenes (Aerobacter aerogenes). Antonie van Leeuwenhoek* **36** 161–177.

Grant, D. J. W. (1971) Degradation of acetylsalicyclic acid by a strain of *Acineto-bacter lwoffii. J. App. Bacteriol.* **34** 689–698.

Grant, D. J. W. (1973) The degradative versatility, arylesterase activity and hydroxylation reactions of *Acinetobacter lwoffii. J. App. Bacteriol.* **36** 47–59.

Grant, D. J. W. and Wilson, J. V. (1973) Degradation and hydrolysis of amides by *Corynebacterium pseudodiphtheriticum* NClB 10803. *Microbios* **8** 15–22.

Grant, D. J. W., De Szôcs and Wilson, J. V. (1970) Utilization of acetylsalicyclic acid as sole carbon source and the induction of its enzymatic hydrolysis by an isolated strain of *Acinetobacter lwoffii. J. Pharm. Pharmacol.* **22** 461–463.

Greenwood M. J. and Hooper, W. L. (1983) Chocolate bars contaminated with *Salmonella napoli:* an infective study. *Br. Med. J.* **286** 1394.

Guyne, C. J. (1973) Growth of various bacteria in a variety of intravenous fluids. *Am. J. Hosp. Pharm.* **30** 321–329.

Guyne, C. J. and Bennett, E. O. (1959) Bacterial deterioration of emulsion oil. *Appl. Microbiol.* **7** 117–125.

Hardy, P. C., Ederer, G. M. and Matsen, J. M. (1970) Contamination of commercially packed urinary catheter kits with *Pseudomonad* EO-1. *New Engl. J. Med.* **282** 33–35.

Hart, A. (1970) The stability of some esters of p-hydroxybenzoic acid to microbial attack. PhD thesis, Sunderland Polytechnic.

Hart, A. and Orr, D. L. J. (1974) Degradation of paracetamol by a Penicillum species. *J. Pharm. Pharmac.* **26** suppl. 70P.

Hikoto, H., Morozumi, S., Wauke, T., Sakai, S. and Kurata, H. (1978) Fungal contamination and mycotoxin detection of powdered herbal drugs. *Appl. Environ. Microbiol.* **36** 252–256.

Hills, S. (1946) The isolation of *Cl. tetani* from infected talc. NZ Med. J. **45** 419–423.

Hirsch, J. I., Canada, A. T. and Randall, E. L. (1969) Microbial contamination of oral liquid medications. *Am. J. Hosp. Pharm.* **23** 625–629.

Hugo, W. B. and Foster, J. H. (1964) Growth of *Pseudomonas aeruginosa* in solutions of esters of *p*-hydroxybenzoic acid. *J. Pharm. Pharmacol.* **16** 209–210.

Kallings, L. O. (1973) Contamination of therapeutic agents. In: *Contamination in the manufacture of pharmaceutical products.* Secretariat of the European Free Trade Association, pp. 17–23.

Kallings, L. O., Ringertz, O., Silverstolpe, L. and Ernerfeldt, F. (1966) Microbiological contamination of medical preparations. *Acta Pharma. Suec.* **3** 219–228.

Kedzia, W., Lewon, J. and Wisniewski, T. (1961) The breakdown of atropine by bacteria. *J. Pharm. Pharmacol.* **13** 614–619.

Kido, Y., Kodama, H., Uraki, F., Uyeda, M., Tsuruoka, M. and Shabata, M. (1988) Microbial degradation of disinfectants. II. Complete degradation of chlorhexidine. *Eisei Kagaku* **34** 97–101.

Komarmy, L. E., Oxley, M. and Brecher, G. (1967) Acquired salmonellosis traced to carmine dye capsules. *New Engl. J. Med.* **276** 850–852.

Lang, D. J., Kunz, L. J., Martin, A. R., Schroeder, S. A. and Thomson, L. A. (1967) Carmine as a source of nosocomial salmonellosis. *New Engl. J. Med.* **276** 829–832.

Lapage, S. P., Johnson, R. and Holmes, B. (1973) Bacteria from intravenous fluids. *Lancet* **ii** 284–285.

Last, P. M. Harbison, P. A. and Marsh, J. A. (1966) Bacteraemia after urological instrumentation. *Lancet* **i** 284–285.,

Lehrfeld, L. and Donnelly, E. J. (1948) Contaminated ophthalmic ointments. *Am. J. Ophthalmol.* **31** 470–471.

Levey, J. M. and Guinness, M. D. G. (1981) Hospital microbial environment: need for continued surveillance. *Med. J. Aust.* 590–592.

Marples, R. R. (1976) Local infections: experimental aspects. *J. Soc. Cosmet. Chem.* **27** 449–457.

McCormack, R. C. and Kunin, C. M. (1966) Control of a single source nursery epidemic due to *Serratia marcescens*. *Paediatrics* **37** 750–752.

McCullough, N. B. and Eisele, C. W. (1951) Experimental human salmonellosis. *J. Infect. Dis.* **88** 278–289.

Meers, P. D., Calder, M. W., Mazher, M. M. and Lawrie, G. M. (1973) Intravenous infusion of contaminated dextrose solution: the Devonport incident. *Lancet* **ii** 1189–1198.

Millership, S. E., Patel, N. and Chattopadhyay, B. (1986) The colonization of patients in an intensive treatment unit with Gram-negative flora: the significance of the oral route. *J. Hosp. Infect.* **7** 226–235.

Mitchell, R. G. and Hayward, A. C. (1966) Postoperative urinary-tract infections caused by contaminated irrigating fluid. *Lancet* **i** 793–795.

Mitvedt, T. and Lindstedt, G. (1970) Metabolism of thalidomide in *Pseudomonas aeruginosa* NCTC A7244. *Acta Path. Microbiol. Scand.* Section B **78** 488–494.

Morse, L. J., Williams, H. I., Grenn, F. P., Eldridge, E. F. and Rotta, J. R. (1967) Septicaemia due to *Klebsiella pneumoniae* originating from a handcream dispenser. *New Engl. J. Med.* **277** 472–473.

Nkibiasala, S. M., Devleeschouwer, M. J., Van Gansbeke, B., Rost, F. and Dony, J. (1989) Disinfectants prepared in a hospital pharmacy: assessment of their microbiological purity and antimicrobial effectiveness. *J. Clin. Pharm. Ther.* **14** 457–464.

Noble, W. C. and Savin, J. A. (1966) Steroid cream contaminated with *Pseudomonas aeruginosa*. *Lancet* **i** 347–349.

Parker, M. T. (1972) The clinical significance of the presence of micro-organisms in pharmaceutical and cosmetic preparations. *J. Soc. Cosmet. Chem.* **23** 415–426.

Parker, M. S. and Barnes, M. (1967) Microbiological quality control of cosmetic and pharmaceutical preparations. *Soap Perfum. Cosmet.* December issue 1–4.

Parrot, P. L., Terry, P. M., Whitworth, E. N., Frawley, L. W., Coble, R. S., Wachsmith, I. K. and McGowan, J. E. (1982) *Pseudomonas aeruginosa* associated with contaminated polaxamer–iodine solutions. *Lancet* **ii** 683–684.

Petersen, N. J., Carson, L. A., Favero, M. S., Marshall, J. H. and Bond, W. W. (1978) Microbial contamination of mist therapy units of six paediatric wards. *Health Lab. Sci.* **12** 41–46.

Phillips, I., Eykyn, S. and Laker, M. (1972) Outbreak of hospital infection caused by contaminated autoclaved fluids. *Lancet* **i** 1258–1260.

Pierce, A. K. and Sanford, J. P. (1973) Bacterial contamination of aerosols. *Arch. Intern. Med.* **131** 156–159.

Reid, F. R. and Wood, T. O. (1979) *Pseudomonas* corneal ulcer: the causative role of contaminated eye cosmetics. *Arch. Ophthalmol.* **97** 1640–1641.

Ringertz, O. and Ernerfeldt, F. (1965) *Microbiological contamination of medical products.* Report to the Royal Medical Board of Stockholm.

Ringertz, O. and Ringertz, S. (1982) The clinical significance of microbial contamination in pharmaceutical and allied products. *Adv. Pharm. Sci.* **5** 201–226.

Rivers, S. M. and Walters, V. (1966) The effect of benzoic acid, phenol and hydroxybenzoates on the oxygen uptake and growth of some lipolytic fungi. *J. Pharm. Pharmacol.* **18** 45S.

Robertson, P. R. (1970) Fungi in fluids: a hazard of intravenous therapy. *J. Med. Microbiol.* **3** 99–102.

Robinson, E. P. (1971) *Ps. aeruginosa* contamination of liquid antacids: a survey. *J. Pharm. Sci.* **60** 604–606.

Rowe, B. and Hall, M. L. (1975) *Salmonella* contamination of therapeutic panel preparations. *Br. Med. J.* **2** 51.

Sack, R. A. (1970) Epidemic of gram-negative organism septicaemia subsequent to elective operation. *Am. J. Obstet. Gynecol.* **107** 394–399.

Salveson, A. and Bergen, T. (1981) Contamination of chlorhexidine cream used to prevent ascending urinary tract infections. *J. Hyg. Camb.* **86** 295–301.

Sanders, C. V., Luby, J. B., Johnson, W. G., Barnett, J. A. and Sanford, J. P. (1970) *Serratia marcescens* infections from inhalation therapy medications: nosocomial outbreak. *Ann. Intern. Med.* **73** 15–21.

Savin, J. A. (1967) The microbiology of topical preparations in pharmaceutical practice. 1. Clinical Aspects. *Pharm. J.* **199** 285–288.

Scott, E. and Bloomfield, S. F. (1990) The survival and transfer of microbial contamination via cloths, hands and utensils. *J. Appl. Bacteriol.* **68** 271–278.

Shooter, R. A., Cooke, E. M., Gaya, H., Kumar, P., Patel, N., Parker, M. T., Thom, B. T. and France, D. R. (1969) Food and medicaments as possible sources of hospital strains of *Pseudomonas aeruginosa. Lancet* **i** 1227–1231.

Smart, R. and Spooner, D. F. (1972) Microbiological spoilage in pharmaceuticals and cosmetics. *J. Soc. Cosmet. Chem.* **23** 721–737.

Smith, G. M. and Worrel, C. S. (1949) Studies on the action of chloramphenicol on enzymatic systems. *Arch. Biochem.* **23** 341–346.

Spooner, D. F. (1988) Hazards associated with the microbiological contamination of non-sterile pharmaceuticals, cosmetics and toiletries. In: Bloomfield, S. F., Baird, R. M., Leak, R. E. and Leech, R. (eds) *Microbial quality assurance in pharmaceuticals, cosmetics and toiletries.* Ellis Horwood, Chichester, pp. 15–34.

Stephenson, J. R., Head, S. R., Richards, M. A. and Tabaqchali, S. (1984) Outbreak of septicaemia due to contaminated mouthwash. *Br. Med. J.* **289** 1584.

Swisher, R. D. (1987) *Surfactant biodegradation,* 2nd edn. Surfactant Science Series No. 18, Marcel Dekker, New York.

Templeton, W. C., Eiferman, R. A., Snyder, J. W., Melo, J. C. and Raff, M. J. (1982) *Serratia* keratitis transmitted by contaminated eye droppers. *Am. J. Ophthalmol.* **93** 723–726.

Theodore, F. H. and Feinstein, R. R. (1952) Practical suggestions for the preparation and maintenance of sterile ophthalmic solutions. *Am. J. Ophthalmol.* **35** (1959) 656–658.

Tremewan, H. C. (1946) Tetanus neonatorum in New Zealand. *NZ Med. J.* **45** 312–313.

Ulrich, K. (1968) Microbial content in non-sterile pharmaceuticals. *Dansk. Tidsskr. Farm.* **42** 1–4, 50–55, 71–83, 257–263.

Victorin, L. (1967) An epidemic of otitis in newborns due to infection with *Pseudomonas aeruginosa. Acta Paediatr. Scand.* **56** 344–348.

Wallhaeusser, K. H. (1977) Microbiological aspects on the subject of oral solid dosage forms. *Pharm. Ind.* **39** 491–497.

Wallhaeusser, K. H. (1978) Microbial quality control of skin care preparations. *Cosmet. Toiletries* **93** 42–48.

Westwood, N. and Pin Lim, B. (1971) Microbial contamination of some pharmaceutical raw materials. *Pharm. J.* **207** 99–102.

Wills, B. A. (1958) Fungal growth in syrup of Tolu. *J. Pharm. Pharmacol.* **10** 302–305.

Wilson, L. A. and Ahearn, D. G. (1977) *Pseudomonas*-induced corneal ulcers associated with contaminated eye mascaras. *Am. J. Ophthalmol.* **84** 112–119.

Wilson, L. A., Kuehne, J. W., Hall, S. W. and Ahearn, D. G. (1971) Microbial contamination in ocular cosmetics. *Am. J. Ophthalmol.* **71** 112–119.

Wilson, L. A., Julian, A. J. and Ahearn, D. G. (1975) The survival and growth of microorganisms in mascara during use. *Am. J. Ophthalmol.* **79** 596–601.

Wolven, A. and Levenstein, I. (1969) Cosmetics: contaminated or not. *Toilet Goods Assoc. Cosmet. J.* **1** 34.

Wolven, A. and Levenstein, I. (1972) Microbiological examination of cosmetics. *Am. Cosmet. Perfum.* **87** 63–65.

3

Microbial ecology of the production process

D. N. Payne
Reckitt and Colman, Pharmaceutical Division, Dansom Lane,
Kingston-upon-Hull HU8 7DS, UK

1   INTRODUCTION

It is necessary to understand the ecology of the total production process in order to be in control of the microbiological quality of the finished pharmaceutical. It is not sufficient to know only the quality of the finished product, since, particularly in the case of a preserved or sterile product, this gives no information of the bioburden inflicted on that product at its earlier stages of manufacture, and therefore the safety margin afforded by any preservative or sterilizing process cannot be assessed.

Furthermore, it is essential not only to be aware of the microbial quality of the raw materials, but also of the packaging materials and the production environment itself. The relative importance of the raw material and the environment will depend largely on the type and quantity of raw material used and on the type of finished product. The microbiology of the environment will thus be of little significance for a tablet or dry powder product whose major constituent is heavily contaminated, while at the opposite extreme an aseptically prepared product, made from sterile ingredients and packed into sterile containers, will be highly susceptible to the environment quality. There are thus three major areas contributing to the ecology of the production process, namely the raw materials, the primary packaging and the environment.

2 RAW MATERIALS

Untreated raw materials derived from natural sources may be expected to be heavily contaminated, whilst those of an essentially synthetic nature are usually free from all but incidental microbial contamination. In 1976 Grigo reviewed the reports of contamination in 282 raw materials and was able to group them into five categories based on their total count (Table 1).

Table 1 — Quality categories of raw materials based on total counts (Grigo 1976)

Category	Maximum average total count $(c.f.u.\ g^{-1}\ or\ ml^{-1})$ for each category
1	10
2	10^3
3	10^4
4	10^5
5	10^6

Category 1 raw materials were principally chemically synthesized or highly purified extracts of natural materials. Category 2 contained synthetic and naturally derived materials and category 3 contained predominantly plant extracts. Categories 4 and 5 were exclusively animal and plant products that had had little or no processing. Of the 282 raw materials, 188 had details of the organisms isolated (Table 2). *Bacillus* species, Enterobacteriaceae, *Staphylococcus aureus* and moulds occurred in all categories, and the Enterobacteriaceae predominated in categories 3, 4 and 5, i.e. those with the most raw materials of natural origin.

Bonomi and Negretti in 1977 surveyed 100 types of raw material in Italy with similar results. Substances of either animal or plant origin were the most heavily contaminated, often with counts exceeding 10^4 c.f.u. g^{-1}, whilst inorganic chemi-

Table 2 — Organisms isolated from raw materials (adapted from Grigo 1976). See Table 1 for total count in each category

Micro-organism	Percentage of raw materials containing the specified organism in each indicated category				
	1	2	3	4	5
Sterile (no organisms detected)	34	0	0	0	0
Bacillus spp.	42	67	55	55	33
Moulds	20	50	30	36	50
Staph. aureus	4	18	15	18	33
Sarcina	0	5	5	9	16
Streptococcus	0	1	0	27	0
E. coli	9	30	55	27	66
Salmonellae	0	4	10	18	83
Enterobacteriaceae (excluding *E. coli* and salmonellae)	1	16	65	73	33
Pseudomonads	0	3	20	0	50
Flavobacterium	0	1	0	0	0
Achromobacter	1	1	5	0	0
Alcaligenes	0	4	10	0	16
Clostridia	0	1	0	9	0

cals, such as sodium bicarbonate, had counts of less then 10 c.f.u. g^{-1}. Undesirable or pathogenic bacteria were isolated from 34 of the 100 raw materials tested, all 34 being of natural origin. Of the 1038 samples tested from these 34 types of raw materials 1.2% (13 samples) contained sulphate-reducing *Clostridia*, 2.9% (30 samples) *Pseudomonas aeruginosa*, 2.6% (27 samples) *Staph. aureus*, 3.1% (32% samples) *Strep. faecalis*, 8.5% (88 samples) *E. coli*, 0.48% (5 samples) salmonellae, and 4.0% (41 samples) other Enterobacteriaceae comprising *Proteus* (23 samples), *Citrobacter* (11 samples), *Klebsiella* (3 samples), *Enterobacter* (1 sample), *Erwinia* (1 sample), *Providencia* (1 sample) and *Yersinia* (1 sample).

Baggerman and Kannegieter (1984) examined the inorganic salts sodium chloride, potassium chloride, calcium chloride and sodium bicarbonate, together with glucose, fructose, sorbitol, mannitol and glycine, all used in large-volume parenteral production, and found all to have minimal contamination, with total counts ranging from 0.1 to 10 c.f.u. g^{-1}.

Crude herbal drugs such as powdered coptis may contain fungi at levels up to 10^4 c.f.u. g^{-1}, and bacteria at levels up to 10^5 c.f.u. g^{-1} (Hitokoto *et al.* 1978; Yokoyama *et al.* 1981). *Aspergillus* and *Penicillium* are the main components of the mycoflora of herbal drugs, with *Aspergillus niger*, *A. glaucus* and *A. flavus* being the most prevalent species among the *Aspergillus*. *Mucor*, *Rhizopus*, *Cladosporium* and *Aureobasidium* may also be isolated. The bacteria isolated are predominantly sporing *Bacillus* with micrococci and staphylococci also being present in some instances.

Data from our own surveys over the period 1984–1989 (Table 3) is in agreement with that of earlier published information. Untreated plant material such as senna pods and ispaghula husk may contain up to 10^6 c.f.u. g^{-1} of bacteria and 10^4 c.f.u. g^{-1} of moulds with Enterobacteriaceae and pseudomonads present, whereas the chemically synthesized or highly refined materials are essentially free of contamination. As in earlier surveys, spore-forming *Bacillus* spp. are the predominant organisms in almost all raw materials.

Table 3 — Microbiological contamination of 34 raw material types representing 781 deliveries over the period 1985–1989

Substance	Numbers of deliveries with total counts (c.f.u. g^{-1} or c.f.u. ml^{-1}) in the indicated ranges:						
	<10	10^1–10^2	10^2–10^3	10^3–10^4	10^4–10^5	10^5–10^6	>10^6
Gum acacia powder			1	8			
Alginic acid		39	2	3			
Aluminium hydroxide	28	3					
Banana flavour	5						
β-Carotene		3					
Calcium carbonate	10	6					
Calcium phosphate	11						
Caramel flavour	6	1					
Carmoisine soluble	2	2	2				
Cocoa powder		3	10	13			
Dextrose, anhydrous	24	2					
Ginger powder[a]							9
Grapefruit flavour	5	5	1	3			
Hydrolysed gelatin	9						
Hydrogenated glucose syrup	13	32	1				
Ispaghula husk[b]					36	32	
Lactose	17	1					
Light kaolin		2					
Locust bean gum			4	1			
Lime flavour	1	2	1				
Magnesium stearate		2					
Magnesium trisilicate	5	18	4				
Maize starch		26	24				
Malt extract	1	6	13	1			
Mannitol	47	25	4				
Orange flavour	5						
Paracetamol/ polyvinylpyrrolidone	33	2					
Raspberry flavour	3						
Senna pods					2	2	
Sodium alginate		21	68	36	4		
Sodium bicarbonate	3	2					
Sugar	9	12	5				
Sunset yellow	6	1	2				
Sterilized talc	28	2					

[a] Salmonellae in one delivery.
[b] *E. coli*, one delivery; pseudomonads, two deliveries.

3 WATER

Water is often the major component of pharmaceutical preparations and can be a very significant source of contamination. Product contamination may arise directly from the process water, indirectly from cleaning operations, or by cross-contamination from the wet areas of floors, sinks and drains to the processing equipment.

3.1 Methods of water preparation

3.1.1 Distillation

Distilled water, immediately after condensation, is sterile, and with proper aseptic collecting and storage precautions may be kept so. In the parenteral industry, distilled water is often maintained at 80°C and circulated around a ring system. This practice maintains the quality of the water by destroying any vegetative organisms that gain access to the system at outlet points, thereby preventing the generation of pyrogens. It is, therefore, important in the construction of circulating ring systems that no dead-legs are created and that outlets are as close as possible to the ring to minimize local areas of lower temperature, where adventitious contamination can survive and grow, and give rise to pyrogens in the final product. Whilst proving effective for the parenteral industry, the maintenance of 80°C throughout the water system is prohibitively expensive, however, for large-scale use in non-sterile pharmaceuticals.

3.1.2 Reverse osmosis

Water produced by reverse osmosis (RO) can be sterile and pyrogen-free as it is forced by osmotic pressure through a semi-permeable membrane which allows only substances of molecular weight less than 250 to diffuse through. Post-RO contamination can occur because of ingress of micro-organisms downstream of the membrane into the storage vessel or distribution system.

3.1.3 Deionization

Purified water prepared by deionization is the most common form of process water for non-sterile pharmaceuticals, yet this has perhaps the highest potential for contamination. The source water for the production of purified water is normally towns water of potable quality. Water suppliers chlorinate the water as it leaves the treatment works in order to maintain its microbial quality throughout the distribution network. However, manufacturing plants at the extremities of the distribution network may receive water with little or no residual chlorine; under these circumstances the potable water received may be contaminated with pseudomonads and other Gram-negative water-borne organisms (Rhodes, personal communication). In this case, on-site chlorination of the water to the storage tanks may be necessary. If possible the towns supply to the purified water plant should come direct from a rising main and not via the main plant storage tanks as these tend to remain static at night, weekends and during plant shutdowns, leading to proliferation of micro-organisms in the tank and thus present a high loading to the deionizers of the purified water plant. In the UK, water authorities will not allow water to be used direct from the rising main and insist on a break tank. This should be as small as possible to minimize the volume of static water.

   Deionized water systems may involve some combination of the following, all of which can harbour micro-organisms: (a) carbon filters, (b) water softeners, (c) cation- and anion-exchangers as either twin or mixed beds, and (d) a storage and distribution system (Chapman *et al.* 1983a).

3.1.3.1   Carbon filters

Carbon filters are effective in removing chlorine and lower-molecular-weight hydro-carbons, but are less effective in removing high-molecular-weight organic materials, such as humic acid, which are common to surface water supplies. These filters are often used to minimize irreversible fouling of the deionizing resins. Microbial growth is supported by organic molecules absorbed onto, and retained within, the activated carbon particles. The highest numbers of micro-organisms occur towards the bottom of the bed because the residual chlorine is removed in the top portion. Organisms leave the filter on particle fines or when they are sloughed off by the local flow conditions and shear forces. Coliform organisms together with *Arthrobacter*, *Alcaligenes*, *Acinetobacter*, *Micrococcus*, *Corynebacter* and *Pseudomonas* species may be recovered from carbon filters (Camper *et al.* 1986).

3.1.3.2   Water softeners

Softeners, which are required when the source water has a high mineral content (especially Ca^{2+} and Mg^{2+}) are generally more susceptible to microbial contamination than cation/anion-exchange resins, since the latter are regenerated with acid and alkali which have a bactericidal effect (Chapman *et al.* 1983b). Sodium chloride regeneration solutions for softeners do not provide the necessaary periodic bactericidal effect. Consequently, situations can develop in which the microbial population steadily increases over the course of the softener's operating life. Some bacteria will be removed or reduced during a backwash operation, but many softeners are designed with minimal head-space and there is insufficient backwash flow (Chapman *et al.* 1983b).

The brine make-up tanks associated with softeners can allow proliferation of halophiles and other salt-tolerant micro-organisms unless adequate precautions are taken. These include agitation or recirculation of the tank contents to prevent stratification, leading to high levels of micro-organisms in the lower salt concentrations at the top of the tank. Maintaining saturated solutions, minimizing the brine holding-time and providing a clean closed system are worthwhile precautions to reduce the risk of microbial contamination and proliferation.

3.1.3.3   Ion-exchange resins

The cation/anion deionizers themselves, if correctly sized, may well present less of a problem than the other major elements of the system. Whilst the deionizers will be repeatedly inoculated with bacteria from upstream in the system, the frequent regeneration by strong acid and alkali usually sanitizes them. Problems may arise with deionizers when either physical pockets of stagnation occur or after prolonged periods of inactivity, e.g. when a stand-by unit comes into operation during regeneration of the primary unit. If regeneration is infrequent the stand-by unit may be seriously contaminated by the time it is called into duty. The adhesive interactions between the micro-organisms and the ion-exchange resins have been classified by Wood (1980) as non-specific, pH-dependent and salt-dependent.

High-molecular-weight organic molecules and their chlorine-oxidized degradation products will be concentrated onto the resin bed from the supply water. This occurs partly due to molecular adsorption onto the bead surface and partly due to the migration of the organics into the matrix of the resin beads. Insoluble organic material will also be retained in the bed due to simple physical filtration. While the resin beads do not, of themselves, support the growth of micro-organisms, microbial proliferation on and between the resin beads is encouraged by the retained organic material (Dudderidge 1988). As the biofilm increases throughout the resin bed, so the chemical and microbiological quality of the water gradually declines. In addition, sudden surges through the bed, caused by shutdowns or start-ups, can lead to sloughing off of portions of the biofilm from the bead surfaces into the water stream.

The extent to which microbial growth will occur within an ion-exchange bed will be a function of the type and level of organic material in the input water, the temperature of the bed, and the operating characteristics of the plant. Typically viable counts made at 22°C can be expected to be 10^3 c.f.u. ml^{-1} from a deionizer prior to regeneration, if that regeneration is undertaken approximately every 24 hours. If the system is so oversize as to need regenerating only weekly, then counts of 10^5–10^6 c.f.u. ml^{-1} are not uncommon. The organisms most often associated with deionizers are *Acinetobacter* spp., the *Alcaligenes* group and *Pseudomonas* species, although Gram-positive rods and cocci may also be found. The organisms originate mainly from the supply water, but may also be present in the resin beds as they are supplied. Karavanskaya *et al.* (1980) found ion-exchange columns to be heavily contaminated with *Moraxella* and *Acinetobacter*, whilst Stamm *et al.* (1969) isolated and identified 44 different bacterial and fungal genera, including pathogens, from the effluent of cation exchangers. Schubert and Esanu (1972) reported *Ps. fluorescens*, *putida*, *lemoignei*, *acidovorans*, *cepacia*, *maltophilia* and *carophylii*, together with *Alcaligenes* group and Gram-positive rods and cocci, as being present in ion exchangers.

Deionizers may be situated between the raw or pre-treated input water and the main storage tank, i.e. outside the distribution ring, and/or within the distribution ring. In either case, accepting that contamination from the deionizers is inevitable, there must be some system of controlling the microbial load in the circulating ring. Two main approaches are used:

(a) *Ultraviolet (UV) light.* UV lamps operating at a wavelength of 254 nm are most often used in the circulating ring main, but there may be occasions where they are better sited at the point of use. UV lamps are effective at controlling the microbial load provided they are correctly sized to cope with the flow rate, optical clarity and expected bioburden of the water. Correct maintenance of UV 'sterilizers', particularly in the regular cleaning of the quartz sleeves covering the UV lamp, is essential if effective light penetration is to be maintained. Lamps need to be changed at the end of their rated hours as the UV output of a lamp decays with time to an ineffective level.

(b) *Filtration*. Filtering water through 0.45-μm or 0.2-μm pore size membrane filters is a method widely used in the pharmaceutical industry for reducing the microbial burden. Pre-filtration may be necessary to protect the expensive bacterial filters from fouling with larger particles or colloids in the source water, and fines shed from the ion exchangers. Some 'water-borne bacteria' will pass through a 0.45-μm pore size filter, and for microbiologically pure water a maximum pore size of 0.2 μm should be used. The correct installation of filters within the housings is crucial if the microbiological quality of the water is to be maintained. Poorly seated filters allow bacteria to pass around the seal and infect the rest of the distribution system. Wherever possible it is advisable to test the integrity of a filter in its housing immediately after installation by, for example, a bubble point or forward flow pressure hold test (see Chapter 9).

3.1.3.4 Distribution system
Once in the distribution system a proportion of the organisms will attach themselves to the surface of pipework, filters, storage tanks and general fittings. Flow rates of 1–2 m s^{-1} are normally recommended for water systems to minimize adhesion. In general, the slower the flow rate and the rougher the internal surfaces, the faster adhesion will occur. The rate of adhesion and subsequent growth will be system-specific, but such biofilms can be difficult to remove and the system may require thorough cleaning followed by disinfection.

If stagnant water is allowed to occur in dead-legs within a distribution system, counts of 10^6 c.f.u. ml^{-1} are quite easily attained, and this culture can effectively seed the main body of recirculating water. Ingress of environmental contaminants will occur if tank vents are not properly protected by bacterial filters and take-off points are poorly handled. The practice of leaving flexible hoses connected to a take-off point is a particular example, where stagnant water in the hose may contaminate the main ring via the valve or meter. Hoses need to be removed and drained immediately after use.

4 PACKAGING
Primary packaging should not be ignored in the total quality equation. It has a dual role in containing the product and in preventing contamination with micro-organisms and the ingress of moisture that may lead to subsequent spoilage (see Chapter 15). The packaging can also act as a source of microbial contamination. In practice, when used for non-sterile dry products or preserved liquids, the packaging seldom contributes significantly to the total bioburden of the product. However, in the case of sterile products, particularly those aseptically prepared, any contamination in the container becomes significant and sterilization of the container becomes essential.

On manufacture, glass containers are sterile, and moulded plastic containers are likely to contain only very low levels of contamination. Incidental contamination may arise during packing, storage and shipment, particularly when card or paper-board is used between the layers of stored bottles or unlined cardboard boxes are employed. Contamination is predominantly with spores of *Penicillium* spp., *Asper-*

gillus spp. and *Bacillus* spp. Laminates, metal foils and blister-pack materials all have smooth impervious surfaces with a high-temperature stage employed in their manufacture and, therefore, have low surface microbial counts. Since they are stored and transported as wound reels, incidental contamination is restricted to the outer surface of the reel.

Negretti (1981) examined 4200 samples of pharmaceutical packaging materials and accessories (glass and plastic bottles, flexible metal tubes, droppers, blisters and cap-liners). The samples most often contaminated were cap-liners (96.4%), plastic bottles (94.8%), droppers (93.6%) and flexible metal tubes (89.7%); less frequently contaminated were the glass bottles (54.6%) and blisters (33.5%). All those contaminated had low microbial counts (only 2.54% in excess of 50 c.f.u. per container) consisting mainly of sporing bacilli (42.4%) and moulds (25%), but pathogenic or hygienically undesirable organisms were occasionally found (Table 4).

5   ENVIRONMENT

5.1   Warehouse

Having obtained good-quality raw materials and packaging components, it is important to maintain that quality throughout storage. Whilst most dry raw materials are nowadays supplied in polythene-lined sacks or kegs, possibly with pallet covers, there is still a potential for contamination if the standard of warehousing is inadequate. Warehouses with racking to hold individual pallets are ideal; air can then circulate around the pallets, allowing the outer packaging to dry out if it has become damp in transit. In unracked warehousing, the close proximity of uncovered pallets to each other may result in damp areas persisting, thereby allowing mould spores present on the outer paper sacks or the cardboard packaging components to germinate and grow. Pallets stored in contact with outer walls may become damp if the wall is at all porous, a situation particularly prevalent in older buildings, with the result that mould growth may occur. The contamination of the outer packaging can be transferred in the dispensaries to the raw material itself as the bags are handled. Small pockets of macroscopic mould on the outer bags can easily be missed by the operators in a busy dispensary. Care needs to be exercised if pallet covers are added at the receiving warehouse since goods must be dry before covers are applied. Conditions ideal for mould growth may be provided if polythene covers are used to overwrap damp materials.

It is essential that pest control measures, against rodents and insects for instance, are maintained, as droppings will be heavily contaminated with enteric pathogens. Strip curtaining or automatic doors should be used at all entrances to warehousing to reduce the risk of birds entering, perching and nesting within the warehouse. Bird droppings, whilst not only being unsightly, are heavily contaminated.

Liquid raw materials preserved by virtue of their high osmotic pressure, e.g. sugar solutions and malt extract, can be susceptible to mould growth if condensation forms on the inner surfaces of the storage vessels and falls back into the liquid thereby causing surface areas of reduced osmotic pressure. Trace heating of tanks to prevent condensation or continuous stirring to mix in any condensation can prevent the problem in large tanks, but small tubs (25 kg) can sometimes be a problem. In our

Table 4 — Microflora present on containers (adapted from Negretti 1981)

Type of container	Numbers examined	Number contaminated	Bacilli	Mould	Number of containers contaminated with:			
					Staph. aureus	*Ps. aeruginosa*	*Strep. faecalis*	Enterobacteriaceae spp.
Glass bottle	1000	546	308	103	25	4	—	*K. pneumoniae* 8, *E. coli* 6
Plastic bottle	1000	948	466	353	40	—	2	*E. coli*, 19, *K. pneumoniae* 7, *Serratia* 6, *Enterobacter* 5, *Yersinia* 5, *Citrobacter* 3
Metal tubes	1000	897	521	248	64	—	5	*E. coli* 11, *Proteus* 7, *K. pneumoniae* 4, *Citrobacter* 3, *Enterobacter* 2, *Hafnia* 2
Droppers	500	468	187	189	11	—	—	*E. coli* 10, *Proteus* 8, *K. pneumoniae* 5, *Enterobacter* 5
Cap-liners	500	482	257	151	14	—	—	*K. pneumoniae* 9, *E. coli* 8, *Proteus* 7, *Serratia* 6
Blister	200	67	42	9	4	—	—	—

experience, malt extract delivered in the summer and stored in a cool warehouse developed condensation on the lids and surface of the malt, allowing the mould spores present to germinate and grow.

5.2   Manufacture of non-sterile dry products (e.g. tablets/granules/powders)

In a manufacturing facility dealing with only dry powder mixing, granulation and drying, and final sacheting or tabletting, contamination of the product from the environment is minimal. The contamination that does occur will be predominantly *Bacillus* and mould spores from the environmental dust, together with micrococci and staphylococci from skin scales shed by the operators. The major source of contamination is cross-contamination from the outer packaging to the raw materials during dispensing. However, in practice, with good handling procedures and suitable ventilation for dust control, cross-contamination is minimal and normally undetectable. Blending and mixing operations are now largely enclosed and ingress of airborne contamination is minimal.

Fluid bed driers and mixer granulator driers pass large quantities of air through the product during the drying and granulation stage and can potentially be a source of contamination depending on the siting of the input air duct. However, in practice, coarse filtration of the input air appears all that is required, and submicron filtration is rarely necessary to prevent large increases in microbial numbers during the drying stage. Bed temperatures of 80–100°C achieved in fluid bed driers and mixer granulator driers cannot be relied upon to destroy vegetative organisms such as the Enterobacteriaceae that may, for instance, be present in a raw material of natural origin, since the heat is essentially dry heat.

Aqueous granulation and drying can become a problem if drying is not carried out immediately or if temperature tray drying is carried out over an extended time. Proliferation of the flora originating from the raw materials may occur during the tray drying stage, which then dies out as the water activity is reduced. High spore counts may be all that remain in the finished product to indicate such a problem.

Tabletting machines exert some antimicrobial effects. The shearing forces and localized heat involved in pressing tablets is sufficient to destroy many mould spores and vegetative organisms, although *Bacillus* spores appear to survive. Reductions of 67–93% in total viable counts of a dry blended product have been reported to be produced by tabletting (Chesworth *et al.* 1977). Increasing compression pressures and tabletting speeds increase the antimicrobial effect (Fassihi and Parker 1987). Sachet or tablet filling operations have no effect on the microbial quality of the product. The accumulation of product dust in vacuum transfer lines, hoppers, tabletting and filling machines is largely a problem of good manufacturing practices (see Chapter 4), and does not pose a microbiological hazard due to the low water activity of the powder preventing growth from occurring.

The method used for cleaning of equipment often has a major influence on the potential for microbial proliferation. Dry vacuuming is the best method as this does not produce conditions conducive to growth, but it may not always be appropriate for product change-overs. On occasions, washing with water may be the only effective form of cleaning, but it carries with it the risk of presenting conditions ideal for microbial proliferation. Unless equipment is thoroughly cleaned and dried, growth is almost inevitable. Poorly cleaned equipment can result in small pockets of product, dried on the outside, but remaining damp in the centre, where growth can occur. Subsequent use of the equipment results in sporadic incidences of contamination which may include Gram-negative organisms originating from the cleaning water supply or moulds from the previous product. Any areas of plant that are not dry at the end of the cleaning operation must be regarded as potential areas for microbial growth. In addition, cleaning solutions themselves require careful attention. Dilute solutions of detergents may well support growth (see Chapter 2). Dilute citric acid solution, used to return stainless steel equipment to a polished appearance, can become heavily contaminated with mould if not freshly prepared (unpublished observations).

5.3   Production of non-sterile liquids, creams and ointments
Cross-contamination from the outer packaging of raw materials is possible in the dispensary, although in practice, with good air handling and dust extraction, it is minimal. *Bacillus* spp., mould spores from environmental dust, micrococci and staphylococci from skin scales are the commonest contaminants at this stage.

Since water is involved in the production of liquids, creams and ointment products, and in the cleaning of the plant, there is a potential for microbial contamination of the production environment. The greatest danger lies in cross-contamination from the manufacturing environment to the product. Water on the floor, in the drains and gulleys of the manufacturing environment and the wash areas, enables *Ps. aeruginosa*, other *Pseudomonas* spp., *Enterobacter* spp. and other Gram-negative bacteria to grow profusely. Counts of 10^6-10^7 c.f.u. ml^{-1} are easily attained in wet areas if regular disinfection and drying is not carried out. However, the total elimination of contamination can never be effected as there is always a reservoir of contamination in the drains. In addition, the feet of the operators and the wheels of pallet trucks are probably a major vector for transferring contamination from one area to another and it is, therefore, important to keep the floors and surfaces as dry as possible.

Similar situations were described in a study of environmental contamination in hospital manufacturing pharmacies, where *Ps. aeruginosa* was isolated from a variety of wet sites, including sinks, drains, taps, draining boards, tank water supplies, label dampers and cleaning equipment (Baird *et al.* 1976). The same strains of *Ps. aeruginosa* were invariably isolated from contaminated products made in these pharmacies, and subsequently from patients who used their products (Baird and Shooter 1976).

Good manufacturing practices are particularly important in preventing cross-contamination from the plant environment to the product (see Chapter 4). Particularly at risk are those operations that may have to be carried out in close proximity to the floor, such as hose connections.

Cleaning equipment can also be a significant source of contamination. Mops, buckets, cloths, scrubbing machines and other items, particularly when stored wet, may provide suitable conditions for the proliferation of Gram-negative bacteria, especially *Pseudomonas* spp. The use of contaminated cleaning equipment has contributed to the spread of infections in hospitals (Maurer 1978) and there is no doubt that contamination in pharmaceutical factories has occurred in the same way.

Cleaning the processing equipment, storage tanks, pipelines and filling machines creates its own potential for contamination because it inevitably has a water rinse as its final stage. If the plant remains moist, then growth of Gram-negative organisms is to be expected. Ideal equipment is crevice-free, smooth-surfaced, easily drained or dried, and is readily accessible. Vessels, mixers and homogenizers with their associated shafts may easily create obstacles to cleaning lances, leaving a shadow of uncleaned equipment area. Inspection ports and inlets for probes, often recessed into the sides of the vessel, can be particularly difficult to clean and dry. Pumps, particularly those with pressure relief valves, need careful attention. Pipelines, with minimal dead-legs that are self-draining, are essential if cleaning is to be achieved without extensive dismantling. Complex filling machines, whilst having smooth inner surfaces and being easily cleaned in place, can be difficult to dry without dismantling. Those areas of the plant that are difficult to clean have the potential for creating areas of dilute product, where organisms may become adapted to preservative levels present in that product.

Compressed air coming into contact with product or primary packaging, e.g. bottle blowers, unless sterilized by filtration, can be expected to be a source of contamination. Gram-negative organisms may colonize the condensate in the air reservoir tanks.

In a well-maintained manufacturing facility operating good manufacturing procedures environmental air is not a significant source of contamination during processing or filling of preserved products. Covered mixing vessels prevent significant ingress of air during the mixing stage and air turbulence created both within and around container openings appears, in practice, to be insufficient to cause significant numbers of micro-organism-laden particles to enter the container.

Chemical disinfectants, used throughout the plant, must be prepared to the correct use-concentration. Over-dilute solutions may become contaminated and thereby represent a source of contamination for the environment to be cleaned (see Chapter 2). Most chemical disinfectants, in particular the halogens, some phenolics and quaternary ammonium compounds, are inactivated in the presence of organic matter and it is essential that all cleaning materials such as buckets are kept clean. Biofilms may arise on the surfaces of dirty containers in which organisms, normally sensitive to the disinfectant solution, may survive and grow. The practice of storing bulk concentrated disinfectant, and preparing use-concentrations daily in clean containers, significantly reduces the chances of contamination. The rotation of disinfecting agents is a wise precaution against the development of resistant strains.

5.4 Sterile products

Many precautions need to be taken in the design and operation of a sterile product-manufacturing facility to minimize both particulate and microbial contamination (see Chapters 4 and 5). The production suite needs to be of a high standard of construction, having impervious smooth walls, floor and ceiling covering, and all dust traps eliminated. All surfaces and equipment should be easy to clean and constructed in materials capable of withstanding repeated chemical disinfection. HEPA-filtered air supplies either to provide conventional air flow in the room space or localized laminar flow at the critical sites of operation are normal in the pharmaceutical industry (see Chapter 5). Regular chemical disinfection of the surfaces, walls and floors, together with maintenance of the air filter integrity and air change rates, can produce areas well within the standards in the unmanned state. Fumigation of areas with formaldehyde is commonly carried out, but provided chemical surface disinfection is thorough this is probably necessary only ofter the integrity of the area has been broken during maintenance. Microbial burdens of 0–3 c.f.u. per 24 cm^2 contact plate immediately after cleaning are easily attained and counts of <10 c.f.u. per 24 cm^2 can be expected even during operation. The level of micro-organisms present in the air is dependent on the type of operation carried out, the number of operators and the size of the room. The greater the complexity of operation and numbers of operators, the higher the level of contamination to be expected in a given space.

The quality of gowning and level of awareness and training of operators is very important in determining the levels of environmental contamination in clean and aseptic areas. Full coveralls with boots, hood, face-mask and sterile gloves afford the maximum protection to the environment. Close-weave fabrics that prevent skin scales from escaping yet allow a degree of air movement give operator comfort and, therefore, high procedure compliance rates. Completely air-impervious garments are extremely uncomfortable and become counter-productive as the only areas from which air can escape are the cuffs and collar. Thus, each time a movement is made there is a tendency to puff skin scales and organisms out into the environment. In addition, hot, uncomfortable and irritable operators are less likely to comply strictly to procedures.

6 OVERVIEW

An understanding of the microbial ecology of production processes and environments enables the industrial microbiologist to appreciate the critical control points, set sensible quality limits and quickly identify reasons for changes in quality. Extended treatments of environmental standards and good manufacturing practices that contribute to good microbiological control are given in Chapters 4 and 5.

7 REFERENCES

Baggerman, C. and Kannegieter, L. M. (1984) Microbiological contamination of raw materials for large volume parenterals. *Appl. Environ. Microbiol.* **48** 662–664.

Baird, R. M. and Shooter, R. A. (1976) *Pseudomonas aeruginosa* infections associated with use of contaminated medicaments. *Br. Med. J.* **2** 349–350.

Baird, R. M., Brown, W. R. L. and Shooter, R. A. (1976) *Pseudomonas aeruginosa* in hospital pharmacies. *Br. Med. J.* **1** 511–512.

Bonomi, E. and Negretti, F. (1977) Studies on the microbial content of raw materials used in pharmaceutical preparations. *Ann. Ist. Super. Sanita* **13** 805–832.

Camper, A. K., Le Chevallier, M. W., Broadaway, S. C. and McFeters, G. A. (1986) Bacteria associated with granular activated carbon particles in drinking water. *Appl. Environ. Microbiol.* **52** 434–438.

Chapman, K. G., Alegnani, G. E., Heinze, G. E., Flemming, C. V., Kochling, J., Croll, D. B., Kladko, M., Lehman, W. J., Smith, D. C., Adair, F. W., Amos, R.

L., Enzinger, R. M. and Soli, T. C. (1983a) Protection of water treatment systems, Part IIa: potential solutions. *Pharm. Technol.* September, 86–92.

Chapman, K. G., Alegnani, W. C., Heinze, G. E., Flemming, C. V., Kochling, J., Croll, D. B., Kladko, M., Lehman, W. J., Smith, D. C., Adair, F. W., Amos, R. L., Enzinger, R. M., Grant, D. E. and Soli, T. C. (1983b) Protection of water treatment systems, Part I: the problem. *Pharm. Technol.* May, 48–57.

Chesworth, K. A. C., Sinclair, A., Stretton, R. J. and Hayes, W. P. (1977) Effect of tablet compression on the microbial content of granule ingredients. *Microbios Lett.* **4** 41–45.

Dudderidge, J. E. (1988) Biofilm growth in water for cosmetics. *Manuf. Chem.* May, 42–44.

Fassihi, A. R. and Parker, M. S. (1987) Inimical effects of compaction speed on micro-organisms in powder systems with dissimilar compaction mechanisms. *J. Pharm. Sci.* **76** 466–470.

Grigo, J. (1976) Micro-organisms in drugs and cosmetics: occurrence, harms and consequences in hygienic manufacturing. *Zentbl. Bakt. Hyg. Abt. I. Orig. B.* **162** 233–287.

Hitokoto, H., Morozumi, S., Wauke, T., Sakai, S. and Kurata, H. (1978) Fungal contamination and mycotoxin detection of powdered herbal drugs. *Appl. Environ. Microbiol.* **36** 252–256.

Karavanskaya, N. A., Yakimenko, A. I., Zemlanskii, V. V. and Listetskaya, N. F. (1980) Degree of microbial contamination of certain types of ion exchange resins and activated carbon. *Mikrobiol. Zh. (Kiev)* **42** 428–431.

Maurer, I. M. (1978) Cleaning the hospital: care with water. *Hospital Hygiene*, 2nd edn. Edward Arnold, London, pp. 42–57.

Negretti, F. (1981) Findings on the microbiological characteristics of pharmaceutical containers. *Boll. Chim.-Farm.* **120** 193–201.

Schubert, R. H. W. and Esanu, J. (1972) On bacterial aftergrowth in drinking and industrial water. I. The influence of ion-exchange plants. *Zentbl. Bakt. Hyg. Abt. I. Orig. B.* **155** 488–501.

Stamm, J. M., Engelhard, W. E. and Parsons, J. E. (1969) Microbiological study of water-softener resins. *Appl. Microbiol.* **18** 376–386.

Wood, J. M. (1980) The interaction of micro-organisms with ion exchange resins. In: Berkely, R. C. W., Lynch, J. M., Melling, J., Rutter, P. R. and Vincent, B. (eds), *Microbial adhesion to surfaces*. Ellis Horwood, Chichester, pp. 163–185.

Yokoyami, H. Yamasaki, K., Sakagami, Y., Nunoura, Y., Umezawa, C. and Yoneda, K. (1981) Investigation on quality of pharmaceutical products containing crude drugs (I). *J. Antibact. Antifung. Agents* **9** 421–428.

4

Good manufacturing practice in the control of contamination

D. P. Hargreaves†
Medicines Control Agency, Market Towers, 1 Nine Elms Lane, London
SW8 5NQ, UK

† The views and opinions expressed are personal ones and are not necessarily those of the Medicines Inspectorate and should not be taken as GMP requirements.

1 INTRODUCTION

Good manufacturing practice (GMP) enshrines the principle that products are consistently manufactured to a quality appropriate to their intended use. GMP is thus an all-embracing philosophy that covers premises, services, equipment, processes, documentation, purchasing, distribution and staff. The control of microbiological contamination is an important aspect of GMP and should form an integral part of it.

Traditionally, microbiological control has been associated particularly with the manufacture of sterile products. However, experience has shown that microbiological contamination can also cause problems with a wide range of non-sterile products, e.g. tablets, creams, ointments and oral liquids. The frequent response to this problem has been the introduction of preservatives, but there is now increasing consumer and medical pressure to remove or reduce the levels of preservatives in products. In turn the pharmaceutical manufacturer has had to respond by increasing the level of microbiological monitoring and control. One of the main consequences of this has been the introduction of microbiological control to existing premises and practices in a piecemeal fashion where it is often expensive and ineffective. An alternative and preferred course of action involves a thorough review of all aspects of the operation with a team consisting of representatives from the microbiology, engineering, manufacturing and training departments. This should ensure that there is a consistent approach throughout the factory and that no important aspects are missed. The food industry is aware of the need for an integrated approach and has developed a system called hazard analysis critical control points (HACCP). This system ensures that the right amount of resource, monitoring and control is in place at the points where microbiological control is required. This is not only cost effective but also gives a high degree of assurance that the finished product will be suitable for its intended use.

GMP has been interpreted in many different ways. The most succinct definition is 'getting it right first time, every time'. One of the best ways of achieving this is to prevent mistakes from occurring at source. Most companies are good at identifying possible hazards for which they then introduce checks or tests at subsequent manufacturing stages to determine whether the hazard has occurred. This is *not* good manufacturing practice. The correct approach is to identify the hazard and prevent it from occurring in the first place. In the long term, this is also probably the most cost-effective approach, but it may take time and effort on the part of the people involved in solving the problem. It is recognized that going from one crisis to another is a common problem in manufacturing industries and that lack of time and resource often prevents the ideal problem-solving approach from being taken. Indeed, there can be considerable commercial pressure to maintain the *status quo* rather than develop better, more secure systems or working practices. In such a situation, a cost–benefit analysis may be necessary to demonstrate that the benefits from an initial investment of staff and resources can often be significant in terms of longer shelf-life (especially in warmer climates), lower rejection rate and fewer customer complaints. It is important, therefore, that scientific and manufacturing personnel are able to present their requirements in such a way that they are readily understandable to the commercial arm of the company. GMP must evolve from, and involve, senior managmeent. Without their commitment, resources may be unduly limited.

2 PRINCIPLES OF FACTORY/HOSPITAL HYGIENE

2.1 Zoning concept

A factory will naturally be divided into specific areas for different activities. Each activity will have different requirements in terms of air handling and filtration, temperature and humidity control, cleaning and protective clothing. By taking this natural segregation of activities one stage further, the zoning concept is achieved. When designing a new factory or renovating an existing one, it is relatively easy to zone activities according to cleanliness requirements and to ensure that these zones are readily identifiable to all employees. One way of achieving this is to paint the zones different colours. Access would be restricted to those people who were correctly clothed, trained and authorized to be in that zone.

Whilst this practice is common in clean-room suites, its extension to cover the whole factory is now becoming more widespread as the need to manufacture non-sterile products to a high microbiological quality is recognized. Traditionally, zones have been classified as black, grey and white. However, with the numerous activities that occur in non-sterile manufacture, a more varied classification is needed. The zoning concept enables the correct amount of resource to be allocated to an area. For example, an oral liquid manufacturing area may require a more frequent and thorough sanitization programme than a non-aqueous ointment manufacturing area. In the same way, clothing, air handling and air filtration should reflect the necessary degree of protection that the products require.

2.2 Clothing

Ideally, all personnel entering or working in pharmaceutical manufacturing areas should be clothed in dedicated factory clothing. This should consist of white shirt, white trousers and appropriate footwear. The clothes should be freshly laundered. It is not unusual to find that people are issued with insufficient changes of clothing, perhaps having to wear the same shirt and trousers for up to one week in the interests of economy. For products that are prone to adventitious microbiological contamination, e.g. oral liquids and creams, and are not manufactured in closed systems, this can prove to be an expensive economy. It is absurd to invest money and time on performing bioburden tests on raw materials when the manufacturing staff are not suitably clothed.

Much has been written on the design of, and the textiles used for, clean-room clothing (Redlin and Neale 1987; Anon. 1987a; Miller 1987; Clemens 1988; Goodwin 1988; Dixon 1989) to which the reader is referred. The purpose of clean-room clothing is to reduce the shedding by personnel of micro-organisms and non-viable particulate matter into the environment. If clean-room clothing is to be effective, therefore, it should be demonstrated to be so, prior to its being worn in the clean room. In this respect, the laundering and sterilization (or sanitization) of clothing can damage it to the extent that it is no longer suitable for its intended use. There are a number of methods available for testing clean-room clothing, and one of these methods or a suitable alternative should be used (Anon. 1968; Australian Standard AS 2013 1977a; Australian Standard AS 2014 1977b; British Standard 3211, 1986). The approximate life of the garments can then be determined so that they can be replaced before becoming defective. This will require stability testing whereby a garment will undergo successive laundering and sterilization cycles until it fails. The rationale behind this is that it is extremely difficult for clean-room monitoring programmes to detect defective garments in a timely manner. A defective garment may be worn only once or twice a month and it may be many months before the monitoring programme will pinpoint the problem. It helps, of course, if all garments are identified and logged so that high microbial counts in the clean room can be correlated to the specific garments worn. Apart from the standard clean-room clothing worn by the regular personnel, there is usually a requirement for clothing for people who are infrequent visitors, e.g. maintenance/engineering personnel and self-inspection audit teams. Disposable clean-room clothing is a popular choice in these circumstances, but this clothing also needs to be vigorously tested for adequacy before a particular make is used; in particular, some types do not have sealed seams over the stitching.

2.3   Cleaning and disinfection
The *Guide to good pharmaceutical manufacturing practice* (Anon. 1983a) contains some general advice with regard to cleaning and disinfection (see sections 2.10, 2.11, 2.12, 4.20, 4.21, 4.22, 9.29, 9.30, 9.41, 9.42, 9.44). Disinfection and sanitization of specific manufacturing areas will be examined in greater detail in subsequent sections of this chapter. Some problems associated with cleaning of equipment are illustrated in Chapter 3. An extensive treatment of cleaning-in-place and sterilizing-in-place is given by Seiberling (1987).

A cleaning and disinfection policy should be prepared that covers the whole factory or hospital manufacturing suite. This should be drawn up in conjunction with a microbiologist, manufacturing and janitorial staff. The cleaning and disinfection policy should cover written cleaning schedules and procedures, including the name of cleaning/disinfection agent; concentration of agent; quality of water to be used in preparation of use dilutions; and shelf-life of diluted agent. The procedures should also include details of how the disinfectant is measured and diluted, e.g. the size of the measuring cylinder should be one appropriate to the quantity being measured. It is not uncommon to find small volumes being measured in large measuring cylinders, a problem which arises particularly when disinfectants are changed, especially to ones that are used at concentrations of 0.5% or below. Both above and below certain concentrations biocidal activity may decrease dramatically.

Validation of disinfectant activity is an area that has been somewhat ignored in the past. Retrospective validation can no longer be accepted, especially where products which are susceptible to microbial contamination are involved. A validation protocol should be prepared and used whenever a new disinfectant is proposed; this should include an initial assessment of the disinfectant's properties (Table 1).

If the results of this initial survey and prospective validation are satisfactory, then

Table 1 — Disinfectant validation protocol

(a) Review manufacturer's data sheet. Determine whether work was done in-house or independently. Obtain copies of references
(b) Literature search. Determine whether further information is available
(c) Determine minimum contact time
(d) Determine compatibility with other disinfectants/cleaning agents in use
(e) Determine compatibility of disinfectant with surface finishes in manufacturing areas, e.g. stainless steel, glass, plastics, vinyl
(f) Determine in-use concentration range
(g) Determine compatibility with any product residues to ensure neutralization does not occur
(h) Determine spectrum of activity

---

the next stage is to consider the current operating procedures. Procedures may need to be rewritten to incorporate such changes as the name of the new disinfectant, its concentration and frequency of use, rotation with other agents, etc. Dilutions may well be different, requiring new measures or containers for diluting and storing the new disinfectant. Another important factor to take into account is user acceptance. If the disinfectant causes irritation of the eyes and throat in sensitive individuals, strict compliance with the disinfection regime may prove difficult. Therefore, user acceptance trials may be of benefit at this stage.

The next stage is the most difficult one: a decision has to be taken to accept or reject the new disinfectant. It is important that the rationale for accepting or rejecting the agent is well documented. If problems are encountered in the future, the documentation could prove to be very useful, especially if there has been a change in staff. When the new disinfectant is brought into use, the level of environmental monitoring must be increased. The extent of this will depend upon the results obtained during the prospective validation study. Once the relevant amount of historical data has been obtained and found to be satisfactory, then environmental monitoring can revert to its previous frequency.

Disinfectants can become contaminated with micro-organisms and special precautions need to be taken to prevent this problem arising (Anon. 1958; Burdon and Whitby 1967; Ayliffe et al. 1969; Bassett et al. 1970; Berkelman et al. 1984; see also Chapter 2). Disinfectants and cleaning agents should be monitored for microbial contamination. Dilutions should be kept in previously cleaned containers and should not be stored unless sterilized. Part-empty containers should not be refilled (Whyte and Donaldson 1989).

The type and condition of mops and buckets used are a frequent source of embarrassment to companies during audits. It is not unusual to find dirty, dilapidated mops stored in a damp condition in a cupboard with inadequate ventilation. This presents a microbiological hazard and generates an excessive challenge for disinfectants. This situation can arise when cleaning and disinfection are performed out of hours and also when outside contractors are used. The examination of cleaning equipment should be part of the self-inspection programme and also, of course, be one of the area supervisor's routine checks.

2.4 Training

Training of personnel is an area to which little practical attention in both time and financial terms is paid, although this would form an integral part of any microbiological audit (see Chapter 17). Training programmes tend to be unimaginative and ineffective as they do not reflect real-life situations. Commercially available programmes may have a professional finish to them but it can be difficult to relate their content to actual work situations. Training programmes produced in-house may not provide a highly polished presentation but, if well constructed, they will at least be relevant to the participants. Initial GMP induction programmes usually have an audience willing and eager to learn; ongoing GMP programmes are much more difficult to produce.

Fortunately, microbiological control is one area in which the theory and practice can be both educational and entertaining. The effects of the operator and the environment on product quality can easily be demonstrated by use of settle plates, swabs, bioburden plates and particle counters. It is important to remember that people need to see bacterial colonies growing on nutrient agar plates in order to appreciate the significance of the training. The theory of microbiological control can be presented in an interesting manner as it can be related to both home and work situations. For example, disinfection of work surfaces in the clean room to prevent microbial contamination of the product can be linked with disinfection of work surfaces in the kitchen to prevent food poisoning. It is essential that personnel understand why they are performing a particular task and what the significance to the end-user of the product may be if that task is not performed correctly. All staff should be encouraged to attend relevant meetings, perhaps in conjunction with managerial staff in order to promote discussion of current working practices.

Training programmes should be documented and each person should have a training manual that details what training has been undertaken, and by whom, and the skills or knowledge attained. Ongoing training and reinforcement are important aspects with regard to microbial control. Periodic assessment of the effectiveness of training programmes should be made. All too frequently, the outcome of an investigation into defective medicinal products that have reached the market-place reveals that human error was involved.

2.5 Motivation

Motivation of staff is an integral part of GMP and is the mainstay of microbial control. No matter how modern the facility, there will always be human interaction. A well-motivated and knowledgeable workforce will be alert to possible contamination risks to the product and will inform the relevant people. If the workforce is not motivated there may be some tell-tale signs such as water filters not being changed according to schedule, equipment not being thoroughly cleaned, damage to fabric not being reported and many other small, but important, items being overlooked.

Disillusionment soon sets in if the principles of GMP learned in training courses are overridden for commercial reasons. It is important to explain to staff if a change is to be made that might appear to be in conflict with their idea of GMP. For instance, the environmental monitoring programme might show that one area is historically well within limits and hence the monitoring is to be decreased, thus releasing staff to work elsewhere. The resource realized by this action might be put into an area that is not so well within limits. The staff in the good area might believe that the decreased monitoring is part of a cost-cutting exercise rather than a fine-tuning of the monitoring programme if they are not told the rationale behind it. Communication between the people involved in monitoring microbial contamination and the manufacturing staff is of the essence if demotivation is not to occur. A typical example of demotivating action is to report only out-of-limit results to the manufacturing department. Even worse is to name individuals associated with these results. This not only creates bad feeling but could ultimately lead to obstructive practices developing between manufacturing and monitoring departments. A feedback system should be developed so that the manufacturing department receives the good news as well as the bad news. If a problem should arise with certain groups or individuals, retraining or reinforcement of GMP principles should be the first step, rather than disciplinary action.

2.6 Self-inspection

A self-inspection or audit team can be a most powerful tool in microbiological control (see Chapter 17). The team has two main functions: to provide a fresh pair of eyes, and to ensure a regular unannounced visit to all manufacturing areas by management. It is a good idea to include in the team someone who has little knowledge of manufacturing or of the area. It is usually this person who asks the most questions and can prove to be an effective challenge of current practices and systems. Regular visits by managerial staff demonstrate that they are interested in the day-to-day life of a manufacturing unit and this helps to reinforce training and increases motivation. Much care needs to be taken with the reporting and feedback of audit results so that they are presented in a positive and constructive manner.

2.7 Procedures

Written procedures have two main functions: they allow all activities to be performed in a reproducible way, and to the same standard every time. They can also encourage the person who writes them to examine current working practices and, perhaps, to improve them.

Written procedures should be kept as simple as possible, should be in easily followed steps and should be written in the imperative. The use of diagrammatic flow-chart procedures should be considered for complex operations as these can be very effective. All too frequently working practice does not reflect the written procedure since it was not written by the person performing the task. Furthermore, the procedures may be inaccessible in the supervisor's office and not available for use in practice. Indeed, the operator may not have seen the procedures, since they may have been prepared for presentation to regulatory authorities or certifying bodies only.

There is a simple rule of thumb to determine whether written procedures are satisfactory: if an experienced person who does not work in that department can follow the procedure without having to ask questions, the procedure works. If questions have to be asked, this indicates that important steps are missing from the procedure.

2.8   Monitoring

Monitoring is the assessment or measurement of a number of parameters in order to estimate the condition of an area, product or process. The purpose is to confirm that the chosen parameters are within defined limits, or whether the limits have been exceeded and corrective action is required. Table 2 summarizes the features required in a microbiological monitoring programme.

Table 2 — Essential features of a microbiological monitoring programme

(a) Reflect the risk to the product
(b) Provide meaningful results (e.g. 'no colony-forming units on a settle plate' does not provide meaningful information)
(c) Initially be all-embracing before concentrating on those areas that show highest risk
(d) Have both warning and action limits
(e) Be flexible, allowing on-the-spot decisions to be taken by monitoring staff
(f) Have a known percentage recovery rate so that results can be converted to actual levels (particularly important for swabs)

It is important that the results of the monitoring programme are documented in such a way that trends are discernible at the earliest possible moment. Any unusual results should be investigated immediately and not assumed to arise from contaminated plates or experimental error.

2.9   Documentation

All too frequently work is performed but not adequately documented. This is particularly true for microbiological investigations of contamination problems. Much work may be done to identify and solve the problem but it may not be written up at the time. Subsequently it can be very difficult to reconstruct the work performed and hence convince an outside person that the problem has been adequately resolved. Furthermore, should a similar problem arise, it may again need to be tackled from first principles in the absence of adequate documentation from the first occasion.

It is now common practice to enter environmental monitoring results onto a computer, in order to aid trend analysis. However, in certain instances it has been found that actual results are converted to averages or means in this process. Whilst this practice may be satisfactory for the purpose of trend analysis, the raw data must be kept, and any reviewer of the data informed about software manipulation of the raw information.

3   INFLUENCE OF PRODUCTION ENVIRONMENT DESIGN

The environment of the manufacturing and storage areas may have an impact upon the microbial quality of the finished product. The extent of this impact will be mainly dependent upon equipment design, operating practices and the process. If closed systems are used then the environmental standards may not be required to be as stringent as those for open systems. However, for this relaxation in standards to be acceptable, the operating procedures and practices must also be appropriate. Two different companies manufacturing the same products, using identical equipment, might have to operate to different levels of environmental standards to achieve the same product quality because of differences in operating procedures and practices. This might at first seem to be unwarranted, but it is important to remember that it is not possible to validate bad manufacturing practices.

A number of key areas need to be addressed when examining the effect of the environment in manufacturing and storage areas on product quality. These are: surface finishes; heating, ventilation and air conditioning (HVAC) systems; drains; equipment; operating procedures; and clothing.

Each of the above points will have a different significance in different manufacturing areas.

3.1 Dry products

There is no doubt that tablets, capsules and powders are, on occasions, susceptible to microbial contamination and this can result in spoilage of the product and, in some cases, harm to the patient (Blair *et al.* 1988). Whilst it is accepted that the main source of contamination is usually the raw material, once an undesirable micro-organism enters a dry products area there are usually a number of places where it can become established to form a reservoir. Subsequent batches of the same or different products may then become contaminated. The correct design, construction and cleaning of manufacturing areas will diminish the risk of microbial contamination. The reader's attention is drawn to the many papers, articles and monographs which have been written on this subject (e.g. Anon. 1983a, 1987b, 1989; British Standard 5295, 1989); some of the more important aspects will be examined here. Drains if present should be regularly monitored and sanitized. Floors should slope towards the drain and there should be no dead areas where water can accumulate. Wash bays should be designed with proper drainage and an adequate air supply and extraction system. Inadequate air extraction often arises since the amount of steam used in cleaning manufacturing equipment is frequently underestimated at the outset. Surface finishes must be robust because of the aggressive nature of steam and some cleaning agents. All too often, insufficient time, effort and expertise are put into designing wash bays since they are perceived not to be directly involved in manufacturing the product.

Water may be used as an ingredient, e.g. in granulation and coating solutions, and as a cleaning agent. The microbial quality of the water may be poor because of the storage conditions or because of unsuitable pipework and valves. Flexible hoses should be removed, drained after use and stored vertically (see also Chapter 3). Some water systems are designed to have point-of-use filters. Unless these filters are changed and sterilized on a frequent basis, they can be a source of microbial contamination. It is usually better practice to design a system that does not require point-of-use filtration in order to obtain water of good microbial quality.

Manufacturing staff can also be a source of undesirable micro-organisms. In particular, fungal spores carried on clothing during the summer months may cause a problem with certain dry products, e.g. paracetamol tablets. Adequate changing facilities should be provided to enable staff to change quickly at the end of working sessions and without contaminating their factory clothing. Another source of fungal spores can be the HVAC system. The air supply to a dry products area should be adequately filtered to prevent the ingress of spores. The system should be so designed that it is easy to examine and replace filters. When filters become blocked there is an increased risk of air bypassing the filters and hence unfiltered air entering the manufacturing areas. Where air extraction systems are used, e.g. to remove local heat, the source of make-up air must be considered.

3.2   Liquids, creams and ointments
Many of the comments made in section 3.1 regarding dry product manufacturing areas are also applicable to areas devoted to the manufacture of liquids, creams and ointments. However, these products may be more prone to microbial contamination as discussed in detail in Chapter 3 and as such require more stringent manufacturing environments. This section refers to non-sterile products only. If closed manufacturing systems are not used then Class J or Class K clean rooms (British Standard 5295, 1989) should be considered for manufacturing these types of products. This approach has two advantages: staff are constantly aware that the products are at risk from microbial contamination, and the products are protected to some degree. These preventative measures may seem extreme but the time and cost involved in eliminating a contamination problem in a manufacturing environment and equipment can be considerable, as can the cost of a product recall.

3.3   Terminally sterilized products
The manufacturing environment for the bulk solution for this type of product should meet Class J (British Standard 5295, 1989). However, if the solution is sterile-filtered via a closed system and then collected in sterile receiving vessels, or filled into the final containers and terminally sterilized within a specified short time period, then a Class K environment may be acceptable. The solution should, however, be filled in a room that meets Class J. Further details on these environments can be found in Chapter 5.

The main source of microbial contamination in these manufacturing areas will be water. It is essential that the area be so designed and built to prevent the accumulation of water on floors. Any flexible hoses used should have quick-release fittings to encourage their removal and suitable hose storage facilities should be available. Water outlets should not have dead-legs exceeding six pipe diameters in length. Where large volumes of solutions are prepared, the environment may become extremely humid, especially if the solutions are heated. This can cause structural damage and allow moulds to become established. Adequate dehumidification systems should be installed in the air-handling units to cope with this problem.

3.4   Aseptic manufacture
The manufacture of aseptically prepared products is one of the most challenging areas within the pharmaceutical industry. The production of a sterile product by this means requires a total quality system. The failure of just one part of the system may result in a batch of product not having a sufficient level of sterility assurance and thus

causing its rejection. The sterility test cannot be used as an alternative to the concept of sterility assurance (see Chapter 9). An important aspect of sterility assurance is parametric rejection, i.e. if a critical parameter is not met during the manufacturing, sterile filtration or filling process then the batch may have to be rejected or reprocessed.

Sterility assurance is highly dependent upon the manufacturing environment. Solutions should be prepared in rooms designed and built to Class J (British Standard 5295, 1989) and it should be demonstrated that they meet this classification, in the unmanned state, on a regular basis (see also Chapter 5). The main sources of contamination are as described in section 3.3.

Aseptic filling rooms should be designed and built to meet Class F (British Standard 5295, 1989) requirements, in the unmanned state. They should not just meet the particulate count requirements but should be well within those limits. In addition, where products are exposed the zone around the product should meet Grade1/A and the room Grade 1/B of the *Guide to good pharmaceutical manufacturing practice* (Anon. 1983a), which are similar to Grades A and B of the *European community guide to good manufacturing practice for medicinal products* (Anon. 1989). It is important to note that the filling zone must meet Grade 1/A in the *manned* state. In order to achieve the necessary environmental standards much thought and care must be put into the design, construction and operation of the area. The advent of computer-aided design can take much of the guesswork out of the design of air-handling systems. The number and locations of air inlets and extracts in relation to the proposed layout can be predicted to achieve the most effective air flow. The reader is referred to Chapter 5 for a more detailed discussion on clean-room design, including the location of services and equipment.

Components and equipment should be sterilized during passage into the aseptic area via a double-door autoclave or oven. It is no longer acceptable to build an aseptic area without a suitable double-door sterilizer. Certain components such as plastic eye-drop bottles will not withstand heat sterilization; in these cases it is acceptable to transfer pre-sterilized components into the aseptic area. These components should be triple-wrapped prior to sterilization so that the first layer can be removed in the air-lock for entry into the Class J area and the second layer removed in the air-lock of the aseptic area. The practice of only double-wrapping is to be deprecated as it does not provide sufficient protection to the components and it can also contaminate the aseptic area. It is standard practice to spray or wipe small items with 70% alcohol as they pass into clean rooms. The alcohol used for this must be sterile and the minimum contact time determined. As alcohol is not sporicidal there are inherent risks in this practice. Large items of equipment cannot always be readily sterilized during passage into the area. This problem can be overcome by the use of fumigating air-locks. The equipment is fumigated within the air-lock with formaldehyde or similar agents. Although this system is expensive to fit, it does provide an effective means of transferring equipment into and out of aseptic areas. It can be justified on the basis of reduced down-time of the area.

Maintaining differential air pressures between rooms of different risk plays an important role in the design and operation of clean rooms (see Chapter 5). Pressures are usually monitored with manometers, which should be identifiable and easily read. The limits should be indicated on them. It is recommended that all manometers be in a central bank and be located in ascending or descending order so that it is immediately obvious that the suite is satisfactory. The practice of referencing between rooms and not to ambient can cause confusion and requires a considerable amount of time to calculate actual and total air pressure differentials. Manometers should be zeroed regularly. Errors in zeroing are frequently found during inspections or audits.

3.5   Form–fill–seal

The design of form–fill–seal equipment can be so varied that it is difficult to determine the influence of production environment design on the product without knowing the exact specification of the equipment. The production environment will have an effect on product quality as form–fill–seal machines are not closed systems and operators will be in intimate contact with the filling zone both at start-up and during filling. If the machine has HEPA-filtered air blown over the filling zone the effect of the environment may be minimal (see Chapter 5). However, the quality of the environment will influence the amount of contamination on the operator and hence the filling zone. If form–fill–seal machines are to be used for aseptic manufacture, they should be located in Class F clean rooms with the operators in sterilized clean-room clothing. In this way the risk of the operator contaminating the product during start-up and during filling is minimized. Location of machines in lower classes of environment may still yield product with a contamination rate which complies with the Parenteral Drug Association guideline of 0.1% for aseptically filled products (Anon. 1980a). Nevertheless, since modern high-speed conventional filling lines can achieve significantly lower contamination rates it seems to be a backward step to accept a lower standard when it is not absolutely necessary. It should be remembered that a terminally sterilized product is expected to achieve a contamination rate of less than 1 in 10^6.

3.6   Isolators

Isolators can be classified into two main types: those where goods are sterilized *in situ* or are transferred into the unit within special transfer containers without sterility being broken, and those where sterile goods are transferred into the unit double-wrapped. In the first case the production environment should have little or no effect whereas in the second case the environment can contaminate the goods and therefore the interior of the isolator. This type of isolator should be located within a clean room in order to minimize the bioburden. Isolator technology is considered in detail in Chapter 5.

4   MANUFACTURING PROCESSES AND THEIR INFLUENCE ON CONTROL OF CONTAMINATION

Manufacturing processes can either increase or decrease the level of microbial contamination of the product. It is important to identify which stages of manufacture may cause a significant change and to ensure adequate control at these stages.

4.1   Chemical raw materials

Chemical raw materials have to be sampled and tested prior to their use in manufacture. Sampling should be performed in a dedicated room which is easily cleanable. It is a common misunderstanding that the rationale behind this is solely to prevent cross-contamination of stored materials. Even if there is no risk or hazard of cross-contamination, sampling should not be undertaken in an open warehouse. Extraneous contamination of the material may occur; flies, other insects and even birds can be found in warehouses.

The next stage of the manufacturing process is the dispensing of chemical raw materials. As this process is carried out in the manufacturing area, the environment is controlled and so the area of risk lies in the scoops and containers used in the dispensary. All equipment which comes into direct contact with the chemical raw materials should be adequately washed, dried and stored. Inadequate drying of containers and unsuitable storage conditions, e.g. in the wash bay, are items frequently missed in self-inspection audits.

4.2   Dry products

The manufacturing process for dry products will usually start with a dry blending process of the active ingredient and the excipients. This process will not usually result in a significant change to the bioburden. The total microbial bioburden of powders, capsules, etc. will usually consist of the sum of the individual bioburdens of the ingredients used.

The wet granulation process used in the manufacture of some tablets can result in a significant change in bioburden (see also Chapter 3). For aqueous granulation the quality of the water used is important. Also, the storage conditions of the granulation solution and the granules, prior to and after drying, should be controlled in order to minimize adventitious contamination. The drying process, whether it be tray drying or fluid drying, can alter the bioburden depending upon the conditions used (Blair *et al.* 1988). Drying at low temperatures, e.g. 45°C, may cause an increase in bioburden in certain susceptible products. Drying at high temperatures may result in the bioburden decreasing. Unfortunately, there is no general rule regarding the effect on bioburden during the granulation process and so individual studies on each product and process need to be performed.

The effect of tablet compression on bioburden is also variable (Blair *et al.* 1988). Only individual studies can ascertain what the effect of compression will be. If tablets are sugar-coated or film-coated, the coating solution should be monitored microbiologically and expiry dates determined.

Whatever the effect of the manufacturing process on bioburden, the process should not be relied upon to control the bioburden.

4.3   Liquids, creams and ointments

These products may be manufactured in open or closed systems. The use of closed systems for manufacture and transfer, together with the use of microbiologically clean raw materials, will help prevent microbiological problems. However, it should be remembered that such systems can be difficult to monitor, e.g. with swabs and contact plates, and so extensive validation of the sanitization process is required (Sieberling 1986; Berman et al. 1986; Myers et al. 1987; McClure 1988). Valves and pipework joints should be of the sanitary type as it is important that there should be no sites of attachment available for micro-organisms. With open systems, there are a number of common problems. In particular, product may remain exposed during stirring, inadequately sloped pipework may impede drainage, and leaking valves and joints may deposit product on the floor. All of these situations can cause unnecessary microbial contamination of the product.

The manufacturing process for many creams, ointments and some liquids includes a heating step which may decrease the bioburden. However, care must be taken during cooling to minimize the ingress of air and prevent excessive condensation on vessel walls and lids, e.g. by ensuring that batch sizes are suitable for the vessels used. If the manufacturing vessels are jacketed, they can be sanitized by using the jacket to heat water in the vessels to 100°C. The filling process for these products needs to be monitored and controlled. Hoppers for creams and ointments should have close-fitting lids. Break-tanks for liquids may require bacterial air-vent filters to be fitted, particularly for extended filling runs. This is necessary because the quality of air in the packing hall may be of a substantially lower standard than that in the manufacturing areas. Filling equipment in contact with the product, e.g. hoses, nozzles, pumps, etc., should ideally be sterilized before use; failing that a validated sanitization programme should be used.

Final containers should be cleaned prior to their being filled unless the containers are manufactured, delivered and stored under an approved quality management system. On delivery containers may be contaminated with insects, dust, glass, swarf and numerous other items; supplier audits are therefore desirable. Ideally, glass containers should be washed before use. Plastic containers should be subject to a vacuum and blowing cycle. Aluminium and laminate tubes usually cannot be cleaned in this way and so supplier audits should be performed in these cases. A number of manufacturers are now manufacturing containers under controlled conditions in clean rooms and are seeking registration to British Standard 5750 (1987). All suppliers should be encouraged to achieve registration to this standard.

4.4 Sterile products
One of the main aims of sterile product manufacture is to maintain as low a bioburden as possible during preliminary stages in order to present a minimal challenge to the sterilizing process. This can be achieved by the use of manufacturing vessels and equipment specifically designed for that purpose. Improvisation and modification of basically unsuitable equipment is unacceptable. This is not to say that manufacturers of sterile products need to have state-of-the-art equipment, but the processes and equipment used should be capable of consistently producing a product of the required quality.

Process validation is an area of utmost importance. However, there is still evidence that 'validation' is being misapplied. It is impossible to validate equipment or processes which are inherently unsuitable for their purpose. As it is not possible to prove that a product is sterile, then much reliance is placed on the concept of sterility assurance. This implies that if one or more parts of the process breaks down or deviates significantly from the norm then there is an increased possibility that the product may not be sterile. It is sobering to realize that if only a small percentage of a batch of product is not sterile there is little likelihood of it ever being detected and removed from the market-place (Ringertz and Ringertz 1982).

4.4.1 Water for injection

One of the processes that is regularly highlighted as causing problems is the manufacture of water for injection for use as an ingredient. In the European Pharmacopoeia (1980) this water must be prepared by distillation, although some non-European countries do allow the use of reverse osmosis for its preparation. Whatever the means of preparation, most problems are caused by inadequate storage and distribution. The more satisfactory systems maintain the water at about 80°C, recirculate and use only sanitary-type valves and fittings (Artiss 1982; Anon. 1983b; Jackman 1988). Other types of systems, for example where water is freshly prepared daily and used within a short time, are acceptable but require more stringent control. Microbiological aspects of water are discussed in Chapters 2 and 3.

4.4.2 Vessels

Manufacturing, holding and filling vessels can cause problems. Lids need to be examined routinely for damage. A warped lid may form an inadequate seal and allow ingress of air during the transfer to other vessels or to the filling line. Damaged or missing 'O' rings from vessels is another common problem. These rings have a finite life and should be replaced on a regular basis and not upon gross failure as they may let by air for a long period of time before detection. Records should be kept of 'O' ring replacement; alternatively, they should be included in a planned preventative maintenance programme.

Bacterial air-vent filters should be used wherever possible on vessels. Integrity testing of these filters can be difficult and time-consuming but they do provide an effective means of protecting the product in vessels.

4.4.3 Filtration

Most sterile solutions undergo a filtration step. Terminally sterilized products may be filtered through a 5-μm pore size filter to remove particulates and then through a 0.45 or 0.2-μm filter to yield a solution with a low bioburden. This second filtration stage may be performed to enable a longer holding time before the terminal sterilization process provided that the pipework and receiving vessels have been sterilized or sanitized. Aseptic filtration is a very demanding process, especially the making of the aseptic connection to the receiving vessel. Operator training and equipment main-tenance play a vital role in successful aseptic filtration. It is not unusual for two sterilizing filters to be used in-line such that if one filter fails the integrity test then adequate sterility assurance is still guaranteed.

The number and type of filters available can be confusing, especially as different terminology and test methods for pore size distribution are used. Users should be aware of the difference between absolute and nominal ratings of filters (Denyer *et al.* 1982). Filters should be integrity tested before and after filtration. There are three main test methods available: bubble point, pressure hold and flow volume (forward flow) (see Chapter 9). Each method has advantages and disadvantages and these should be looked at in detail and the limitations of the chosen method understood. Limits should be based upon the solutions being filtered and not based upon water. The bubble point is sometimes incorrectly performed as the compressed air line is regulated to a maximum pressure below the bubble point.

If cartridge filters are used, the style of cartridge and holder is important. A straight, single 'O' ring push-fit with a spring to hold the centre is not satisfactory, as under moderate pulsing the filter will bounce or flex in the housing causing random bypass from the non-sterile to the sterile side. A bayonet lock with two 'O' rings, or similar, is a more secure system.

4.4.4 Bioburden
Bioburden studies are very useful in determining the effect the manufacturing equipment and processes have on the microbial content of the product. These studies should initially be performed at each stage of the manufacturing process so that potential problem areas can be identified, rectified or monitored. These studies should then be repeated at regular intervals to ensure that no significant changes have occurred. When sufficient data have been collected, bioburden limits may then be set.

4.4.5 Filling
There is a wide variety of filling equipment available, ranging from fully automated, microprocessor-controlled lines to simple hand-filling lines. Information to date shows that fully automated aseptic filling can approach the sterility assurance level of terminally sterilized products. However, aseptic hand-filling is still practised and the sterility assurance level can be as low as 1 in 1000. Consequently, hand-filling should only be performed when absolutely necessary, i.e. when the benefit outweighs the risk. The level of sterility assurance of aseptic filling is commonly determined by running broth fills (media fills, system suitability tests). This particular test can provide much useful information if run correctly. The test should challenge both the aseptic filtration and the filling process. The filling of previously autoclaved broth provides little useful information on the sterility assurance of the total manufacturing process. Again, the broth fill cannot be used to validate inadequate or unsuitable manufacturing equipment or processes. Detailed guidance on broth fills and powder fills is provided in *Parenteral Drug Association monographs* (Anon. 1980a, 1984b).

4.4.6 Sterilization methods
There are four main methods of sterilizing components and finished product: autoclaving, hot air, ethylene oxide and irradiation (see Chapter 8). There are many texts available on the validation and operation of these processes (Anon. 1980b, 1981, 1984a, 1988a, 1988b; see also Chapters 8 and 9).

Double-ended sterilizers should be used for components entering aseptic areas and for terminally sterilized products leaving the filling area. If double-ended sterilizers are not used there is an increased risk of product mix-up between sterilized and non-sterilized product. The use of indicator tape on its own does not provide sufficient evidence that a product has undergone a sterilization cycle. In one particular instance, rolls of indicator tape were subject to a sterilizing cycle to obtain the colour change and pieces of this tape were then attached to the product after it had completed its sterilization cycle. The rationale for this was that if the tape was attached to bottles before sterilization, then it was very difficult to remove the tape afterwards. This one example illustrates just how easy it is for a system to be made inherently unsafe.

The cooling media in autoclaves can be a source of microbial contamination. Cooling water should be sterile and air should be filtered through a sterilizing-grade filter during the cooling cycle. One hundred per cent leak testing of containers should detect any leakers but this is a check system, not a prevention system. There have been instances of sterility failure owing to the necks of vials becoming contaminated during the cooling process. The dye solution used for leak testing should be monitored microbiologically and appropriate limits set. It is important that the sensitivity of detection be determined. It should be remembered that some products will decolorize certain dyes.

Sterilizers play such an important role in the manufacture of sterile products that it is surprising to find that their maintenance and upkeep is sometimes left to unqualified and untrained personnel. Unless the person understands the theory and practice of sterilization and has adequate knowledge of the sterilizer, potentially hazardous alterations to the equipment may unwittingly be made. Any work performed on a sterilizer should only be done by authorized personnel. It is not unusual to find that sterilizers have been modified over the years; these modifications should be well documented and engineering drawings prepared to illustrate the total system and highlight the modifications.

5 OVERVIEW

In both hospital and industrial pharmaceutical environments, microbiological control is an area which requires a total understanding of the manufacturing systems, constant vigilance and an enquiring mind. One company's problem may be another's in the future and so a regular review of specialist journals is recommended. In this way, it is possible to recognize potential problems and prevent them from occurring. Lack of time is no excuse for ignorance.

The cost of monitoring and checking is an ongoing expense. The cost of prevention is usually one-off. Application of modern rapid microbiological detection methods should be considered (see Chapter 6B) in an attempt to eliminate the retrospective nature of traditional microbiological cultural methods. Historical information could lead to difficult decisions having to be made.

6 REFERENCES

Anon. (1958) Bacteria in antiseptic solutions. *Br. Med. J.* **2** 436.

Anon. (1968) *Sizing and counting particulate contamination in and on clean room garments* . American Society for Testing and Materials, no. ASTM F51-68.

Anon. (1980a) *Validation of aseptic filling for solution drug products.* Parenteral Drug Association Inc. Technical Monograph no. 2, Philadelphia.

Anon. (1980b) *Validation of steam sterilization cycles.* Parenteral Drug Association Inc. Technical Monograph no. 1, Philadelphia.

Anon (1981). *Validation of dry heat processes used for sterilization and depyrogenation*. Parenteral Drug Association Inc. Technical Report no. 3. Philadelphia.

Anon. (1983a) *The guide to good pharmaceutical manufacturing practice*. HMSO, London.

Anon. (1983b) *Design concepts for the validation of a water for injection system*. Parenteral Drug Association Inc. Technical Report no. 4, Philadelphia.

Anon. (1984a) *Process control guidelines for gamma radiation sterilization of medical devices*. Association for the Advancement of Medical Instrumentation, Arlington, VA.

Anon. (1984b) *Validation of aseptic drug powder filling processes*. Parenteral Drug Association Inc. Technical Report no. 6, Philadelphia.

Anon. (1987a) *Garments required in clean rooms and controlled environment areas*. Institute of Environmental Sciences no. RP-CC-003 87T, Institute of Environmental Sciences, Mount Prospect, USA.

Anon. (1987b) *Pharmaceutical premises and environment*. Pharmaceutical quality group, Institute of Quality Assurance, London.

Anon. (1988a) *Process design, validation, routine sterilization and contract sterilization*. Association for the Advancement of Medical Instrumentation, Arlington, VA.

Anon. (1988b) *Validation and routine monitoring of sterilization by ionizing radiation*. UK Panel on Gamma and Electron Irradiation.

Anon. (1989) *The rules governing medicinal products in the European Community Vol. IV. Guide to good manufacturing practice for medicinal products*. HMSO, London.

Artiss, D. H. (1982) Materials, surfaces and components for WFI and other sanitary piping systems. *Pharm. Technol.* August issue 37–48.

Australian Standard AS 2013 (1977a) *Clean room garments*. Standards Association of Australia, North Sydney, NSW.

Australian Standard AS 2014 (1977b) *Code of practice fo clean room garments*. Standards Association of Australia, North Sydney, NSW.

Ayliffe, G. A. J., Barrowcliff, D. F. and Lowbury, E. J. L. (1969) Contamination of disinfectants. *Br. Med. J.* **1** 505–511.

Bassett, D. C. J., Stokes, K. J. and Thomas, W. R. G. (1970) Wound infection due to *Pseudomonas multivorans*. A water-borne contaminant of disinfectant solutions. *Lancet* **i** 1188–1191.

Berkelman, R. L., Anderson, R. L., Davis, B. J., Highsmith, A. K., Petersen, N. J., Bono, W. W., Cook, E. H., Mackel, M. S., Faucio, M. S. and Martone, W. J. (1984) Intrinsic bacterial contamination of a commercial iodophor solution. *Appl. Environ. Microbiol.* **47** 752–756.

Berman, D., Myers, T. and Chrai, S. (1986) Factors involved in cycle development of a steam-in-place system. *J. Parenter. Sci. Technol.* **40** 119–121.

Blair, T. C., Buckton, G. and Bloomfield, S. F. (1988) Preservation of solid oral dosage forms. In: Bloomfield, S. F., Baird, R., Leak, R. E. and Leech, R. (eds), *Microbial quality assurance in pharmaceuticals, cosmetics and toiletries*. Ellis Horwood, Chichester, pp. 104–116.

British Standard 3211 (1986) *Method for the measurement of the equivalent pore size of fabrics (bubble pressure test)*. British Standards Institution, London.

British Standard 5295 (1989) *Environmental cleanliness in enclosed spaces*. British Standards Institution, London.

British Standard 5750 (1987) *Quality Systems* (ISO 9000–1987). British Standards Institution, London.

Burdon, D. W. and Whitby, J. L. (1967) Contamination of hospital disinfectants with *Pseudomonas* species. *Br. Med. J.* **2** 153–155.

Clemems, S. W. (1988) Packaging people to protect products from contamination in the hospital pharmacy. *Aust. J. Pharm.* **18** 74.

Denyer, S. P. (1982) Filtration sterilisation. In: Russel, A. D., Hugo, W. B. and Ayliffe, G. A. J. (eds.), *Principles and practice of disinfection, preservation and sterilisation*. Blackwood Scientific Publications, Oxford, pp. 569–608.

Dixon, A. M. (1989) Garments: a clean approach. *Med. Dev. Diagnost. Ind.* February issue 44–61.

European Pharmcopoeia (1980). Maison Neuve, Sainte Ruffine.

Goodwin, B. W. (1988) *Cleanroom garments and fabrics. Handbook of contamination control in micro-electronics*. Noyes Publications, Park Ridge, New Jersey, pp. 110–135.

Jackman, D. L. (1988) Troubleshooting your pharmaceutical water system. *Pharm. Eng.* **8** 22–28.

McClure, H. (1988) Sterilization in place: how to sterilize liquid filling equipment at point of contact. *Pharm. Eng.* **8** 14–17.

Miller, W. F. (1987) Clean room garments: a day in the life. *J. Soc. Environ. Eng.* **26** 12–13.

Myers, T., Kasica, T. and Chrai, S. (1987) Approaches to cycle developments for clean-in-place processes. *J. Parent. Sci. Technol.* **41** 9–15.

Redlin, W. J. and Neale, R. M. (1987) Garments for clean room operators: the demands of the 1990's. *J. Soc. Environ. Eng.* **26–1** 17–19.

Ringertz, O. and Ringertz, S. (1982) The clinical significance of microbiol contamination in pharmaceutical and allied products. *Adv. Pharm. Tech.* **5** 201–226.

Seiberling D. A. (1986) Clean-in-place and sterilize-in-place applications in the parenteral solution process. *Pharm. Eng.* **6**, 30–35.

Seiberling, D. (1987) Clean-in-place/sterilize-in-place (CIP/SIP). In: Olson, W. P. and Groves, M. J. (eds), *Aseptic pharmaceutical manufacturing: technology for the 1990's*, Interpharm Press, Prairie View, IL, pp. 247–314.

Whyte, W. and Donaldson, N. (1989) Cleaning a clean room. *Med. Dev. Diagnost. Ind.* February issue 31–35.

5

The design of controlled environments

P. J. P. White
Pharmacy Department, Leicester Royal Infirmary, Leicester LE1 5WW, UK

1   INTRODUCTION

1.1   The need for environmental control

Contamination control technology has undergone a major revolution over the last thirty years, and levels of cleanliness which were once literally unattainable are now regarded as commonplace and routine. It is now universally accepted that all pharmaceuticals should be produced under 'hygienic' conditions, and that some presentations require more comprehensive environmental control during their preparation (see Chapter 4).

Many formulations are potentially vulnerable to microbial spoilage (Smart 1972; Beveridge 1975), and under some circumstances even non-sterile products may present a health hazard to patients (Parker 1972; Ringertz and Ringertz 1982) if microbial contamination is not controlled within closely defined limits. In recognition of the potential hazards arising from excessive contamination of oral and topical dose forms, various official standards (e.g. United States Parmacopeia 1990) specify maximum total viable counts (TVCs) for such preparations, and require them to be free from certain bacterial species. For terminally sterilized products, low initial bioburdens are central to a high confidence level in the sterilization process, and ensure that satisfactorily low levels of endotoxins are achieved in the final product. Injectable products must also meet limits for non-viable particulate contamination, although Boom et al. (1981) and Whyte (1983) have convincingly established that environmental factors contribute relatively little to a product's overall particulate load.

The thermolabile nature of many modern synthetic drug molecules and the current upsurge in biopharmaceuticals production have resulted in a dramatic, industry-wide increase in aseptic manufacturing. In hospital practice, therapeutic techniques such as total parenteral nutrition (TPN) and intravenous chemotherapy have produced a significant requirement for aseptic processing of individualized doses, and several companies have recently entered this field on a commercial basis. The maintenance of asepsis during any mechanical or human manipulation is critically dependent on environmental control, and the demands placed on facility design and operational procedures are the most stringent found in the pharmaceutical sector. This chapter will therefore concentrate principally on the design and specification of facilities suitable for aseptic work, in the knowledge that many of the features described can be selectively employed for less critical applications.

1.2   The scale of the problem

In an uncontrolled environment, the atmosphere forms a natural aerosol of particles which originate from a wide variety of sources. Those particles which harbour culturable micro-organisms are referred to as viable, while inanimate particles are termed non-viable. The particle size distribution of a typical atmospheric air sample is shown in Table 1, from which it can be seen that particles $\leqslant 1$ μm constitute almost

Table 1 — Size distribution of a typical atmospheric dust sample

Particle size range (μm)	Proportionate particle count	% by particle count	% by weight
10–30	1 000	0.005	28
5–10	35 000	0.175	52
3–5	50 000	0.25	11
1–3	214 000	1.07	6
0.5–1	1 352 000	6.78	2
0–0.5	18 280 000	91.72	1

99% of the numerical particulate load, but account for only 3% of contaminant weight, which has important implications for filtration systems. The concentration of suspended particles is generally in the range of 10^8–10^{13} m^{-3}, and the ratio of viable to non-viable particles has been variously estimated at between 1:500 and 1:20 000 (De Vecchi 1986). The characteristics of the natural aerosol vary with the location as well as with climatic conditions. In highly populated areas, both the total particulate load and the proportion of viable particles tend to be high, so that aero-microbial concentrations within an urban public building can approach 10^6 c.f.u. m^{-3}.

Clearly this level of microbial concentration constitutes a massive contamination potential for pharmaceutical processes, but fortunately modern filtration techniques render the surrounding atmospheric quality almost irrelevant to the environment within a properly designed clean room. It is now possible to operate fairly modest clean rooms which will consistently achieve aero-microbial contamination levels well below 1 c.f.u. m^{-3}, in the unmanned state. However, once personnel enter a clean room the situation can change dramatically, as shown in Fig. 1. It is important to realize that the atmospheric characteristics within a manned clean room differ markedly from those of the 'natural aerosol' in an uncontrolled environment.

Within a high-grade clean room, 80–90% of particulate contamination originates from the personnel (Austin 1966a; Heuring 1970), since the release of particles from surfaces and inanimate objects is minimal and the air input is essentially particle-free for pharmaceutical purposes. People continuously shed dead skin cells and fragments of hair, as well as exhaling liquid droplet aerosols. Each person sheds a complete layer of skin cells every 1–2 days, variously estimated to be equivalent to between 10^7 (Noble 1978) and 10^9 (MacIntosh et al. 1978) particles of >5 μm. Skin cells are around 40 μm in size, but often fragment, resulting in a median particle size of about 20 μm, with up to 10% of skin-derived particles being less than 10 μm (MacIntosh et al. 1978). The rate at which an individual sheds particles is not constant, but varies markedly with the level and type of activity. Austin (1966b)

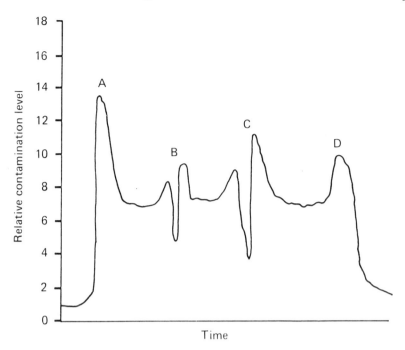

Events A : Start of working day
       B : Morning break
       C : Lunch
       D : End of working day

Fig. 1 — Effect of personnel on contamination levels.

determined the average number of particles of >0.3 μm dispersed from a motionless person as 10^5 per minute, rising to 10^7 per minute for brisk walking or climbing stairs.

Since the great majority of particles within a manned clean room are derived from personnel, the ratio of viable:non-viable particles is much higher than in the outside atmosphere. A further distinction is that most of the viable particles carry bacteria such as staphylococci, micrococci and diphtheroids, which are resident flora on human skin (Noble 1981), whereas the 'natural aerosol' contains a preponderance of yeasts, moulds and fungal spores. The total number of resident bacteria carried by an individual varies markedly, with males tending to carry significantly larger numbers than females (Noble *et al.* 1976), and individual men and women may show variable rates of bacterial dispersal, depending on their personal characteristics, general health and skin condition (Luna 1984). MacIntosh *et al.* (1978) determined ratios of viable:non-viable skin particles of >5 μm shed from six individuals as between 1:2 and 1:45, with an average of 1:4. Combined with an observed 40-fold variation in the total rate of particle shedding, this 25-fold variability in the incidence of viable contamination resulted in 1000-fold differences in the rate of dispersal of bacteria-carrying skin particles.

Whyte *et al.* (1982) have demonstrated that virtually all contamination occurring during aseptic manufacture results from poor operator technique or airborne viable particles. Assuming a properly trained workforce, the crucial factor for achieving very low levels of contamination probability in the final product is the concentration of viable particles in the air surrounding a vulnerable process. It might therefore seem logical to define environmental standards for aseptic manufacturing on the basis of c.f.u. per unit air volume within an operational facility, and such an approach has indeed been suggested (Hempel 1976; Whyte *et al.* 1979). However, the variability in workforce shedding characteristics and the very low levels of microbial contamination required would render a microbiological-based industry standard for clean-room performance inherently imprecise and difficult to apply consistently. In practice, the need for a rapid, quantitative measure of environmental control has led to air quality being defined in terms of total particulate counts, allowing facilities to be characterized by periodic or continuous monitoring. Thus sterility assurance relies upon the exclusion from the immediate work zone of all particles which could be viable, rather than attempting to define an acceptable limit for viable particle concentration.

2 STANDARDS

The technology of contamination control is subject to relatively few regulatory standards and statutory controls, and no universally recognized standard exists for clean-room performance. Many multinational organizations adopted the original US Federal Standard 209A (1962) as the basis for their in-house performance specifications, and the various revisions of 209 (B, C and D) (1976, 1987, 1988) have therefore been widely used outside the USA.

In Britain, the corresponding national standard is BS 5295, *Environmental cleanliness in confined spaces* (1976, 1989). The basic philosophy of the two standards is similar, as considered below.

2.1 Federal Standard 209D

The current standard establishes classified performance specifications for the control of airborne particulates, and defines methodology for validating room classification and monitoring air cleanliness. As in previous editions, no attempt is made to differentiate between total particulate burden and the extent of viable contamination. All operational aspects of clean-room technology, including guidance on construction techniques and surface finishes, are now covered by a series of Recommended Practices (RPs), as listed in Appendix 1 (US Institute of Environmental Sciences 1988).

Table 2 shows the six classifications included in 209D, which compares with the three classes of 100, 10 000 and 100 000 defined in earlier editions. As before, classification is in terms of limits on the number of particles of given sizes which may be present in a cubic foot of air, and is based on a logarithmic relationship, as shown in Fig. 2. Class 100 remains the appropriate environment for all aseptic work and other critical production processes, whilst any of the lower three classifications could be appropriate for controlled areas within a pharmaceutical facility, depending on the nature of the work undertaken. The latest version of 209 introduces a statistical

Table 2 — Environmental classification: Federal Standard 209D

Class	Class limits, in particles per cubic foot, of sizes greater than or equal to sizes shown (μm)				
	0.1	0.2	0.3	0.5	5.0
1	35	7.5	3	1	—
10	350	75	30	10	—
100	—	750	300	100	—
1 000	—	—	—	1 000	7
10 000	—	—	—	10 000	70
100 000	—	—	—	100 000	700

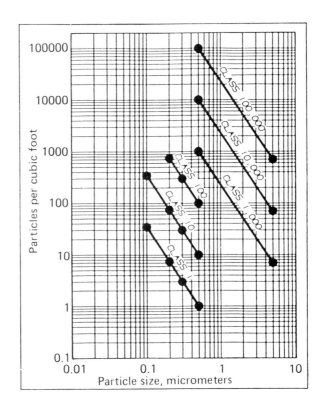

Fig. 2 — Relationship between particle size and particle concentration
(Federal Standard 209D).

approach to performance validation, calling for the mean concentration of replicate samples taken at each location to fall within class limits, and for statistical analysis of the mean concentrations at individual sites to indicate, at a 95% confidence level, that the population mean for all sampling locations lies within the limits.

A second difference from previous standards is in the definition of alternative test conditions, which now allows compliance to be specified 'as built' (i.e. complete but empty), 'at rest' (fully equipped but unmanned) or, most relevantly, 'during operation' (i.e. fully manned). Earlier versions of 209 had simply required compliance with class limits in the unmanned state, which allowed facilities with low flushing rates or poor air distribution to meet the criteria for Class 100, even though particulate contamination could rise to unacceptably high levels during operation. In practice it may well prove much easier to demonstrate Class 10 conditions 'at rest', than to achieve Class 100 performance in the same facility when fully manned. Determining reproducible particulate levels during operation is obviously beset by a range of practical difficulties, due to variations in personnel behaviour and physical characteristics, and operational factors such as cleaning protocols. However, the purpose of environmental control is to afford products the maximum overall protection against contamination, whatever its source, and the facility within 209D for the assessment of in-use performance should therefore prove beneficial.

2.2 BS5295: 1989

The original 5295 defined four classifications of environmental cleanliness. Class 1 was appropriate for aseptic manufacture and Class 2 for the bulk preparation of solutions for terminal sterilization. The manufacture of microbially vulnerable non-sterile products required Class 3 conditions and Class 4 was adequate for all other pharmaceutical production.

In contrast to the original standard, the revised edition (1989) (Part 1) does not include any requirement for minimum rates of air replacement, but simply defines particulate limits for ten classes of environment, C–J. Reference to Table 3 shows

Table 3 — Environmental classification: BS 5295 (1989)

Class	Class limits, in particles per cubic metre, of sizes greater than or equal to sizes shown (µm)				
	0.3	0.5	5.0	10	25
C	100	35	0	—	—
D	1 000	350	0	—	—
E	10 000	3 500	0	—	—
F	—	3 500	0	—	—
G	100 000	35 000	200	0	—
H	—	35 000	200	0	—
J	—	350 000	2 000	450	0
K	—	3 500 000	20 000	4 500	500
L	—	—	200 000	45 000	5 000
M	—	—	—	450 000	50 000

that Classes F, J, K and L are essentially comparable to Classes 1–4 in the original BS 5295, whilst Classes C and D correspond approximately to Classes 1 and 10 FS 209D. The new standard defines the same alternative test conditions as specified in 209D, but does not adopt statistical analysis of results, relying instead on the use of relatively large sampling volumes. The revised edition also includes a structured method for specifying a clean room (Part 2), the operational aspects of running and maintaining controlled facilities (Part 3), and guidance on the type and frequency of testing to be performed (Part 4).

2.3   Guides to good pharmaceutical manufacturing practice
Similar specifications for environmental quality are included in the *Guide to good pharmaceutical manufacturing practice* (Anon. 1983) and more recently in the European Community's *Guide to good manufacturing practice for medicinal products* (Anon. 1989). These guides define grades of environmental quality in terms of both particulate concentration and aero-microbiological contamination levels; the latter are summarized in Chapter 17.

3   STRATEGIES FOR PRODUCT PROTECTION
Since any activity which requires human intervention will inevitably be subject to viable particulate contamination, a wide range of measures have been evolved which will avoid or minimize the problem.

The most obvious strategy is to segregate the work process from environmental and operative-derived contamination by manufacturing the product within a completely closed system. By adopting sealed mixing vessels, closed pipework sytsems etc., the product is intrinsically protected from environmental contamination during processing, and the cleaning and sterilization of equipment between batches is a relatively straightforward and reliable operation. Nevertheless, despite ingenious plant design, many products will still be exposed, however transiently, to the surrounding environment, and therefore some form of control is necessary. Form–fill–seal technology is an interesting example of a highly automated production system which is almost, but not entirely, enclosed; practical experience has shown the desirability of environmental protection, even for this sophisticated equipment (HM Inspectorate 1989).

The logical approach to controlling environmental quality in the immediate vicinity of a critical process is to isolate the process itself from the general surroundings. Purpose-built, dedicated enclosures have long been used in conjunction with specific items of production equipment, such as freeze-driers and ampoule-fillers. The production equipment and its surrounding enclosure are gas sterilized prior to production, and thereafter sterility is maintained by a true hermetic seal around the critical operation. Although such equipment is expensive and sometimes cumbersome, it is usually possible to develop successful design solutions to problems such as control setting and maintenance. The improved versatility and reduced costs of flexible film isolation technology may well make this an increasingly attractive option for high-throughput sterile production lines of the future. Within the last few years increasing interest has been focused on stand-alone isolators as a means of providing a suitable local environment for small-scale aseptic processing. Practicality has dictated that most of this proprietary equipment has been designed and operated as 'contained workstations', rather than as genuinely sterile isolators.

In the foreseeable future there will continue to be many circumstances in which it is impractical to maintain a physical barrier between personnel and the material being processed, and in this situation the risk of product contamination is minimized by a variety of strategies, including flushing the work area with high-quality air, containing the particulate debris shed from personnel, and constructing easily cleanable facilities. Clean-room technology incorporates all these measures, and in conjunction with fastidious operational procedures can provide the high levels of sterility assurance required for aseptic manufacture.

4 CLEAN-ROOM TECHNOLOGY

4.1 Air quality

The quality of air supplied to pharmaceutical facilities is closely defined by the standards previously described, and can be accurately measured by modern particle-counting equipment. Aseptic facilities demand supply air with an extremely low concentration of 0.5-μm particles, and an absence of 5-μm particles. For practical purposes, air of this quality will be free from viable contamination, since micro-organisms are almost invariably associated with larger, inanimate particles which protect them from desiccation in the airstream. There is therefore no inherent advantage to be gained by reducing the concentrations of particles in the range 0.1–0.3 μm within pharmaceutical clean rooms. Although various techniques such as electrostatic precipitation may be involved in cleaning air for general factory areas, all air supplied to controlled areas within a pharmaceutical plant will have been subjected to filtration.

4.1.1 Mechanisms of filtration

Filtration is not a straightforward process, but is the sum effect of several different mechanisms, whose relative contributions vary markedly with particle size and the velocity of air passing through the filter medium. The sieving effect is the simplest filtration mechanism, but is only of real significance for comparatively large particles which would normally be arrested on coarse pre-filters. Three additional mechanisms are responsible for retaining smaller particles on the fibres which make up a filter medium, as shown diagramatically in Fig. 3.

4.1.1.1 Inertial impaction

As air flows around the randomly orientated fibres, the inertia of suspended particles precludes rapid changes of direction, and they become embedded on the fibres. This mechanism is of major significance for particles of >1 μm and becomes more effective as air velocity through the filter medium increases.

4.1.1.2 Electrostatic retention

Particles of 0.5–1.0 μm have very low mass and can be trapped by electrostatic attraction to fibres with which they come into close proximity.

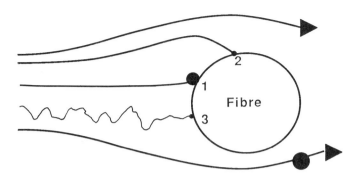

1   Inertial Impaction
2   Electrostatic retention
3   Diffusive retention

Fig. 3 — Schematic representation of mechanisms of filtration.

4.1.1.3   Diffusive retention

Particles of <0.5 μm are principally retained by impaction resulting from randomized particle movement (i.e. Brownian motion), and this mechanism operates most efficiently at lower flow velocities, and very small particle sizes.

The critical particle size at which none of these three mechanisms operate particularly effectively is around 0.2 μm.

4.1.2   Filtration efficiency

Owing to the complex interrelationship between filter medium characteristics, airflow and particle size, it is not possible to design a universally efficient filter for all circumstances. Overall filtration efficiency is normally greatest when the velocity of air passing through the actual filter medium is in the range 0.025–0.050 m s^{-1}. Filters are therefore designed to achieve a stated efficiency against a specific particle size, when operated under the volume flow rate which corresponds to the optimum filtration velocity across the entire surface area of pleated medium. Efficiency (%) is defined as:

$$\frac{\text{particle concentration upstream} - \text{particle concentration downstream}}{\text{particle concentration upstream}} \times 100$$

The measured collection efficiency of a filter has practical relevance only when related to the test aerosol providing the particulate challenge. Coarse and medium-efficiency pre-filters are usually challenged with American Society of Heating, Refrigerating and Air Conditioning Engineers (ASHRAE) synthetic dusts, whilst hot or cold generated dioctylphthalate (DOP) aerosols or atomized sodium chloride is used to test high-efficiency filters (Denyer *et al.* 1982). For high-efficiency filters, the concept of particulate penetration is also employed. This may be defined as the complement to collection efficiency and represents the fraction passing through the filter. A recent trend is to rate filters in terms of a simple ratio, known as the decontamination factor (DF):

$$(DF) = \frac{\text{particulate concentration upstream}}{\text{particulate concentration downstream}}$$

Table 4 illustrates the relationships between these three parameters for various hypothetical filters, and it can be seen that DF provides the clearest differentiation of filter performance.

Table 4 — Performance parameters for filters

	Efficiency (%)	Penetration (%)	Decontamination factor
Filter I	95	5	20
Filter II	99.99	0.01	10 000
Filter III	99.999	0.001	100 000
Filter IV	99.9997	0.0003	333 333

4.1.3 High-efficiency particulate air (HEPA) filters

Air filtration technology has now advanced to allow commercial production of ultra-low particulate air (ULPA) filters, which are 99.99996% efficient against 0.12-μm particles. For even the most stringent pharmaceutical purposes, filters possessing 99.9997% efficiency against 0.3-μm particles are entirely adequate for final filtration of air entering controlled areas. This specification would fall just within the upper performance limit for filters classified under the imprecise generic term 'HEPAs'.

HEPA filters, also misleadingly called 'absolute filters', are disposable, extended-media filters in rigid carcasses. The filter medium employed is normally a non-flammable, water-repellent microglass material, having individual fibre diameters of around 0.1 μm. Conventional HEPA filters are pleated as shown in Fig. 4, to provide a large filtration area within compact overall dimensions. Each pleat is spaced by a corrugated separator which supports the filter medium and maintains even packing; this is vital for the achievement of uniform face velocities. Separators are generally made of Kraft paper or aluminium, with the latter material being preferable for low shedding and improved durability. The medium and separators are bonded to the rigid carcass with a low-solvent adhesive to minimize shrinkage, polyurethane being a commonly used material. The carcass itself can be metal, chipboard, or more recently plastic, with anodized aluminium being suitable for almost all pharmaceutical applications. Chipboard has been extensively used in the past, but can cause problems due to inadequately flat gasket faces and particle shedding from cut edges.

A comparatively recent manufacturing refinement has resulted in 'minipleat'

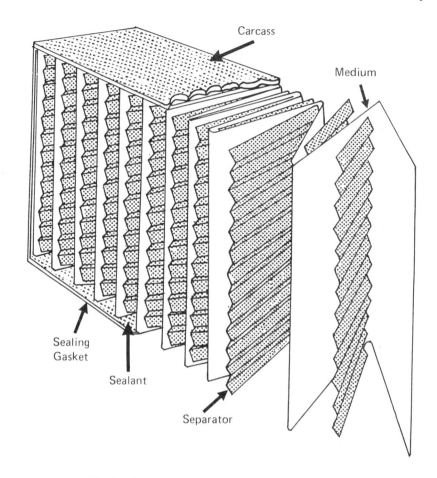

Fig. 4 — Construction of conventional HEPA filter panel.

designs from several filter suppliers. The construction of these filters dispenses entirely with separators, and uses bonded glass threads, ribbons or moulded media to maintain close, regular packing of the pleated filter material. Compared to a conventional HEPA filter panel of equivalent dimensions, 'minipleat' construction provides considerably greater volume flow capacity, more uniform face velocities, and a significant reduction in weight. Whereas the relatively loose packing of conventionally constructed filters allows the filter medium to oscillate in transit, which can occasionally lead to small ruptures in the filter material, 'minipleat' construction results in a comparatively robust component. This quality is further enhanced in some designs by the incorporation of integral expanded-metal grids to protect both faces of the medium from mechanical damage, particularly during installation.

The modern 'minipleat' HEPA filter has evolved into an extremely dependable component, providing consistently high performance and good durability, and being virtually free from 'pinhole' leaks. A typical final filter for aseptic areas would be flow-rated for a face velocity of 0.45 m s^{-1}, which because of the large filtration area corresponds to a media velocity of 0.025 m s^{-1}. A newly installed filter in such an application would demonstrate a dynamic resistance of approximately 170 Pa (1.7 mbar).

4.1.4   HEPA filter installation
As a general principle, the final filters for all air supply systems into critical areas should be terminal to any distribution ductwork or balancing dampers, in order to prevent entrainment of contaminated air through flanged duct joints, etc. The only air system components downstream from a final filter should be a diffuser grille, if required, or a simple protective grille or splashguard. Obviously the frame assemblies in which the filter panels are mounted must themselves be securely fixed and sealed to their apertures in the ceiling or walls of the clean room. Any opportunity for relative movement between ductwork, frame and surroundings will allow leaks to develop under the effects of vibration or cyclic thermal stress. The joint between filter frame and the plenum chamber or duct which feeds it is particularly critical, as the contaminated, high-pressure air behind the filter panel can force very large numbers of particles into the room through the smallest of leaks!

Wherever considerations of space and access permit, the filter housing should be designed for rearward replacment of the filter panels. This arrangement results in a neater, easily cleanable installation, as shown in Fig. 5, and also allows the clean room to be protected from the dirty interior of the ductwork during filter replacement. Furthermore, the detection and diagnosis of edge leaks is more straightforward, due to the absence of air turbulence, and *in situ* sealing of minor leaks is more likely to be successful.

4.1.5   Filter seal systems
Whereas ductwork and frames are permanent installations, it is obviously necessary to replace filter panels periodically, as they possess relatively limited service lives. The breakable joint between filter panel carcass and its mounting frame is normally sealed by a compressible gasket, and in practice most problems associated with unsatisfactory supply air quality arise from this joint. Gaskets are usually made from closed-cell neoprene foam, and alternative materials such as PTFE and moulded polyurethane do not appear to offer any significant advantage.

The mounting frame design may take a variety of forms, including a simple flat mating face, a returned knife-edge, and 'bevel-seal' profiles fabricated from extruded aluminium. Satisfactory sealing can be achieved by any of these variants, provided that the frames are truly flat, smooth and free from imperfections such as inadequately ground and polished welds. Filter panel gaskets are compressed against their frames by clamping frames or individual screwed clamps, which should be evenly distributed, in order to prevent local distortion of the frame or filter panel. Some designs apply the clamping force through springs, which helps maintain an even, consistent pressure over the full service life of the panel.

A relatively recent development which offers an attractive alternative to conventional compressed gaskets is the gel-seal system. The filter mounting frame is fabricated from a stainless steel channel, and the aluminium extrusion from which

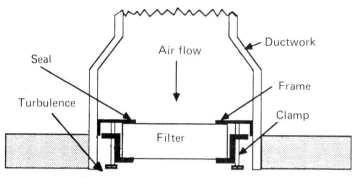

POOR DESIGN; FRONT MOUNTING

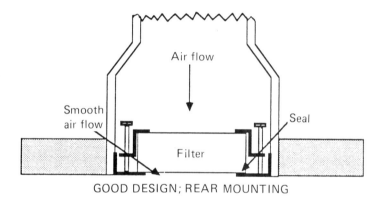

GOOD DESIGN; REAR MOUNTING

Fig. 5 — HEPA filter installation.

the filter carcass is formed carries an integral knife-edge, which locates within the channel. The assembly is hermetically sealed by a chemically inert, non-volatile thixotropic gel, which flows around and seals to each of the components, as shown in Fig. 6. This technique is particularly suited to horizontal filter panel installation, and lends itself admirably to the modular construction of vertical-flow rooms.

4.1.6   Pre-filtration
Any filter subject to a particulate load will eventually become clogged. In order to extend the useful life of expensive final filters and minimize clean-room downtime, pre-filters are used to remove the gross contamination found in untreated air. A typical installation might use washable, adhesive-coated metal filters to remove particles of >15 μm, such components being reused more or less indefinitely. Disposable intermediate filter panels, or in larger installations bag filters, would then remove particles of around 4 μm and upwards, before the air is fed to the final filters.

Since the rate of filter clogging depends on the extent of aerosol challenge, filter life varies with factors such as rainfall, location of the facility, and proximity to major

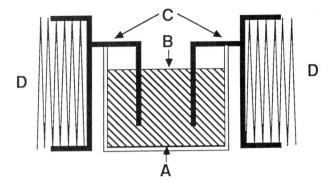

A: Stainless steel channel frame
B: Thixotropic gel
C: Extruded aluminium filter carcasses
D: HEPA filter media

Fig. 6 — Gel seal system for filter installations.

traffic routes. As a general guide, intermediate filters are usually replaced on a quarterly basis in an urban environment. It is good design practice to ensure that other air system components such as heater batteries are protected by upstream filtration, which will prevent heat exchanger cores from becoming blocked and starving the facility of supply air. In a well-designed system, final HEPA filters should have service lives of around two years continuous, full-duty operation, although high recirculation ratios may considerably extend replacement intervals. In order to maintain the design performance of an air supply system throughout the service lives of final HEPA filters, it is necessary to compensate for filter blockage by progressively increasing the pressure differential across the filters. In modern systems, automatic fan compensation is usually achieved electronically, using an orifice plate, or other equivalent means, to generate a constant-resistance reference source.

4.2 Airflow management
Clean-room technology is founded upon the use of HEPA-filtered air to provide products with protection from airborne contamination, by continuously sweeping away operative-derived particulates from the immediate work zone. Since airflow protection of the working area is quite easily disrupted, a secondary objective of clean-room design is to control the surrounding particulate challenge to the protected work zone at the lowest achievable level. As personnel continuously shed large numbers of particles, the concentration of particulates within a manned clean room will represent a dynamic equilibrium between the rate at which debris is generated or released, and the rate at which particulates are purged from the clean room. The ability of an aseptic suite to maintain low equilibrium levels of particulates under fully operational conditions is a direct measure of the suite's contribution to sterility assurance, and under the revised standards (see section 2) is a specifiable performance criterion.

4.2.1   Laminar flow

Laminar airflow is defined as the movement of air within confined boundaries at essentially uniform velocity, and along parallel flow lines. In practice, a small amount of lateral mixing occurs in the airstream, and the term 'unidirectional flow' is a more accurate description. In order to achieve optimally efficient removal of particles from the vicinity of an aseptic manipulation, the air velocity around the work should generally be within the range 0.45 m s^{-1} ($\pm 20\%$). Around this critical velocity, particles of <15 μm are transported in suspension by the airflow, which can therefore be directed so that viable contamination shed by an operative is systematically flushed away from the working area. Below this velocity the rate of particulate removal is unacceptably slow, and eddy currents produced by operator movements will readily induce counter-flow of contaminated air towards the product. As the velocity of air flowing around the work increases above 0.6 m s^{-1}, turbulence will begin to develop, and the controlled, systematic removal of contamination will be replaced by a randomized mixing between filtered supply air and air contaminated by the operative.

Any physical obstruction to airflow will create downstream turbulence, which may compromise product protection. However, at 'laminar flow' velocity there is little tendency for turbulent flow to develop upstream of an obstruction, and uniform flow is usually re-established downstream at a distance equivalent to 3–6 times the cross-stream dimension of the obstruction (Fig. 7). The selection of a horizontal or vertical protective airstream depends on the relative disposition of products, equipment and personnel, and the nature of human interaction in the production process.

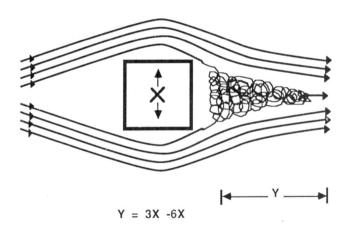

Y = 3X -6X

Fig. 7 — Effect of obstruction on airflow patterns.

4.2.2   Conventional (turbulent) flow rooms

In a conventional aseptic room, the localized protection for critical operations is provided by 'laminar airflow' (LAF) cabinets or workstations. These items of equipment are usually self-contained, and incorporate pre-filtration, fans and a plenum chamber supplying a HEPA filter, which may be installed either vertically or horizontally as shown schematically in Fig. 8. Critical work is therefore performed

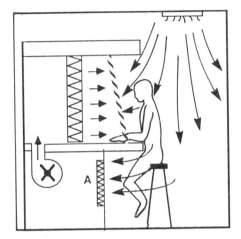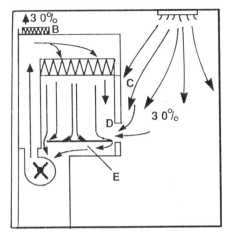

A: Prefilter
B: Exhaust HEPA filter
C: Glazed panel

D: Controlled air entry
E: Dished work-top,
   with peripheral slots

Fig. 8 — Schematic diagram of horizontal and vertical LAF workstations, and interaction with room air inlets.

directly in front of, or beneath, the HEPA filter, within an envelope of controlled airflow. In order to ensure that face velocities are uniformly within the 'laminar' range across the full area of HEPA panels, workstations should possess adequately deep plenum chambers, supplemented if necessary by baffles or diffusers, to maintain even pressure distribution behind the HEPA filters.

Although viscosity effects result in much reduced air velocities immediately adjacent to worktop and other surfaces, the airflow across the working area of a horizontal LAF workstation should be essentially regular and uniform. In contrast, downflow cabinets inevitably exhibit some airflow distortion above the worktop. In order to minimize turbulent or stagnant areas in this critical zone, some designs of cabinet incorporate heavily perforated worktops. However, this construction is notoriously difficult to clean effectively, and most current designs rely on carefully shaped and proportioned peripheral slots to achieve satisfactory airflow patterns.

As well as rigidly constructed workstations, aseptic areas may be provided with LAF modules for local protection of equipment such as filling lines. Various studies (e.g. Whyte *et al.* 1979) have demonstrated that product protection will be seriously impaired if the airflow from such modules is unconstrained, since velocity will decline rapidly as air moves away from the filter face, and particulate debris can then be entrained into the critical area. As an alternative to rigid side panels, dowflow modules may employ flexible plastic sheeting or even peripheral high-velocity air curtains to contain the 'laminar' airflow over the working area.

The correct choice between vertical or horizontal airflow protection should be made to ensure that an undistorted, uncontaminated airstream flows over critical points, such as the open necks of vials, whilst operatives' hands should ideally be downstream, or at least to one side of the vulnerable components. Thus, when significant obstructions to airflow are positioned above a critical process, as in most filling operations, horizontal flow is often advantageous in minimizing turbulence at the point of fill. Processes in which operative movements are predominantly in the vertical plane are also probably best performed within horizontal airflow. Conversely, unavoidable obstructions alongside a critical process or predominantly horizontal operative movements could dictate the use of dowflow to minimize airflow disruption. Regardless of airflow direction, mechanical or human movement within the working area should be slow, deliberate and as infrequent as possible, in order to minimize the generation of vortices and eddy currents.

For all critical work, LAF workstations must be sited within a clean room, in order to reduce the challenge to the airflow protection they afford. Conventional clean rooms are provided with an independent HEPA-filtered air supply, which is intended to flush particulates from the room by a process of dilution. Air within the body of the room should therefore be thoroughly mixed with the input air by inducing turbulent conditions throughout the room. For this reason, supply air normally enters a conventional room at relatively high velocity, through wall or ceiling inlets which are comparatively few in number and small in size.

Despite the use of inlet diffusers to improve the lateral distribution of supply air, it is virtually impossible to prevent the occurrence of stagnant areas, resulting in inefficient particulate purging. In order to minimize this deficiency, it is important that the relative positions of supply inlets and air outlets or leakage points optimize the air's flushing potential by precluding ineffectual 'short-circuiting' of supply air to outlets. In the simplest case, a ceiling-mounted inlet for a small aseptic room would normally be sited diagonally opposite a low-level outlet. In larger facilities it is essential that multiple inlets, fed from a common air-handling unit, can be individually balanced by means of dampers, so that 'dead' areas of low air movement can be minimized during initial commissioning tests.

In order to achieve satisfactorily low equilibrium levels of particulate contamination, air must be supplied at a rate sufficient to maintain adequate dilution of debris released within the room. The air-flushing performance of a clean room is normally expressed as air changes per hour, which can of course only be calculated on a notional basis, since in practice air at some points within a turbulent flow room will be changed at many times the rate of air replacement in stagnant areas. The original BS 5295 (1976) required a calculated minimum of 20 air changes per hour within a Class 1 area, and many suites were therefore built to this criterion. However, this notional rate of air replacement may be insufficient to maintain low particulate concentrations within poorly designed or heavily manned clean rooms, and the current (1989) standard relates only to the maintenance of stated air quality under various operational conditions (see section 2.2).

Fortunately, the diluting effect of a room's air supply is supplemented by the recirculatory action of LAF modules sited within it, due to continuous cycling of room air through workstation HEPA filters. In this respect, horizontal LAF workstations are more effective than internally recirculating downflow units, as the entire throughput of the cabinet 'refines' room air quality. The recirculation pattern adjacent to a horizontal cabinet also results in efficient removal of operative-derived contamination, particularly if the pre-filter intake is below the worktop (Fig. 8). In terms of particulate removal, the effective volume filtration rate may therefore exceed the calculated air change rate by a wide margin; thus adequately low particulate levels can be achieved in turbulent flow rooms, provided that manning levels are modest in relation to LAF module throughput.

One potentially significant problem which is often overlooked in the layout of conventional suites is the possibility of interference between room air supplies and the protective airflow within LAF workstations. Air input velocities are generally significantly above 0.45 m s^{-1}, and as shown in Fig. 8 contamination can be transported from operatives directly into the working area of a poorly sited workstation. As downflow cabinets present a physical barrier to high-level entrainment into the work zone, their performance is less easily compromised by external air currents.

4.2.3 Unidirectional flow rooms

Unidirectional flow rooms (UFRs) are widely used in industry, and in many ways represent a fundamentally superior approach to contamination control. Whereas tubulent flow rooms achieve a reduction in airborne contamination by a dilution mechanism, UFRs eliminate particulates by a more consistent and predictable displacement action. The design objective for a UFR is to move filtered air evenly and uniformly through the entire volume of the room, so that the air displaces suspended particulates in a continuous, piston-like manner. In order to achieve this effect, one complete wall or the entire ceiling of a UFR is formed by a bank of HEPA filters, producing horizontal or vertical flow rooms as shown in Fig. 9.

When worktops are arranged in front of or beneath the filter bank, the local environment for aseptic procedures is essentially equivalent to that achieved within a LAF workstation. The fundamental advantage of UFRs lies in the rapid and consistent removal of operative-derived debris from the room, resulting in much lower equilibrium particulate concentrations for a given level of human activity. The challenge to the local environment is consequently much reduced, and the stable and predictable airflow patterns facilitate optimal arrangement of equipment and deployment of personnel within the room. Since airflow is essentially uniform throughout the entire room, stagnant areas and high-velocity turbulence are eliminated, and as the airflow provides both product protection and room flushing, interference between these functions cannot occur.

The selection of horizontal or vertical airflow depends upon the criteria outlined for conventional clean rooms, but the relative positions of workers within a UFR assumes increased importance. For large aseptic facilities, with critical locations distributed throughout the floor plan, downflow may be the only realistic option, since this arrangement should provide good environmental control at any point within the room, regardless of adjacent personnel. Vertical-flow rooms require very high volumetric flow rates. They are therefore expensive to construct and operate, and significant difficulties may be encountered in maintaining acceptably uniform

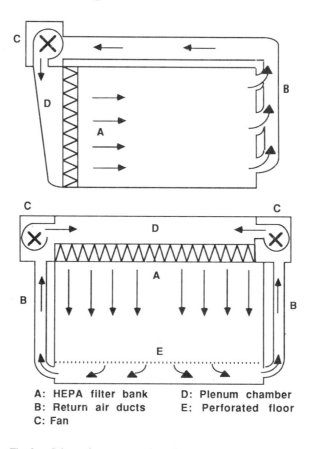

A: HEPA filter bank   D: Plenum chamber
B: Return air ducts   E: Perforated floor
C: Fan

Fig. 9 — Schematic representation of unidirectional flow rooms.

airflow patterns at worktop height. If the exhaust outlets are around the periphery of a large downflow room, airflow may be distorted to such an extent that the advantages of undirectional flow are negated. A perforated, raised floor can provide optimally regular airflow, but is difficult to construct and clean. The most satisfactory compromise is often to provide a series of low-level outlets at regular intervals throughout the room, or possibly at strategic points around critical locations. The degree of protection offered to products on an open bench within a vertical-flow room may not be entirely comparable with that afforded by a downflow cabinet, due to the absence of a physical barrier to exhaled particles and debris shed from the operator's upper body. Various studies (Whyte *et al.* 1979; Howorth 1987) have demonstrated that *partial* vertical-flow rooms are unsatisfactory, as entrainment of contamination into the critical area is inevitable as personnel move into or out of the protected zone.

For smaller facilities, horizontal flow provides outstanding product protection, with no cross-contamination between adjacent operatives working in front of the filter wall. However, debris shed from each individual forms a well-defined 'wake' of

contaminated air, rendering the downstream environment unsuitable for unpro-
tected aseptic work. Airflow distortion is not a significant problem, provided that the
outlets in the rear wall are adquately sized and evenly distributed. In contrast to
downflow rooms, partial horizontal-flow rooms, as shown in Fig. 10, can provide

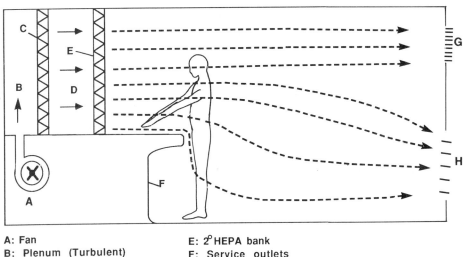

A: Fan
B: Plenum (Turbulent)
C: 1° HEPA bank
D: Plenum (Uniform flow):

E: 2° HEPA bank
F: Service outlets
G: Outlet grille
H: Pressure control valves

Fig. 10 — Partial horizontal-flow room.

excellent contamination control in a very cost-effective manner. When combined
with an aerodynamically effective worktop profile, the stagnant under-bench area
encourages air to flow smoothly down and around the operator, eliminating any
tendency for counter-flow or turbulence to develop under adverse conditions.
Biasing exhaust outlet distribution toward floor level ensures acceptably uniform
airflow throughout the body of the room, as indicated schematically in Fig. 10. An
additional refinement shown in this diagram is sequential HEPA filtration, in which
the primary filter bank acts as a diffuser for the secondary bank, thereby ensuring
consistently uniform airflow over the critical area. The overall filtration efficiency is
exceptionally high, and the useful life of the secondary filters is greatly extended,
minimizing service downtime.

Since the air supply to a UFR provides product protection, the velocity of the
supply air must remain within the 'laminar' range. The volumetric flow rate of air
entering the room will consequently depend on the dimensions of the wall or ceiling
HEPA filter bank. Elementary geometry dictates that the calculated air change rate
will be a direct function of the room's length or height, and because airflow is uniform
throughout the room the actual rate of air replacement at any point within a UFR
should agree closely with the calculated value. Although UFRs typically operate at

300–600 air changes per hour, it must be appreciated that this is a consequence of the design concept, and is not necessarily a design objective. The financial implications of single-pass temperature/humidity control and filtration for UFRs has led to most facilities being designed for recirculation of exhaust air. Owing to the high volumetric flow rates within UFRs, 10% fresh air make-up is normally quite adequate for ventilation requirements. For smaller UFRs it is often possible to employ adjacent accommodation as a reservoir of comfort-conditioned air, so that air passing through the aseptic facilities requires filtration only.

4.2.4 Room over-pressures
As well as flushing away contamination released within the clean room itself, the air supply also pressurizes the room, thereby preventing the ingress of contamination from uncontrolled surrounding areas. The layout of facilities and the design of the air supply system should result in a 'cascade' of airflow from the most critical (aseptic) areas through intermediate accommodation (e.g. preparation areas) to the least stringently controlled areas. In order to ensure that air flows through a facility in the correct sequence, BS 5295 (1989) specifies a minimum pressure differential of 10 Pa (0.1 mbar) between adjacent areas of differing classification.

A significant proportion of air exhausted from an aseptic room would normally flush out through a three-stage changing facility, which provides the only access route for personnel entering or leaving critical areas. Since extremely large numbers of viable particles can be released as personnel remove outer garments and don clean-room uniforms, it is especially important that debris is flushed out of the changing area in an efficient manner. Materials, equipment and products usually enter and leave clean rooms through double-ended transfer chambers which serve several functions. The two doors are normally interlocked to prevent simultaneous opening, thereby avoiding an open aperture between rooms of differing environmental quality. Items are placed in the chamber for chemical disinfection prior to removal into the clean room, but contaminated air from the 'dirty' area inevitably becomes trapped within the chamber. It is therefore important that ample clean air flushes outwards through the chamber whilst both doors are closed, to ensure that contaminated air does not enter the clean room along with the materials. Considering the obvious nature of this requirement, it is surprising that some proprietary transfer chambers are fitted with elaborate draught seals!

Air is exhausted from a clean room through either pressure-control valves (PCVs), or by leakage through fixed grilles, transfer chambers and around doors. PCVs usually take the form of counterweighted pivoted flaps, which open under increasing pressure differential to provide a progressively larger aperture for room air exhaust. Some proprietary designs of PCV are insufficiently sensitive for effective control, and designs in which the blade is pivoted on ballraces are to be preferred. The ratio of controlled exhaust:uncontrolled leakage should be at least 2:1, to ensure overall stability in a suite's air system performance. If the majority of exhaust air is dissipated through uncontrolled leakage, cyclic fluctuations can develop whenever the overall flow resistance of the suite is altered by events such as the operation of a transfer chamber. Adequate PCV capacity damps out minor changes in system resistance, and also accommodates small changes in the air supply's volumetric flow rate.

When personnel enter or leave clean rooms, the prompt closure of sensitive PCVs will divert all surplus air out through the open doorway, providing maximum airflow protection to the controlled area. Well-designed facilities equipped with a high-performance air supply sytem may well operate at up to 50 Pa (0.5 mbar) over-pressure, and be able to demonstrate measurable over-pressure even when the entrance door is partially open. Under normal circumstances, the velocity of air flowing out through PCVs or apertures around conveyors should exceed 2.5 m s^{-1}, which will deny access to airborne debris or even flying insects.

4.2.5   Validation and monitoring of clean rooms

The commissioning of a clean room suite involves comprehensive checks on the quality and quantity of air supplied to each area, and the methodical adjustment of supply fans, dampers, diffusers and PCVs in order to obtain the desired airflow patterns and differential over-pressures. Once the suite is functioning within its design specification, parameters such as filter face velocities can be characterized, so that subsequent physical monitoring will indicate that the suite continues to perform satisfactorily. In the case of pharmaceutical facilities, a further period of intensive microbiological monitoring would normally precede the suite being brought into production.

As mentioned in section 2.2, BS 5295 (1989) Part 4 introduced a specification for monitoring clean rooms to ensure continuing compliance with environmental classification. The methodologies described in the standard, and the minimum frequencies specified for each monitoring process, are essentially a description of current 'good practice' amongst clean-room operators, the principal requirements for Class F suites being summarized in Table 5.

Table 5 — Summary of routine physical monitoring requirements for Class F suite: BS 5295 (1989)

Parameter	Action	Frequency
Room over-pressures	Indication Check Record	Continuous Hourly Every 8 hours
Leak tests on HEPA filter installations (using challenge aerosols)	Test Record	6-monthly + Whenever an HEPA filter is disturbed/replaced
Induction leak tests	Test and record	Commissioning/ revalidation
Particulate contamination within rooms	Test and record	Weekly (minimum) or continuous

The standard calls for frequent monitoring of room over-pressures by regular checking of manometer or 'Magnahelic' gauge readings. In many modern suites, manual checks are supplemented by audio-visual alarms, which activate when room over-pressures (or safety cabinet performance) drift outside limits. Assuming that PCVs are functioning correctly, satisfactory over-pressures depend primarily on the volume of air supplied to the suite, and it is normal practice to monitor the pressure drop across supply HEPA filters, as this provides an indication of filter condition, and is also a check on the ability of the fan to deliver the design flow volume against the total system resistance.

As a direct measure of volume flow rates within a suite, it is also good practice to record filter face velocities on a regular basis, using an accurate anemometer. Whilst it is probably sufficient to measure room supply system velocities on a monthly basis, any filters providing direct product protection should ideally be monitored daily.

Although BS 5295 specifies a six-monthly minimum frequency for HEPA filter installation leak tests, it is usual to perform checks with a light-scattering particle counter on a more regular basis. If the room supply HEPA filters are subject to a continuous natural aerosol, as in a single-pass system with conventional pre-filtration, such checks may be an adequate substitute for periodic DOP testings. Workstation HEPA filters within high-grade clean rooms certainly require aerosol challenge testing, as the 'equilibrium' particulate levels within clean rooms are too low for statistically reliable testing of recirculating systems, even in the manned state. Either form of installation leak detection should concentrate on gasket seals, particularly at the corners of filter panels, and should also cover the total area of filter medium in an overlapping, backward and forward scanning pattern.

The requirement for weekly determinations of particulate levels within Class F clean rooms is the one aspect of the new standard which might be considered somewhat contentious, since most users of small aseptic suites currently perform such measurements on a monthly or quarterly basis. Assuming that a suite's design performance is adequate, and that room over-pressures, filter face velocities and input air quality are all within specification, the routine measurement of particulate levels within manned clean rooms is primarily an assessment of staff adherence to operational procedures, and the continuing effectiveness of clean-room clothing. It might therefore be argued that the microbiological monitoring which is invariably performed during aseptic processing provides a valid alternative to frequent particle-counting within small suites, and particularly in horizontal-flow rooms, where air quality 'downstream' from the critical process may be of limited significance in the maintenance of product sterility.

4.3   Facility design

4.3.1   *General layout*

In common with all pharmaceutical manufacturing facilities, sterile production suites should allow logical and clearly defined workflow, with minimal back-tracking. The layout must achieve good segregation between sterilized and non-sterilized material, as well as preventing cross-contamination between dissimilar products. In order to facilitate stringent environmental control, the critical facilities must be effectively segregated from general factory areas, and should not be accessible to unauthorized personnel. Ideally, the general arrangement and detailed design of the suite should allow all routine maintenance to be undertaken from outside the controlled areas. Sterile manufacturing places considerable demands on the workforce, and a thoughtfully designed and well finished suite can help to minimize sensations of isolation or claustrophobia, whilst encouraging compliance with operational procedures and individual pride in high standards of work.

It is usual for aseptic areas and injectable filling rooms to be serviced from an adjacent preparation area, which allows supporting personnel to assemble or prepare materials and equipment for processing by staff within the critical area. Raw materials and disposable items such as syringes and filters can be stored in quantity within the preparation area, minimizing the amount of packaging taken into the aseptic areas. The juxtaposition of supporting accommodation and changing facilities, and the location of doors, grille outlets and apertures such as conveyor tunnels should ensure that exhaust air from the critical areas flows through intermediate areas into uncontrolled surroundings. Air from facilities where potentially hazardous activities are undertaken should never be exhausted through other manned accommodation.

As a generalization, aseptic areas should be as compact as possible to maximize air-flushing efficiency and avoid unnecessary cleaning workload. Ceilings should be as low as practicable to facilitate routine cleaning. Careful consideration should be given to the relative positioning of workstations, transfer chambers, equipment such as conveyors and filling machines, control panels and service outlets or connections. In conjunction with compact overall dimensions, optimizing layout of these features will minimize personnel movement and eliminate unnecessary traffic within the clean room, thereby significantly reducing the particulate load on the facility.

Within the clean room itself, it is often possible to arrange workflow to ensure that the most critical operations are afforded maximum environmental protection. For example, in a horizontal-flow room used for small-scale aseptic production, filling and sealing of containers would be performed immediately adjacent to the HEPA filter bank, whereas solution preparation and mixing could be carried out as a semi-closed process downstream from the filling station.

4.3.2   Design features

Ease of cleaning is the overriding consideration in terms of detailed design for critical areas. Every effort must be made to eliminate avoidable ledges and potential dirt traps such as architraves, window sills and surrounds. The object is to achieve smooth, flat impervious surfaces, with all equipment and fixtures flush-fitting wherever possible. All junctions between floors, walls and ceilings should be seamless and coved with a uniform radius of around 50 mm. As well as easing the cleaning, the absence of joints precludes the development of bacterial reservoirs. This potentially serious problem can arise when capillary action causes liquids to be drawn into a crack, which affords contaminating micro-organisms protection against disinfection procedures, and may result in any subsequent spillage flushing out very large numbers of organisms.

Whenever practicable, major items of equipment should either be movable for cleaning, or be built into the structure of the room to present smooth, cleanable surfaces and eliminate inaccessible gaps and recesses. Exhaust-ducted safety cabinets can be incorporated into the plane of a wall, so that the working area within the cabinet effectively forms an alcove in the wall, with a smoothly finished knee recess beneath. The junction of benchwork to walls often present problems, as flexure of the working surface produces relative movement at the joint and a crack develops which is difficult to seal effectively on a permanent basis. Unless the clean room is finished in thermoplastic sheet, which can provide a continuous, flexible surface across the joint, consideration should be given to free-standing stainless steel tables as an alternative to fixed benching.

Windows in controlled areas should not of course be openable, and are frequently mounted in neoprene gasket surrounds. Although this construction is reasonably satisfactory, the neoprene surrounds are not usually sealed to either the glazing or the surrounding wall surface, and there is the potential for capillary entrapment of water during cleaning. Overall, a better solution is to seal the glazed panel into a rebated mounting using an epoxy adhesive, which can subsequently be polished to provide a flush, joint-free assembly. When a window is located between two controlled areas, it should be double-glazed to preserve a flush construction on both sides of the dividing wall. Alternatives to glass can be considered for window panels, as replacement of a cracked panel can result in extensive disruption of the clean-room environment. Polycarobonate is virtually unbreakable, but even expensive scratch-resistant grades are vulnerable to abrasion. Acrylic also scratches easily and can darken with age, whilst PVC is commendably tough and offers the possibility of welded construction, although it is not available in a truly glass-clear grade.

Communication between adjacent clean rooms is usually by means of 'speech panels' which are normally mounted within window assemblies. Speech panels employ a polymeric membrane to transmit sound whilst maintaining an airtight seal, and should be used back-to-back in double-glazed units. When mounted in a critical location, the protective acrylic grille should be omitted from the assembly as it is not readily cleanable. Telephone and intercom systems should be sited in preparation areas in preference to aseptic areas, and should be purpose-designed, flush-mounted instruments, featuring wipeable, touch-sensitive control panels.

Light fittings should ideally be flush-fitting, permanently sealed units with access for lamp replacement gained from a service void above the clean room. If lamp replacement from within the clean room is unavoidable, the diffuser assembly should at least seal onto a gasket, and under no circumstances should corrugated diffuser panels be used in critical areas. A logical refinement for use in vertical-flow rooms is a slimline, teardrop-section fluorescent fitting which integrates into the modular construction of a filter ceiling, reducing turbulence and disruption to airflow in the vicinity of each light fixture.

Doors should be positioned and hinged so that their opening produces minimum airflow disturbance at critical locations within the clean room, and air flows smoothly out into the lower classification areas. Doors should normally open into the more stringently controlled area, so that personnel can back through the doorway without contaminating gloved hands, and room over-pressure will assist in closing doors promptly. In order to re-establish controlled over-pressure in critical areas as quickly as possible, it is important that doors self-close efficiently. Unfortunately, conventional door closers are not readily cleanable, and closers which are concealed within the edge of the door itself tend to be unreliable in action. Conventional doors can be covered in melamine laminate, or preferably clad entirely in welded PVC sheet, which is more durable and easily repaired. Urethane-filled, moulded glass-rein-forced polyester (GRP) doors offer very cleanable surfaces for applications where mechanical damage is unlikely. Whatever a door's construction, ironmongery should be restricted to a simple D-handle fitted to its 'clean' side. An effective alternative to conventionally hinged doors is offered by one-piece solid polypropylene doors which have ligament-type flexing hinges formed by grooves machined in the sheet material. These are very easily cleaned, and once installed the material's elastic memory provides a self-closing door with no moving parts.

All doors communicating with a changing area should be interlocked to prevent more than one door being open simultaneously, thereby preserving overall pressure differentials as personnel enter or leave the critical areas. Electromechanical bolt systems were commonly used in early suites, but are potentially dangerous in the event of fire, and are unnecessary in facilities operated by a highly trained and disciplined workforce. An indicator light system controlled by door-mounted mic-roswitches provides adequate operational security, and allows incorporation of a manual override 'privacy' switch within the changing area. Indicator lights should be wall-mounted at eye level, adjacent to door handles.

Washing facilities are usually provided as flush-fitting, self-contained proprietary units, featuring foot controls for water, antibacterial liquid soap and hot air. These units are intended to draw air from the changing area for the hand-drier fan, and therefore it is important that their casings are sealed to prevent heavily contaminated air from the wall cavity becoming entrained into the hot air stream. The water supply within such scrub units can be fitted with a 0.2-µm filter cartridge. Heated traps are often fitted to the waste outlets for washing facilities, but they can cause problems by generating microbial aerosols as they warm up to full temperature. However, provided that basin outlets are plugged before their traps are activated, they can be a useful adjunct to routine disinfection. Cross-over barriers are best designed as movable items to facilitate routine cleaning, and should stand well clear of the floor so that debris released during changing is effectively flushed out of the controlled area.

4.3.3 Construction materials and surface finishes
The short-term criteria for a clean room's interior finishes are simply that they should provide smooth, non-shedding, washable surfaces, free from cracks, crevices or unsealed joints. Until comparatively recently, many clean rooms employed essen-tially conventional building methods, and were finished in gloss paint. Given sufficient attention to detail, it is possible to achieve an adequate standard of finish using conventional techniques, although forming smoothly radiused junctions is always problematic. However, all 'natural' materials are subject to warping, shrin-kage or cracking, and repeated cleaning and disinfection of walls and ceilings leads to comparatively rapid degradation of the paint film. Various polymeric paints have been developed as improvements over conventional gloss paints, and these do possess considerably enhanced elasticity, which theoretically should accommodate

any relative movement in their substrate. Some of these purpose-developed paints also incorporate fungicides and 'cobwebbing agents' which allow the applied paint layer to bridge across junctions between dissimilar materials. In practice, the localized strain at the site of a crack in the underlying plasterwork can exceed the elastic limit of even a polymeric paint, and the film itself will then also crack. In addition, the paint film is vulnerable to mechanical damage due to the softness of the substrate materials, and disruption of the film usually exposes materials which harbour micro-organisms and shed prolific numbers of particles.

The importance attached to ease of cleaning throughout a facility's service life has led to the adoption of fundamentally more durable constructional materials and surface finishes. The use wherever possible of monolithic materials also avoids exposure of substrates through wear and mechanical damage, or due to delamination. Sheet materials such as melamine-faced laminates provide good surface finish, but cannot be effectively joined or repaired, are prone to delamination along edges, and are brittle and easily chipped. The interiors of many large industrial clean rooms are now constructed in modular fashion from rigid panels of materials such as solid PVC, polymer-coated steel and GRP. Whilst the individual panels offer excellent surface characteristics, the junctions between panels constitute a potential problem. In order to allow some freedom for thermal expansion, such joints are usually sealed with RTV silicone, which introduces the possibility of sealant gradually deteriorating and losing adhesion. In addition, the modular nature of rigid panels is a serious limitation in forming irregular shaped features and equipment enclosures. Floors are usually of epoxy resin, which is extremely durable but difficult to form into smoothly radiused upstands, or an antislip grade of PVC sheet, which contains mica chips embedded in the polymer, and often provides the optimum compromise between safety and ease of cleaning.

An alternative construction technique which offers many advantages is the cladding of all interior surfaces with flexible thermoplastic sheet. The material used is normally 2-mm thick PVC, which can be bonded to any suitably smooth and flat substrate, such as plywood or chipboard. Coved junctions are easily formed by the use of extruded PVC formers which underlie the sheet material, and adjacent sections of material are permanently joined together by thermowelding. This technique is extremely versatile, providing the clean room with a smooth, continuous and impervious 'cocoon', with worktops and other features clad as an integral part of the surface finish. As 2-mm PVC sheet combines flexibility with considerable tensile strength, normal building movements will not disrupt the surface finish, and major mechanical damage can be readily and effectively repaired. Flexible PVC sheet may also be thermowelded to rigid PVC, and by fabricating components such as transfer chambers, window assemblies, light diffusers and door frames in this material it is possible to achieve totally flush, homogeneous, all-welded surfaces within a clean room, and virtually eliminate the need for sealants and other jointing techniques. Clean rooms constructed in this manner can be expected to provide at lest ten year's continuous service, without requiring any maintenance to their internal finishes.

Where the use of a sealant is unavoidable, such as around metal components, the materials used are normally urethanes or RTV silicones. Urethanes offer good adhesion, but tend to 'sink' gradually into cracks. Silicones are more resilient and stable, but can lose adhesion over a period of time. A high-hysteresis grade should therefore be selected, and the sealant applied as 45° fillets, avoiding feathered edges.

5 ISOLATION TECHNOLOGY

The concept of segregating personnel from work in progress is neither new, nor unique to the pharmaceutical industry. Glovebox technology has long been used for remote handling of radionuclides, and the use of Trexler-type isolators to house experimental animals is widespread.

Isolation technology is based upon the containment and close control of the environment immediately surrounding a work process, thus avoiding operator-derived product contamination and protecting personnel from hazardous materials. Unfortunately, this simple objective is normally complicated by provision of adequate access for manual intervention, and the need to introduce materials and remove products without compromising containment. Although isolation technology has been used in certain areas of the pharmaceutical industry for some years, the potential financial and operational advantages of the technique have only recently been widely recognized, particularly within the hospital sector.

As well as purpose-built, industrial containment systems, a variety of proprietary 'sterile isolators' are now available, some of which are promoted as alternatives to conventional clean rooms for small-scale aseptic processing. Although these devices show considerable diversity in their design philosophy, they can be broadly categorized as genuine isolators providing hermetically sealed containment, and hybrid machines which are best considered as contained workstations. Genuine isolators are normally loaded with sufficient equipment and materials for a work session, prior to sealing and subsequent gaseous sterilization of the isolator interior and its contents. Once the sterilant has been flushed from the isolator, all aseptic manipulations are completed before isolation is broken. By contrast, most contained workstations resemble conventional downflow workstations with a glove-ported, sealed front panel, and are intended to allow aseptic processing of small numbers of items on a sporadic basis. Owing to the unpredictable nature of such work, gaseous sterilization is impractical, and some form of double-door transfer hatch provides the only barrier between the contained work zone and the environment in which the isolator is sited.

The choice of the most appropriate isolator specification depends upon the nature, extent and predictability of work to be undertaken, the quality of the environment in which the equipment will be installed, and the degree of confidence required in the microbial integrity of the final products. Consideration of the various design features may help in this selection process.

5.1 Containment

Currently available isolators are either of rigid construction or employ a flexible canopy as the containment medium. Rigid isolators are normally constructed from polymer-coated or stainless steel, along similar lines to vertical LAF cabinets, although alternatives such as moulded acrylic have been used with satisfactory results. Vision panels are permanently bonded into neoprene gaskets, or form a hinged front panel which clamps onto conventional seals to effect containment. Experience has shown that, without hinged front panels, access to all parts of the enclosure for cleaning and disinfection may be difficult, although such panels obviously introduce a potential for leakage. Rigid isolators are the only practicable choice for radiopharmaceutical work, where lead-glass vision panels, lead-shielded cabinet construction and inherent aerosol containment combine to offer excellent overall protection. On balance, the mechanical durability of rigid construction may be preferable for all isolators operated under negative pressure, although recently introduced flexible isolators with internally zoned airflow should offer comparable levels of product security.

Flexible film isolators are normally fabricated from 0.5-mm transparent PVC, using radio-frequency welding to ensure airtight seams. The flexible canopy is supported by a tubular metal framework, which is also used to mount various transfer devices. Early flexible isolators incorporated the floor into a complete bubble, but this was found to be extremely vulnerable to damage by sharp or heavy objects. More recent designs have employed a rigid dished floor tray formed from GRP or stainless steel, with an open-bottomed flexible canopy sealed to the flanged tray by a clamping strip. This modified construction has improved the durability of flexible isolators whilst retaining the advantages of light weight, all-round visibility and improved operator comfort and lateral reach.

5.2   Personnel access systems

The two principal methods of gaining manipulative access to the interior of an isolator are through two or more sleeves, or by means of a half-suit. Most current isolators use multi-component sleeves which allow the use of coventional latex gloves, affording the sensitivity required for aseptic processing. The sleeves themselves are fabricated from material such as nylon-lined PVC, which offers operator comfort whilst presenting an impervious, wipeable surface within the work zone. The sleeves are secured to the flexible canopy or rigid vision panel by means of demountable rigid plastic rings, which allow the sleeves themselves to be replaced periodically. The service life of the sleeve is of the order of three months under normal use. The sleeve retaining rings of some rigid isolators include very sharp changes of section, combined with low wall thickness. Given the non-compliance of glass panels it seems feasible that continual flexure may eventually lead to the development of fatigue cracks, which could allow undetected leakage of contaminated air into a negative pressure isolator.

At the wrist end the sleeves seal onto rigid plastic cuff rings, which in turn carry the gloves. The cuff rings are so designed that gloves can be changed without breaking containment. Gloves should always be changed on each occasion that the operator enters the isolator, as they are prone to tearing if reused.

Half-suits are fabricated from the same material as sleeves, and use the same cuff rings for glove attachment. A transparent helmet is sealed to the neck of the suit, which is normally ventilated by its own pressurized air supply, maintaining operator comfort over prolonged work sessions. The advantage of a half-suit is that the operator has around 80% greater reach radius, and can also manoeuvre larger or heavier items. Half-suit isolators are generally flexible film types, and are usually employed as dedicated production equipment or for commercial aseptic compounding of materials such as TPN regimens.

5.3 Ventilation

All isolators incorporate an HEPA-filtered air supply which is intended to purge particles from the working area, just as in a conventional clean room. Equipment intended for processing hazardous materials such as cytotoxic drugs are normally operated under approximately 50 Pa (0.5 mbar) negative pressure, in order to ensure operator protection. Aseptic processing of non-hazardous materials is performed in isolators over-pressured to a similar level, since product protection is the sole criterion. In the absence of truly relevant design standards for isolators, some manufacturers have adopted the specification of 20 volume changes per hour mentioned in the original BS 5295 (1976) in relation to 'clean tents'. These designs use perforated baffles or slotted tubes to diffuse filtered air through the volume of the isolator, relying on turbulence to avoid stagnant areas. In a sealed, positive-pressure isolator which has been gas sterilized prior to aseptic work, there should theoretically be a complete absence of viable contamination, and this arrangement is therefore probably adequate, provided that the work process itself does not generate excessive particulate load.

Designs of rigid isolators which are intended as stand-alone alternatives to aseptic dispensing suites mostly employ full-area HEPA filtration to provide vertical laminar flow within the containment area. High flushing rates are certainly essential in these applications as the nature of the workload necessitates frequent transfer of material into and out of the containment area, and product integrity therefore depends heavily on airflow protection. Several of the most recent isolator designs combine flexible film containment with internally zoned undirectional airflow. These machines are intended to offer the convenience and practicality of flexible isolators, whilst providing a safeguard against possible product contamination due to canopy defects.

5.4 Transfer devices

A key factor in developing practical and effective systems of working in isolators is the technique adopted for passing materials into and out of the containment zone. In terms of preserving truly hermetic, sterile isolation, the simplest method for material introduction is through a diaphragm port or hinged door, but the disadvantage of this system is that once the work session is in progress further access cannot be gained without breaking containment. Airlocks featuring two or more sealed doors can be built onto an isolator, allowing items to be sterilized within the airlock before entry into the containment zone. This approach is simple but protracted and cumbersome.

For quicker and more convenient material transfer, a technique used in the nuclear industry has been adapted to produce 'rapid transfer ports' (RTPs) and associated container systems. The sealed lids of these containers dock on to specially designed ports, and are secured in place by bayonet fittings, as shown schematically in Fig. 11. The port access door is so designed that the contaminated outer surface of the container lid is sealed against the outside of the port door as it is locked in place,

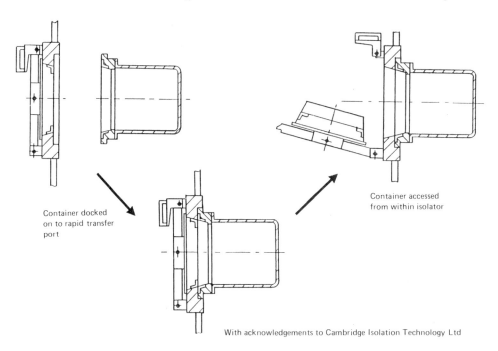

Container docked
on to rapid transfer
port

Container accessed
from within isolator

With acknowledgements to Cambridge Isolation Technology Ltd

Fig. 11 — Schematic diagram of a rapid transfer port and associated container.

and is not exposed to the isolator interior when the access door is open. It is therefore possible to gain immediate access to or from the isolator, without compromising the microbial or particulate integrity of the contained environment. The contents and interior surfaces of rapid transfer containers can be gas sterilized, or the whole assembly can be autoclaved. By pre-sterilizing several containers, it is possible to process a considerable amount of material through an isolator before containment is broken.

When numerous small items, such as pre-filled syringes, are prepared in an isolator, they can be passed out through an irradiated polyethylene sleeve, by heat-sealing units into individual overwraps, thereby preserving containment. For large-scale work, two or more isolators can be interconnected via large-diameter PVC sleeves equipped with RTP flanges at each end, or isolators can be docked directly to purpose-designed flanges around the doors of freeze-driers, autoclaves or heat-tunnel exits.

In the case of the earlier designs of contained workstation, which were primarily intended for aseptic dispensing, materials were introduced to or removed from the working area through simple, double-doored transfer chambers. Since the nature of this work resulted in chamber doors being opened a number of times during the course of a working session, significant quantities of contaminated air could enter the containment zone as eddy currents in the wake of items removed from the chamber into the working area. In order to minimize this problem, more recent equipment features transfer chambers which are flushed by their own HEPA-filtered air supply, thus providing a much more effective barrier against the ingress of contamination. The most sophisticated variants are fitted with time-delay interlock systems and/or pneumatically inflated door seals, making the chamber into an effective decontamination zone. Nevertheless, the official view of regulatory authorities remains that such equipment should be sited in controlled areas, particularly when operated under negative pressure (HM Medicines Inspectorate, 1989).

5.5 Instrumentation

Equipment performance is monitored by relatively simple instrumentation. The two fundamental parameters which require continuous monitoring are containment over- or under-pressure, and the volume flow rate for contained zone ventilation. It is also normal for the pressure differentials across HEPA filters to be monitored, since this measurement is the most direct indicator of filter condition. A potential problem with any isolator operated at negative pressure is that a small undetected defect in a canopy, gasket or door seal could direct a high-velocity stream of contaminated air towards the work zone, even though the exhaust system maintains the correct pressure differential. Since containment validation is normally peformed infrequently, this possibility should not be ignored.

5.6 Sterilization

The only practical method for reliable sterilization of the interior surfaces and contents of an isolator is by pumping a vaporized sporicidal agent through the equipment's ventilation system. The materials used are usually formaldehyde or solutions based on peracetic acid. Formaldehyde is a potential carcinogen, and is readily sorbed by polymers such as PVC, making peracetic acid the agent of choice in most circumstances. The vaporized sterilant normally passes through the isolator's air supply HEPA filter into the volume of the isolator, before being ducted to atmosphere on a total-loss basis. Several companies now offer purpose-built gas generators, which enable an average-sized four-glove isolator to be subjected to a complete sterilization and purge cycle in about one hour. More sophisticated versions of these generators provide digital or analogue records of each cycle, facilitating effective process validation.

5.7 Validation

The general approach to the initial validation and subsequent monitoring of a contained workstation is very similar to that used for comparable LAF cabinets. Airflow velocities and particle count should be checked regularly, and supply HEPA filters should be DOP-challenged on a scheduled basis. Gaskets and seals should be regularly inspected for leaks, but it is often impractical to perform any kind of pressure hold test on this type of equipment. Initial validation should establish the airflow patterns within the work zone and transfer chamber(s). Particular attention should be paid to the turbulence created during the passage of items into or out of the work zone, so that operational procedures can be tailored to the equipment's performance characteristics. Routine microbial monitoring of the equipment, for example by settle plates or by centrifugal samplers, is highly desirable.

Isolators intended to preserve a hermetic barrier at all times should of course be capable of maintaining a static pressure differential with minimal decay. Flexible isolators should be tested at 250 Pa canopy inflation pressure, with the ventilation system valves closed, and should allow <10% pressure loss over 30 minutes. If leakage exceeds this rate, the defect can be traced using DOP, Freon or ammonia-based detection tests. Of these methods, DOP is possibly the most relevant technique, since it monitors the permeability of the canopy to particles rather than gases.

6 NUMERICAL ASSESSMENT OF CONTAMINATION RATES

In an ideal situation, every aseptically produced item would obviously be totally free from viable contamination. However, the maintenance of asepsis during manufacture is a matter of probability, and measures such as high-quality air supply and good operator technique merely increase the likelihood that a completed item will be sterile. Owing to the statistical nature of sterility assurance, it is necessary to define a failure rate which is both tolerable and realistically achievable in practice. The World Health Organization's original recommendation (1973) was that the contamination rate for aseptically produced pharmaceuticals should not exceed 0.3%, but this guidance has been generally superseded by the Parenteral Drug Association's suggested maximum failure rate of 0.1% (1980). When considering formulations which are potentially capable of supporting microbial growth, it is particularly important to strive for a nil failure rate, and most authorities would now regard contamination rates of <0.01% as easily achievable (Sharp 1989).

The practical determination of ultra-low contamination rates is both laborious and expensive and a theoretical model for predicting failure rates from easily quantified parameters has obvious attractions. Whyte *et al.* (1982) demonstrated that virtually all contamination in aseptically produced vials originated from the air or operator's hands. Whyte (1981, 1984, 1986) has subsequently developed a numerical model for assessing the frequency of product failure arising from airborne contamination. Several workers (e.g. MacIntosh *et al.* 1978) have determined the median diameter for viable particles in a clean room to be approximately 20 μm. Noble *et al.* (1963) calculated the equivalent mean diameter (i.e. the diameter of a sphere with unit density, which would have equivalent settling rate in still air) for such particles to be approximately 12 μm. The possible mechanisms by which such particles could enter a container during aseptic production are similar to those operating in a filtration process, and include inertial impaction, gravitational settling, direct interception and electrostatic attraction. Whyte showed both theoretically and experimentally that gravitational settling accounts for the majority of particle deposition in a clean room. The settling velocity of 12-μm particles can be derived from Stokes' law as 0.46 cm s^{-1}, and the number of particles entering a container by this mechanism is then easily determined as:

$$\text{number deposited} = 0.46\,(CAt) \qquad (1)$$

where

C=concentration of airborne viable particles (cm^{-3})
A=area of exposed surface (e.g. open neck of container) (cm^2)

t=time (s).

It is worth noting that the settling velocity of these particles is only around 1% of LAF velocity, which accounts for the highly efficient removal of skin debris in an unobstructed horizontal airstream. However, Whyte contended that the airflow immediately in front of an operator is largely turbulent, even when working at an LAF workstation, and that gravitational deposition is essentially unhindered. In practice, significantly turbulent airflow around the necks of open containers would usually reflect poor operator technique, badly designed or sited equipment, or an inappropriate choice of airflow direction.

Assuming that pre-sterilized containers are not open for long periods, inertial impaction is the only other significant mechanism for airborne contamination, although it only operates when the airflow direction is parallel with the axis of the open container. In this situation, relatively large and massive particles are projected into the open neck of a container according to the following equation:

$$\text{number of particles impacted}=CAVEt \tag{2}$$

where
V=air velocity (cm s^{-1})
E=efficiency of system.

Whyte (1981) derived the efficiency of impaction for 12-μm particles to be:

$$E=4.7\times10^{-4}\frac{V}{l} \tag{3}$$

where l =diameter of the container neck (cm).

Since the efficiency of inertial impaction during a typical aseptic filling operation is only around 2%, it can be seen that the relative contribution of this mechanism to product contamination is usually small, with the possible exception of small containers filled under a vertical airstream. As a reasonable approximation, Whyte (1986) calculated the number of viable particles settling into various sized containers over differing exposure periods, and expressed the results as percentage failure rates. Assuming a very low aero-microbial concentration of 0.2 c.f.u. m^{-3}, the projected failure rate for 500-ml bottles exposed for an average of 10 minutes was 0.023%, whereas 2-ml ampoules which were opened and closed within 5 seconds would have an expected failure rate of only 0.00001%.

If the average concentration of viable particles in a fully manned clean room is determined by volumetric air sampling, equations (1) and (2) can be used to predict failure rates for various aseptic procedures performed within that facility. The same equations can be used to relate volumetric sampling results to expected settle plate contamination rates, and can also be used to determine the total exposed area of plates necessary to give statistical confidence in the monitoring process. Conversely, establishing a 'tolerable' failure rate for a critical process would allow the determination of a suitable environmental quality specification from a knowledge of process parameters.

In highly automated aseptic processes, the relationship between environmental quality and product failure rates may well be described reasonably accurately by these or similar equations, since the process mechanics are standardized, and aero-microbial concentration in the critical zone can be characterized. In situations involving significant human manipulation this approach has less relevance, as the air quality in the immediate vicinity of a container will be largely dependent on individual operator technique, and may not reflect aero-microbial concentrations measured at adjacent monitoring sites. For labour-intensive, predominatly 'closed system' aseptic processing, such as the preparation of TPN solutions, this limitation in accuracy of modelling is exacerbated by the heightened significance of direct touch contamination, which is probably the single most important route of product contamination in such situations. In the absence of convincing data on the aero-microbial environment *immediately* around such critical sites as vial necks, models for predicting product contamination levels may be of limited use.

7 REFERENCES

Anon. (1983) *The guide to good pharmaceutical manufacturing practice.* HMSO, London.

Anon. (1989) *The rules governing medicinal products in the European Community vol. IV. Guide to good manufacturing practice for medicinal products.* HMSO, London.

Austin, P. R. (1966a) Understanding fluctuations in airborne contamination. *Contam. Control* **5** 26–32.

Austin, P. R. (1966b) Austin Contamination Control Index: how it works. *Contam. Control* **5** 11–19.

Beveridge, E. G. (1975) The microbial spoilage of pharmaceutical products. In: Gilbert, R. J. and Lovelock, D. W. (eds), *Microbial aspects of deterioration of materials.* Academic Press, London, pp. 213–235.

Boom, F. A., Graatsma, B. H. and Oremus, E. Th. H. G. J. (1981) Bereiding van parenteralia in zeikenhuisapotheken 111: Toetsing aan de hand van het produkt. *Pharmaceutisch Weekblad* **116** 724.

BS 5295 (1976, 1989) *Environmental cleanliness in enclosed spaces.* British Standards Institution, London.

Denyer, S. P., Russell, A. D. and Hugo, W. B. (1982) Filtration sterilization. In: Russell, A. D., Hugo, W. B. and Ayliffe, G. A. J. (eds), *Principles and practice of disinfection preservation and sterilization.* Blackwell Scientific Publications, Oxford, pp. 569–608.

DeVecchi, F. (1986) Environmental control in parenteral drug manufacturing. In: Avis, K.E., Lachman, L. and Lieberman, H. A. (eds), *Pharmaceutical dosage forms: parenteral medications, Vol. II.* Marcel Dekker, New York, pp. 309–359.

Hempel, H. E. (1976) Large scale manufacture of parenterals. *Bull. Parent. Drug Assn.* **30** 88–95.

HM Medicines Inspectorate (1989) Personal communication.

Heuring, H. (1970) People: the key to contamination control. *Contam. Control* **9** 18–20.

Howorth, F. H. (1987) Prevention of airborne infection in operating rooms. *NAT News. Br. J. Theatre Nursing* **24**, 13–15.

Luna, C. J. (1984) Personnel: the key factor in cleanroom operations. In: Avis, K. E., Lachman, L. and Lieberman, H. A. (eds), *Pharmaceutical dosage forms: parenteral medications, Vol. I.* Marcel Dekker, New York, pp. 427–455.

MacIntosh, C. A., Lidwell, O. M., Towers, A. G. and Marples, R. R. (1978) The dimensions of skin fragments dispersed into the air during activity. *J. Hyg. Camb.* **81** 471–479.

Noble, W. C. (1978) Dispersal of bacteria from human skin. *J. Environ. Sci.* **21** 25–28.

Noble, W. C. (1981) *Microbiology of the human skin,* 2nd edn. Lloyd-Luke, London.

Noble, W. C., Lidwell, O. M. and Kingston, D. (1963) The size distribution of airborne particles carrying micro-organisms. *J. Hyg. Camb.* **66** 385–391.

Noble, W. C., Habbema, J. D. F., von Furth, R., Smith, I. and de Raay, C. (1976). Quantitative studies on the dispersal of skin bacteria into the air. *J. Med. Microbiol.* **9** 53–61.

Parenteral Drug Association (1980) Validation of aseptic filling for solution drug products. *Technical Monograph No. 2.*

Parker, M. T. (1972) The clinical significance of the presence of micro-organisms in pharmaceutical and cosmetic preparations. *J. Soc. Cosmet. Chem.* **23** 415–425.

Ringertz, O. and Ringertz, S. (1982) The clinical significance of microbial contamination in pharmaceutical and allied products. *Adv. Pharm. Sci.* **1** 201–225.

Sharp, J. (1989) Manufacture and control of sterile products. *Manuf. Chem.* **60** 49–53.

Smart, R. (1972) Microbial spoilage in pharmaceuticals and cosmetics. *J. Soc. Cosmet. Chem.* **23** 721–737.

United States Federal Standard 209A, B, C and D (1962, 1976, 1987, 1988) *Cleanroom and workstation requirements, controlled environment.* Washington, DC.

United States Pharmacopeia (1990) Twenty-second revision. The United States Pharmacopeial Convention, Rockville, MD.

Whyte, W. (1981) Settling and impaction of particles into containers in manufacturing pharmacies. *J. Parent. Sci. Technol.* **35** 255–261.

Whyte, W. (1983) A multicentred investigation of clean air requirements for terminally sterilized pharmaceuticals. *J. Parent. Sci. Technol.* **37** 138–144.

Whyte, W. (1984) The influence of cleanroom design on product contamination. *J. Parent. Sci. Technol.* **38** 103–108.

Whyte, W. (1986) Sterility assurance and models for assessing airborne bacterial contamination. *J. Parent. Sci. Technol.* **40** 188–197.

Whyte, W., Bailey, P. V. and Hodgson, R. (1979) Monitoring the causes of cleanroom contamination. *Man. Chem. Aer. News* **50** 65–81.

Whyte, W., Bailey, P. V., Tinkler, J., McCubbin, I., Young, L. and Jess, J. (1982) An evaluation of the routes of bacterial contamination occurring during aseptic pharmaceutical manufacturing. *J. Parent. Sci. Technol.* **36** 102–106.

World Health Organization Report (1973) Sterility and sterility testing of pharmaceutical preparations and biological substances. *Technical Report Series No. 530.*

APPENDIX:
US Instute of Environmental Sciences: current and planned recommended practices for contamination control

	Current	Planned
RP1	HEPA Filters	Guidelines for planning and design of controlled environments
RP2	Laminar-flow clean-air devices	
RP3	Garments required in clean rooms and controlled environmental areas	Clean-room surfaces Flooring for controlled environments
RP4	Wipers used in clean rooms and controlled environments	Clean-room cleaning and maintenance
RP5	Clean-room gloves and finger-cots	Documentation and stationery for clean rooms
RP6	Testing clean rooms	Particle-counting
RP8	Gas-phase adsorber cells	Process liquids, cleanliness and control
RP9	Compendium of standards, practices and methods relating to contamination control	Static control in clean rooms and controlled environments
RP11	Glossary of definitions	Liquids filtration
RP13	Equipment calibration or validation procedures	Equipment calibration procedures
RP15	Clean-room product and support equipment	Clean-room swabs

6A

Monitoring microbiological quality: conventional testing methods

Rosamund M. Baird
Formerly NETRHA Pharmaceutical Microbiology Laboratory, St Bartholomew's Hospital, London†

† Present address: Summerlands House, Yeovil, Somerset BA21 3AL, UK

1   INTRODUCTION

Microbiological control begins with the design of plant and premises and ends with testing of the finished product for microbial contamination. As in any production chain, the quality of that finished product hinges upon the weakest link in the chain. Quality must therefore be built in at every production stage; by definition it cannot be inserted into the final product (see Chapter 4).

Microbiological control is applied at several key points during the manufacture of both sterile and non-sterile products. Raw materials, including water, must meet the required specifications before being approved for use. In-process monitoring will indicate whether product quality has been compromised during manufacture, abnormal results often providing the first indication of an earlier problem in processing. Finished product tests will demonstate whether release specifications have been met. These results, combined with other accumulated data, provide the vital documentary evidence that the product is fit for its intended use.

Regardless of whether the product under examination is a raw material, a sterile or a non-sterile product, all samples withdrawn for testing should be selected on a statistical basis, with the sampling method taking account of the individual product type. Similarly the test method, whether quantitative or qualitative, should be adapted to the product characteristics. A number of contributory factors are known to influence the outcome of the test, including the choice and sensitivity of the test method itself, the effectiveness of antimicrobial neutralization techniques and the choice of resuscitation and enrichment media. Test methods used in pharmaceutical microbiology have traditionally been based upon the techniques developed for use in food, water and dairy microbiology; newer techniques involving rapid methods have also been introduced in recent years with some success, as discussed in Chapter 6B.

As with other control laboratories, the quality of service provided by the pharmaceutical microbiology laboratory should be monitored by a process of continuous self-inspection and regular external audit. Factors such as the choice, standardization and validation of test methods will clearly need to be reviewed.

2 SAMPLING

In any sampling scheme, the quality of a given batch is assessed from the results of samples drawn from that batch. Any sampling process therefore involves the selection of appropriate indicators of quality, known as attributes, which are assumed to be homogeneously distributed throughout the batch. In microbiological sampling, however, contaminants may not always be randomly distributed in a product. In the case of heat-sterilized products, samples selected for sterility testing are normally taken from the coolest part of the autoclave, where the risk of sterilization failure is deemed to be higher. Likewise non-aqueous products may not always be homogeneously contaminated since pockets of contaminants may occur. For example, surface contamination of an antibiotic eye ointment was reported to have occurred through the condensation of water onto the ointment surface, thereby enabling local proliferation of *Pseudomonas aeruginosa* in an otherwise hostile environment (Kallings *et al.* 1966). Similarly, aerobic contaminants may grow preferentially on the surface of topical products. In such cases sampling schemes should take account of this difference in distribution. Aqueous products are assumed to be homogeneously contaminated; nevertheless, the contents of individual containers should be mixed thoroughly before samples are withdrawn.

2.1 Sampling techniques

The likelihood of accidental contamination occurring whilst taking samples should clearly be minimized. Personnel involved in sampling will not necessarily be microbiologists but they should have been properly trained in the use of aseptic techniques.

Samples taken should obviously be representative of the batch as a whole. Sampling procedures should document the method of sampling, the equipment and type of sample container to be used, the quantity of sample to be taken and how it should be treated thereafter. Equipment should be properly cleaned after use and reserved only for sampling purposes.

Microbiological sampling of pharmaceuticals should precede other quality-control tests. Previously unopened packs should be sampled and each pack should be suitably marked so that it can be identified in the case of a failure. The interval between sampling and examination should be kept to a minimum, particularly when sampling water supplies. Contaminants may multiply during this time, leading to erroneously high counts. If necessary, samples should be refrigerated.

In the case of aseptically prepared products, both random and non-random sampling is required; one-quarter of the required samples should be taken from the beginning of the filling run and similarly from the end of the run, the remaining half being randomly selected from the finished batch. As mentioned before, for heat-sterilized products samples should be taken from specified sites in the load, previously identified as the slowest to reach sterilizing temperatures. Samples for pyrogen testing should be collected from amongst the last filled containers. Oily products, creams and ointments frequently present sampling problems. This may be overcome to some extent by homogenizing the product with a suitable emulsifying agent, such as Tween 80. The British Pharmacopoeia (BP 1988) and the United States Pharmacopeia (USP) XXII (1990) then recommend warming the resulting homogenate to not more than 40°C and 45°C, respectively, for an unspecified period of time. Since preservative action is temperature dependent, the microbial count may well be reduced by doing this, thereby providing misleading information on product quality.

2.2 Sampling schemes

In formulating any sampling scheme a decision must first be made as to the level of assurance required. This in turn will determine the size of the sample and the number required. Sampling rates can then be found in British Standard (BS) 6001 (1972). Clearly, for greater assurance, the number of samples must increase accordingly. In those instances where test results indicate a deterioration in product quality, sampling plans can be switched from a normal inspection to a tightened inspection, as stated in BS 6000 (1972) and BS 6002 (1979). Sampling will then remain at this level until test results show that normal inspection levels are again warranted.

2.2.1 Single sampling

Conventional sampling plans are usually based upon the examination of single samples taken from a predetermined number of containers in a batch. Traditionally this number has been $\sqrt{n}+2$, where n is the number of containers in the batch. Such samples are mixed together and a further sample from this is then analysed, resulting in the acceptance or rejection of the batch concerned. Results on individual products may be examined for trends over a period of time.

An alternative but somewhat time-consuming approach involves the use of cumulative sum (cusum) charts, whereby trends in microbiological quality can easily be observed. Such a system can provide an early warning that product quality is not being maintained. It has also been successfully used in monitoring the quality of water supplies as shown in Fig. 1 and in environmental monitoring programmes (Russell *et al.* 1984).

2.2.2 Attribute sampling

More recently, a different approach to sampling has been introduced in the form of two- and three-class attribute sampling schemes. As before, a number of samples are taken but these are then analysed separately. Although more costly in terms of staff resources, such schemes are considered to offer a greater degree of assurance and to provide rather more useful information on the batch concerned. By definition such schemes incorporate so-called tolerances, allowing a small proportion of samples to show slight deficiencies; clearly, however, they are unsuitable for the testing of sterile products.

2.2.2.1 Two-class attribute plan

In this plan both the number of samples to be taken and the maximum permitted number of positive results are stated. Such a scheme is used in the examination of water supplies where *Escherichia coli* is not allowed in any sample and only two out of five samples may contain Enterobacteriaceae (Anon. 1982). Thus two quality levels are defined by the required absence of *E coli* and by the limited number of samples which may contain Enterobacteriaceae.

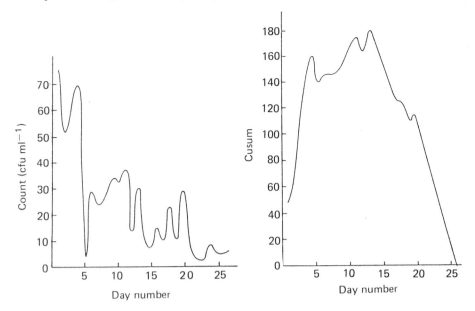

Fig. 1 — Variations in bacterial counts of deionized water over a period of time, (a) plotted traditionally and (b) depicted as a cusum chart. In the case of the latter trends are more easily discernible, thus enabling corrective action to be taken at an early stage, if required. Reproduced, with permission, from Microbiological control of raw materials by M. Russell. In: Bloomfield, S. F., Baird, R., Leak, R. E. and Leech, R. (eds), *Microbial quality assurance in pharmaceuticals, cosmetics and toiletries*. Ellis Horwood, Chichester, 1988, pp. 40–41.

2.2.2.2   *Three-class attribute plan*

Here three levels of quality are acknowledged: the fully acceptable, often known as the acceptable quality level or AQL; the marginally acceptable; and the unacceptable. Such schemes are closely associated with the establishment and use of microbiological reference values and have been used successfully in food and cosmetic microbiology in recent years (Mossel 1982; Anon. 1986). In pharmaceutical microbiology their use has been largely restricted to the in-house testing of raw materials and non-sterile products; they have not as yet been incorporated into the various pharmacopoeial specifications. Nevertheless, when used they are considered to provide invaluable, detailed information on the batch concerned. Additional information can then be obtained by comparing data amassed from different batches.

3   CULTURE MEDIA

Over the years a wide range of culture media has been developed for the isolation and identification of micro-organisms from different ecological niches. The range of available media has expanded considerably through the introduction of new selective agents and the adaptation of existing formulae, particularly in the field of food microbiology. Both non-selective media, rich in nutrients, and highly selective, specific media are used for the detection of the increasingly large number of known microbial types.

In contrast, the range of media used in pharmaceutical microbiology is comparatively narrow and has altered very little in recent times. Media used in the pharmacopoeial tests are required to recover a relatively small number of microbial types or to demonstrate that contaminants cannot be recovered from the product in question. In-house tests on pharmaceutical products, however, frequently employ a less restricted range of culture media.

Culture media used in the identification and isolation of microbial contaminants may be in a liquid or solid form. They are generally formulated to contain a source of carbon, nitrogen, buffers, sulphur, phosphorous, inorganic salts and a significant proportion of water. In addition, nutritional supplements such as serum, blood, carbohydrates, vitamins and certain salts (calcium, magnesium, manganese, sodium and potassium, for example) may be added. Selective agents (antibiotics and dyes) may also be included to inhibit unwanted organisms, thereby increasing the selective properties of a given medium. Media are usually formulated with a pH close to neutral, so providing optimum conditions for growth.

In the past a wide range of culture media have been prepared and stocked for identification purposes. The often laborious task of identifying microbial isolates has nowadays become much simpler through the introduction of commercially available kits; these contain dehydrated reagents to which suspensions of individual bacterial cultures are added. Following incubation, the biochemical reactions are recorded according to observed colour changes and these are then converted to a score which corresponds to a certain bacterial type and species.

3.1 Preparation and use of culture media

Culture media may be purchased in a ready-to-use form with a limited shelf-life or in a more stable dehydrated form to which water is added. Less commonly, culture media may be prepared from the component raw materials. Good laboratory practice requires that culture media are prepared to pharmaceutical and not 'cookbook' standards. Thus culture media and their components should be purchased from approved suppliers and dated on receipt; media should be prepared according to master formulae and written procedures; sterilization methods should be carefully followed so that the resulting product is sufficiently processed, but not overheated, thereby affecting its nutritive properties; the finished product should be given a batch number and an expiry date. Culture media and its component raw materials should be stored in appropriate conditions, as recommended by the manufacturer.

Quality-control tests on the final product should include not only tests on sterility and pH but also performance tests on the medium's selectivity, productivity and ability to produce distinctive colonies. Significant differences in productivity may occur between brands of media and even between different batches of the same brand.

With the exception of fertility tests carried out on sterility test media, the importance of performance tests has been largely overlooked in pharmaceutical microbiology. In food microbiology, however, their importance has been recognized through the publication of an international pharmacopoeia, detailing test methods, test strains and monographs on the most commonly used media (Baird *et al.* 1985; Baird *et al.* 1987).

The performance of a given culture medium is known to be affected by three factors (Mosell *et al.* 1980). The so-called 'intrinsic' properties are of primary importance since they include not only the available nutrients, the water activity (A_w), the redox potential (E_h) and pH of the medium at the time of inoculation and during incubation, but also any antimicrobial agents which may be present. 'External' factors such as the temperature and gaseous environment can also markedly affect the performance of media during the incubation period. Other 'implicit' factors may also be significant during this period, depending upon the vitality of the inoculum itself and the likelihood of synergism or antagonism between competing cells.

3.2 Culture methods

Recovery of microbial contaminants from pharmaceutical products involves both an isolation and identification stage. Additionally, an initial resuscitation stage may be required to recover sublethally injured cells. Such cells may result from exposure to preservatives, antimicrobial compounds or other toxic components, extremes of osmotic pressure or pH, or from the injurious effects of processing generally, including heat. Micro-organisms surviving such conditions carry sublethal lesions which inhibit their development on selective media, although quite suitable for non-stressed cells of the same species. The use of selective media for counting purposes may therefore result in a gross underestimation of the number of cells present.

Food microbiologists have long recognized the damaging consequences of exposure to sublethal effects. Recovery methods frequently therefore incorporate a resuscitation step when cell repair can take place. This may take the form of recovery in a liquid medium, such as in a simple salts solution at room temperature for a period of 2 hours. In other cases a longer period may be required, for example up to 6 hours. In such cases liquid medium repair is inappropriate since it would allow multiplication of both uninjured and repaired cells, leading to erroneously high counts. In these instances a solid medium repair technique is used, where dilutions of the product are spread onto a rich non-selective agar and held at room temperature for 4–6 hours. Subsequently, a suitable selective agar at 44°C is overlayered, allowed to set and then incubated at an appropriate temperature.

Apart from the recommended techniques used to recover specified organisms from non-sterile products (see BP 1988), resuscitation techniques have been largely overlooked in pharmaceutical microbiology. This clearly illustrates the need for closer co-operation between microbiologists of different disciplines.

An additional stage in the examination of pharmaceutical products is a neutralization step to inactivate any antimicrobial agents which may be present (see Chapter 13A). This should take place at an early stage of culture and before any attempt at resuscitation is made. In some cases, for example alcohols and phenols, the antimicrobial activity may simply be diluted out. The success of this method depends upon the product having a high dilution coefficient. In the case of phenol with a dilution coefficient of six, a threefold dilution will result in a decrease of activity of 3^6-fold. Where dilution is inappropriate, various inactivating agents may be added to the culture media as shown in Table 1. Where a specific inactivator is not available a multipurpose neutralizing agent, such as 3% Tween 80 or 4% Lubrol W, may be used. In sampling pharmaceutical products of unknown origin, a non-specific neutralization method should be used. A further detailed treatment of neutralization methods is given in Chapter 11.

4 MICROBIOLOGICAL TESTS

4.1 Control of raw materials

Raw materials, including water, used in the manufacture of both sterile and non-sterile pharmaceuticals may contain a variety of microbial contaminants. During processing these may be reduced in number or conversely they may be given a suitable opportunity to multiply. Hence, the purpose of microbiological quality-control tests is, first, to establish whether contaminants are present and in what sort of numbers and, second, to determine which organisms are present and whether they represent a potential hazard either from a health or from a spoilage point of view.

The microbiological quality of the final product is determined by the quality of the starting materials; materials with a known low bioburden should be purchased whenever possible. Poor-quality raw materials will not only compromise the quality and life of the final product but also contribute to the overall level of background contamination in the manufacturing plant. Particularly in the case of free-living opportunist organisms, reservoirs of contamination may be established in the manufacturing environment, thus providing a potential source of contamination to successive products. Gram-negative bacilli found in water supplies have often caused notable problems in the past (see also Chapters 2 and 3).

Microbiological standards for raw materials will vary according to the type of product and its susceptibility to contamination. Table 2 summarizes the microbiological test requirements for selected raw materials of the BP 1988 and the USP XXII. Although a wide range of raw materials is used in pharmaceutical production, it is not necessary to monitor the microbiological quality of all starting materials. Sampling regimens should therefore be adapted accordingly by manufacturers, based on a given product's known bioburden. Susceptible products, such as tragacanth powder, should be examined at every delivery; less susceptible products may be sampled at defined intervals; others may not need to be sampled routinely.

Products of natural origin, whether plant, mineral or animal, are likely to be heavily contaminated and may well contain pathogenic organisms, for example talcum powder may contain *Clostridium* spp. and pancreatin extracts may contain *Salmonella* spp. and *E. coli*. Microbiological control of such products may rest with the supplier, who must provide materials of an agreed specification, detailed on an accompanying certificate of analysis. In contrast, synthetic materials are rarely contaminated and generally provide contaminants with poor growth opportunities. In other instances the manufacturing process itself may have a profound effect on the microbiological quality of the raw material concerned. For example, extremes of pH employed in an extraction process will significantly reduce the natural bioburden. For other materials which do not meet the required microbiological standard, some form of in-house treatment may, however, be required.

Table 1 — Methods of inactivating antimicrobial compounds

Antimicrobial compound	Method/addition of:
Alcohols	Dilution (+Tween 80)
Ampicillin, benzylpenicillin	β-Lactamase from *B. cereus*
Antibiotics, other	Membrane filtration
Bronopol	Cysteine hydrochloride
Chlorhexidine	Lecithin+Tween 80 or Lubrol W
Cresols	Dilution+Tween 80
Halogens	Sodium thiosulphate
Hexachlorophane	Tween 80
Mercurials	Sodium thioglycollate or cysteine
Parabens	Dilution+Tween 80
Phenolics	Dilution+Tween 80
Quarternary ammonium compounds	Lecithin+Tween 80 or Lubrol W
Sorbic acid	Dilution+Tween 80
Sulphonamides	*p*-Aminobenzoic acid

Table 2 — Comparison of BP (1988) and USP (XXII) microbiological test requirements for selected raw materials

Raw material	BP requires absence of:	USP requires absence of:
Acacia	*E. coli*[a]	Salmonellae
Agar	*E. coli*[a]	Salmonellae
Aluminium hydroxide	*E. coli*[a]	*E. coli*[b]
Aluminium phosphate	Pseudomonads	
Bentonite	[a]	*E. coli*
Cochineal	*E. coli*, salmonellae	
Digitalis, powdered	*E. coli*	Salmonellae
Gelatin	*E. coli*, salmonellae[a]	*E. coli*, salmonellae[b]
Kaolin	[a]	*E. coli*
Lactose	[a]	*E. coli*, salmonellae[b]
Pancreatin	*E. coli*, salmonellae[a]	Salmonellae
Starch	*E. coli*[a]	*E. coli*, salmonellae
Sterculia	*E. coli*	
Talc, purified	[a]	[b]
Tragacanth	*E. coli*, salmonellae[a]	*E. coli*, salmonellae

[a]EP requirement in some member states for TVC (see individual monographs in BP).

[b]USP requirement for TVC (see individual monographs).

4.2   Control of sterile products

4.2.1   *Sterility test*

Much has been written about the deficiencies of the sterility test, as described in BP
1988 and USP XXII (see also Chapter 9). In order to make an objective assessment
of its value, it is necessary to understand not only the microbiological problems
involved in carrying out the test, but also the difficulties which may be encountered in
obtaining representative samples from a given batch. Although essentially a qualitative test, the sterility test can be adapted to provide quantitative information on the
numbers and types of contaminants present. Such data can be invaluable when
investigating potential sources of contamination.

4.2.1.1   *Statistical considerations*

By its nature the test is destructive and clearly cannot be applied to the entire batch.
The test therefore relies heavily on a statistical method of withdrawing random
samples; results are determined both by the number of samples taken and the
incidence of contamination in the batch. In mathematical terms this may be written
as:

$$\text{The probability of rejection } 1-(1-p)^n$$

where p is the proportion of contaminated containers and n is the number of
containers tested.

The number of containers to be tested in a given batch is determined by the size of
the batch and the type of product. Table 3 summarizes these requirements as stated

Table 3 — Sample requirements of BP and EP for sterility testing

Product	Batch size	Minimum no. samples required
Parenterals (single and multidose, large-volume parenterals)	<100	10% or 4, whichever is the greater
	101–500	10
	>500	2% or 20, whichever is the less
Ophthalmics	<200	5% or 2, whichever is the greater
	>200	10

in BP 1988 and the European Pharmacopoeia (EP) 1980, Addendum 1986. Clearly,
as the sample size increases, so the probability of approving a defective consignment
decreases. Conversely, the probability of approving a defective consignment
increases as the incidence of contamination decreases. Based on the results of a
single test and taking no account of possible microbiological problems, the prob-

ability of rejecting single batches of different sizes and varying frequencies of contamination is shown in Table 4.

Table 4 — Probability of rejecting a batch as non-sterile according to sample size (based on one EP sterility test)

Batch size	Sample size	Probability of rejection according to frequency (%) of contamination in batch				
		0.1	1.0	5.0	10	50
40	4	0.004	0.039	0.185	0.344	0.937
100–500	10	0.010	0.096	0.401	0.653	0.999
1000	20	0.020	0.180	0.640	0.878	0.999

Adapted from Brown and Gilbert (1977).

In the event of a positive sterility test result, the possibility of operator contamination must be considered (Kelsey 1972) and in such cases a total of two retests are permitted. From a statistical point of view, the probability of approving a defective batch in fact increases with additional tests.

In mathematical terms the probability of passing a defective batch at the first retest is:

$$(1-p)^n [2-(1-p)^n]$$

A further complication may be introduced when the sample size itself is reduced. BP 1988 states that the minimum quantity to be tested per container may vary according to the container size. For parenteral products of less than 1 ml volume, the entire contents must be sampled; whereas for those containing more than 20 ml only 10% of the contents are required. On the other hand, the USP XXII requires the entire contents of parenteral products of less than 1 ml and of 50 ml and over to be tested; for intermediate volumes, a proportionate sample is allowed (1 ml for volumes less than 10 ml, 5 ml for volumes between 10 and less than 50 ml). Clearly, such testing schemes can have a profound effect on the results of samples with low levels of contamination.

4.2.1.2 *Microbiological considerations*
There are a number of inherent problems in devising a test to demonstrate the sterility of a product. Since the identity of all potential contaminants is unknown, a compromise on the choice of media is inevitably required. In practice only two media, soya bean casein digest broth and fluid thioglycollate, are recommended in the most recent editions of BP, EP and USP. It is worth noting that fluid thioglycollate is known to be toxic to damaged cells. Compromises on incubation temperatures and times are also required.

The nature of the product under test may pose problems from a sampling point of view. In the case of oily products, such as eye ointments, microbial cells may well be embedded within the matrix of the product, thus requiring extraction with a suitable solvent, for example sterile isopropyl myristate. Likewise the product itself or its components (including preservatives) may possess antimicrobial activity and these will need inactivating either by a dilution technique or by the addition of a specific inactivating agent to the culture medium (see Table 1). In some instances specific inactivators may not be available, in which case a multipurpose neutralizing agent such as Lubrol W or Tween 80 may be used. A third method involves the physical separation of microbial cells from the antimicrobial components of the product using a membrane filtration technique. A hydrophobic-edged membrane filter is used for such purposes and this is then washed with a sterile diluent, such as peptone saline or $\frac{1}{4}$ strength Ringer's solution. Antibiotic preparations have traditionally been sampled in this way.

Microbial cells exposed to the effects of such antimicrobial compounds are likely to be sublethally damaged, as are cells exposed to a heating process, as discussed earlier. It is noteworthy that the current sterility test method fails to incorporate a resuscitation step to recover such cells.

As far as the test itself is concerned, appropriate precautions should be taken to avoid accidental contamination of the sample under test. In practice the test is carried out in a laminar airflow cabinet using sterile equipment and sterile diluents. Personnel responsible for sterility testing should be appropriately clad, usually in clean-room clothing, and should be properly trained in aseptic manipulations. Rotational staff are considered unsuitable for such work.

Accidental contamination of test material will inevitably occur from time to time and a retest, or even a second retest, is permitted where distinguishable isolates are found in the two tests. As mentioned earlier, the practice of retesting actually increases the probability of passing a defective batch and must therefore be considered of dubious value.

4.2.1.3   Test methods
BP (1988) recommends the use of two test methods: membrane filtration and direct inoculation. Two culture media are recommended: fluid thioglycollate medium, incubated at 30–35°C for not less than seven days is used primarily for isolating anaerobic bacteria, but will also sustain the growth of aerobic bacteria; soya bean casein digest medium, incubated at 20–25°C for not less than seven days, is intended primarily for the culture of aerobic bacteria, but will also support the growth of fungi. Where a direct inoculation method replaces a membrane filtration technique, the incubation period is increased to 14 days.

Quality control tests on all batches of culture media should include the following: a sterility test; a productivity test to demonstrate the growth of small numbers of organisms (approximately 100 cells), including where appropriate an aerobe such as *Staphylococcus aureus*, a spore-forming aerobe *such as Bacillus subtilis*, an anaerobe such as *Clostridium sporogens* and a fungus such as *Candida albicans*; and a similar test in the presence of the product to demonstrate effective neutralization of antimicrobial activity in the test sample.

(a) *Membrane filtration.* This is the method of choice for aqueous and alcoholic preparations that can be filtered and for preparations miscible with, or soluble in, oily solvents. Fluids are filtered through a sterile cellulose nitrate or cellulose acetate membrane filter, pore size not greater than 0.45 μm. Cells retained on the surface of the filter will then multiply when placed in appropriate growth media. In practice the filter may be divided into two portions after filtration or the sample itself may be filtered through two separate filters. Suitable filtration equipment includes both traditional glass, metal or polycarbonate filter holders and a number of dual-purpose, commercially available enclosed filter units. In the case of the latter, appropriate media may be introduced and incubated directly, thereby reducing the risk of operator contamination.

(b) *Direct inoculation.* Using this technique, any antimicrobial agents must first be inactivated before the sample is added directly to the culture medium. The sample should be diluted by approximately tenfold in the case of liquids and a hundredfold in the case of solids. Where large volumes of liquid are concerned, the growth medium may be added directly to the sample in a concentrated form.

4.2.1.4   *Overview*
In summary, the time-honoured sterility test, first described in the 1932 BP and the 1936 USP, has in recent years lost some of its former standing. Nowadays it is regarded by most industrialists as a rather poor indicator of product quality. In the case of terminally sterilized products, alternative methods are now available for assessing the probability of sterility. In such cases confidence can be justifiably placed in the proper control of the manufacturing and sterilizing processes and in the associated use of biovalidation data (see Chapter 9). However, in the case of aseptic preparations, heat-labile and filter-sterilized products, the sterility test must still be regarded as an essential quality-control test. It should not be forgotten, however, that the sterility test can only provide information on the sample tested under the conditions specified.

4.2.2   *Testing for pyrogens*
The traditional way of detecting pyrogens has involved the injection of test material into rabbits and the measurement of any subsequent febrile response (see British Pharmacopoeia 1988). The test has a number of drawbacks, mainly relating to its biological nature. In recent years the *Limulus* amoebocyte lysate (LAL) test has been used as a promising alternative *in vitro* method for the detection of microbial lipopolysaccharides, known as endotoxins; the test will not, however, detect other pyrogens and in such cases the rabbit test remains the method of choice. The test is based on the highly specific interaction of microbial endotoxin with amoebocyte lysate, producing turbidity, precipitation or gelation of the mixture. This relatively simple, sensitive and inexpensive test provides rapid results, the rate of reaction being dependent on the concentration of endotoxin, the pH and the temperature. Some therapeutic products are known, however, to interfere with the test reaction. A more recent development of this test involves the use of chromogenic assay (Friberger 1987).

In recent times considerable experience has been gained in both the performance of the *Limulus* test through collaborative studies and also in refinement of the test to improve its sensitivity. The *Limulus* test continues to gain acceptance amongst the pharmacopoeial bodies, the licensing authorities and individual manufacturers; it is now increasingly used for bacterial endotoxin detection not only when screening raw materials, in monitoring production processes and in testing high-purity water systems but also when releasing selected sterile products. For a more detailed discussion of the test, the reader is referred to Pearson (1985).

4.3   Microbiological tests on non-sterile products

Microbiological control of pharmaceuticals has become increasingly important in the past two decades. Three factors in particular have contributed to this development. In recent years the occurrence of microbial contamination in medicines has been widely reported; the origins and avoidance of such contamination have been well documented; at the same time there is now a better understanding of the health risks presented to patients from the inadvertent exposure to contaminated medicines.

4.3.1   *Control of finished products*

Microbiological quality-control tests will establish whether the finished product meets its release specification. Where appropriate, the pharmacopoeial standard is used (see current edition of BP, USP and EP). In other cases an in-house specification may be used alone or in combination with the pharmacopoeial standard. In-house specifications are generally more detailed, reflecting the known inherent microbiological problems associated with the product itself or its manufacture.

4.3.2   *Microbiological methods*

Essentially, microbiological quality-control tests comprise both quantitative techniques for counting micro-organisms and qualitative tests to show the absence of specified organisms. Both sets of test are recognized by the various national pharmacopoeias: the EP test is based on the former, the BP on the latter and the USP includes both sets of tests.

4.3.2.1   *Pour plate*

In this method the sample is mixed with molten agar at 44°C in Petri dishes and allowed to set. Following incubation, colonies are counted and a total viable count per millilitre or gram can then be calculated. The method is more sensitive for counting small numbers of colonies than the spread plate technique, since a larger sample volume (up to 5 ml) can be examined. However, in preparing the plates it is important not to exceed the holding temperature of the molten agar, as this may affect the count. Colonies held within the matrix of the agar will require an increased period of incubation (usually an extra 24 hours) before they can be seen. Colonies should not be confused with undissolved particles of test sample, nor with air bubbles, introduced through vigorous mixing of the plate contents.

4.3.2.2   *Spread plate*

Aliquots (usually 0.1 ml) of the prepared sample are spread in duplicate over the plate surface and incubated. Colonies are counted and results may then be converted to total viable counts using the appropriate dilution factor. Non-selective media, such as nutrient agar or tryptone soya agar, are usually employed for counting purposes.

4.3.2.3 Drop count
Less commonly used, the drop count method may be useful as a screening test when relatively high viable counts are suspected. The technique is a variation of the surface count method developed by Miles *et al.* (1938). Aliquots (0.002 ml) of the diluted sample are deposited from a special dropper onto previously dried plates. Following incubation, individual colonies are counted; the total viable count can then be calculated using the appropriate dilution factor.

4.3.4.2 Most probable number (MPN)
This technique uses liquid culture media and depends upon the observation of certain growth characteristics, such as turbidity, acid or gas production. Decimal dilutions of the sample are first prepared from which aliquots are inoculated into the broth concerned. Following incubation, the number of tubes showing the required growth characteristics are counted. Through the use of reference tables (Meynell and Meynell 1970), the most probable number of organisms in the original sample can then be calculated. In using the tables it is assumed firstly that micro-organisms are randomly distributed in the sample and secondly that a positive reaction is obtained if, and only if, the aliquot of sample tested contains one or more micro-organisms.

Although the MPN technique has been widely used for counting coliforms in the water industry, it is regarded as somewhat cumbersome for pharmaceutical purposes. It has, however, been recommended for counting micro-organisms in USP XXII and is also considered to be useful when counting small numbers of micro-organisms (van Doorne *et al.* 1981).

4.3.2.5 Filtration
Membrane filtration techniques, as described earlier, are commonly used to examine water and other liquid samples. Following filtration, membranes (0.45 μm pore size) are transferred to solid media for incubation. Resulting colonies are counted and a total viable count/sample volume may be calculated.

4.3.3 Tests for specified micro-organisms
Individual methods vary according to the particular organism sought. In most instances a broth enrichment step precedes the isolation stage on solid media which is then followed by confirmatory tests to establish the identity of isolates. The latter are generally based upon the growth characteristics of pure cultures on selective media and on their biochemical reactions to selected tests. A detailed discussion of identification schemes is outside the scope of this chapter, but appropriate reference sources should be consulted (e.g. Cowan 1974).

As discussed previously, those organisms considered to be hazardous from a health point of view are reflected in the various pharmacopoeial requirements. BP 1988 details tests for the absence of Enterobacteriaceae, *E. coli* salmonellae, *Ps. aeruginosa* and *Staph. aureus*. Whilst recognizing why these particular organisms have been selected for pharmacopoeial standards, the presence of other organisms in pharmaceuticals cannot be overlooked. Nowadays it is well known that the presence of many other Gram-negative organisms, and particularly *Pseudomonas* spp. cannot be condoned. Such contaminants often have simple nutritional requirements and are able to multiply to appreciable numbers within a product. Furthermore the presence of such opportunist pathogens can be particularly hazardous for certain patients, for example the very young, the elderly, immunosuppressed patients or those with burns.

Nowadays therefore many in-house specifications for non-sterile pharmaceuticals include a requirement to test for the presence of additional organisms, other than those detailed in the various pharmacopoeias. An upper limit in the number of so-called undesirable organisms is often specified.

BP 1988 lists methods for the isolation and identification of Enterobacteriaceae, *E. coli* salmonellae, *Ps. aeruginosa* and *Staph. aureus*, as summarized in Table 5. In all cases the methods incorporate an initial recovery step, a broth enrichment stage (non-selective in the case of casein digest, but selective in the case of Enterobacteriaceae enrichment broth–Mossel), followed by an isolation stage on solid media. Confirmation of isolates is then based upon suggested biochemical tests and observed growth characteristics on selective media.

Although such tests will provide the required microbiological evidence that specified organisms are indeed absent, the methods may be considered to be time-consuming and somewhat cumbersome in practice, particularly when large numbers of samples must be examined. In-house specifications for both raw materials and non-sterile products are often therefore based on more generalized screening methods combining counting techniques with isolation techniques for specific microbial types. The latter have also been widely used in various surveys comparing the incidence of microbial contamination in different types of pharmaceutical products (Anon. 1971; Baird 1985).

4.4   Environmental controls

Significant advances in clean-room design and construction in recent years have had a considerable impact on the overall microbiological quality of manufacturing environments for both sterile and non-sterile products. In addition the development of clean-room standards (see Chapters 4 and 5) have in turn identified the environmental conditions required for the manufacture of both sterile and non-sterile products. The monitoring of contamination levels in such environments is largely based upon air and surface sampling methods.

4.4.1   Air sampling

The traditional method of monitoring air quality has involved the use of settle plates. Petri dishes, usually containing a non-selective agar, are exposed to the atmosphere for defined periods of time. Following incubation, colonies are counted and results from different exposure areas may then be compared. However, this 'passive' method is of limited quantitative value since the results are affected by air currents in the immediate area, the particle settling rate and the time of exposure. Moreover, the technique will not detect those organisms which remain suspended and hence fail to settle on the agar surface.

Air quality can also be usefully monitored using 'active' techniques, such as slit samplers, centrifugal samplers and those using liquid impingement and membrane filtration. All provide a quantitative evaluation of the number of organisms per volume of air sampled. Such devices should be regularly calibrated and used according to the manufacturer's instructions. Successful use of these samplers is dependent on the statistics of sampling. Sample volumes of air should therefore be

Table 5 — Isolation and identification tests for specified micro-organisms (BP 1988)

Organism	Enrichment	Primary test	Secondary test	Confirmation
Enterobacteriaceae	Lactose broth 35–37°C for 2–5 h	EEB–Mossel 35–37°C for 24–48 h	VRBGLA 35–37°C for 18–24 h	Growth of Gram-negatives
E. coli	As above	MacConkey broth 43–45°C for 18–24 h	MacConkey agar 43–45°C for 18–24 h	Indole at 43.5–44.5°C/biochemical
Salmonella	As above for 5–24 h	TBBG broth 42–43°C for 18–24 h then subculture on: DCA, XLDA or BGA for 35–37°C for 24–48 h	TSI agar 35–37°C for 18–24 h	Biochemical/serological
Ps. aeruginosa	Saline peptone 35–37°C for 2–5 h	Casein digest broth 35–37°C for 24–48 h	Cetrimide agar 35–37°C for 24–48 h	Oxidase test
Staph. aureus	As for Ps. aeruginosa above		Baird-Parker 35–37°C for 24–48 h	Coagulase, catalase, DNase tests

EEB–Mossel, Enterobacteriaceae enrichment broth–Mossel; VRBGLA, violet red bile agar with glucose and lactose; TBBG, tetrathionate bile brilliant green broth; DCA, deoxycholate citrate agar; XLDA, xylose lysine deoxycholate agar; BGA, brilliant green agar; TSI, triple sugar iron agar; DNase, deoxyribonuclease test.

adjusted according to expected contamination levels, for example in a critical (filling) area larger volumes of air will be required to provide statistically valid results, than in a less clean environment, where higher levels of contamination might reasonably be expected.

4.4.2   Surface sampling
Surface sampling will indicate the effectiveness of cleaning and disinfection policies. 'Rodac' or contact plates containing non-selective media can be pressed lightly onto flat surfaces. Following incubation, numbers of colonies can be counted, thus providing a quantitative estimate of contamination levels. Other less accessible surfaces are best sampled using the non-quantitative technique with moistened swabs. These can be cultured directly onto solid media or first incubated in nutrient broth and then subcultured onto solid media.

4.4.3   Monitoring programmes
The frequency and extent of environmental monitoring should be defined in a testing programme, according to the class of manufacturing environment and the work undertaken there. Routine microbiological monitoring should then be carried out to prove continued compliance with such requirements. BS 5295 (1989) states that the frequency of monitoring of clean rooms or clean-air devices should not be less than that required for particulate monitoring, but gives no specific guidance on appropriate standards. FDA guidelines (Anon. 1987) state, however, that air in critical areas should be monitored daily and should meet a standard of no more than one colony-forming unit per 10 cu. ft. In controlled areas a standard of not more than 25 colony-forming units per 10 cu ft is required (see also Chapter 17).

Microbial limits for surface counts are not defined in either of these documents. Nevertheless, it is recommended that maximum microbial limits for individual manufacturing units should be drawn up on the basis of what can be achieved under optimum operating conditions. Additionally a definitive course of action should be established should such limits be exceeded. Many manufacturers adopt a three-class attribute plan for implementing environmental limits, thus defining acceptable, warning and action levels for the results obtained.

5   AUDITING MICROBIOLOGICAL ACTIVITIES

As in other areas of pharmaceutical production, the activities of the microbiology laboratory should be audited on a regular basis (see Chapter 17). Depending on the nature of the work undertaken there, this will require a critical appraisal of the following aspects: the use and suitability of existing premises; the use and maintenance of equipment; the type and range of activities in relation to the changing demands of production activities; staffing levels and staff ability, particularly with regard to the individual's training needs.

5.1   Premises
Sufficient working space should be available to segregate the various activities of the laboratory and to provide a streamlined direction of work-flow through the laboratory. Separate areas should be designated for the following activities: sample receipt,

sample preparation and testing, including a separate area for sterility testing with adjacent changing facilities, sample incubation, the preparation of culture media, decontamination and wash-up, the reading of results, documentation and office work. The work-flow through these areas should be such that the opportunity for cross-over of samples is kept to a minimum.

5.2 Equipment
A wide range of equipment may be found in the microbiology laboratory, all of which requires regular maintenance. Separate log books should be kept for each item of equipment. Good laboratory practice requires that detailed records are kept on the operation of equipment, including for example daily fluctuations of temperature within incubators and temperature, pressure and time readings monitored during autoclave cycles.

5.3 Activities
The quality of the microbiological service provided by the laboratory is clearly an important issue. The suitability, reproducibility and precision of methods for isolating, counting and identifying microbial contaminants should be reviewed from time to time and modified if necessary. In the past the quality control of culture media has been sadly neglected in pharmaceutical microbiology laboratories. All batches of media should meet release specifications, as discussed earlier. Technical skills of individual members of staff may need to be examined from time to time. Consideration should be given to the setting up of a national quality control scheme, such as that operated by the Public Health Laboratories.

As in other areas of quality control, the microbiologist's involvement in laboratory-based activities, particularly in end-product analysis, has in recent years been overtaken by a more open approach to quality-assurance activities generally. Nowadays he may well be expected to advise on the microbiological aspects of building and equipment design, equipment cleaning and sanitization methods, as well as cleaning and disinfection policies. Staff training may also form an important part of his job, involving both the teaching of basic microbiology and the education of production personnel in aspects of cleanliness and hygiene. In addition the microbiology laboratory has an important function in monitoring whether acceptable conditions are being maintained, particularly in the testing of environmental and water samples. This involves not only the setting of appropriate standards with warning and action levels, but also close monitoring of test results against such limits.

Some laboratories will clearly be unable to meet all these requirements and some work may well be contracted out to a specialist microbiology laboratory. The work of such laboratories should be carried out to an agreed specification and audited on a regular basis. Certain aspects of the work, including environmental testing, are, however, best carried out in-house so that corrective action may be taken at an early stage, if required.

5.4 Staff
Demands on staff time change constantly as new problems arise within the laboratory. Sufficient trained staff should be available to cope with these demands, which may range from time-consuming challenge testing or stability testing of new

formulations to the simple examination of in-process samples. Additionally, there should be sufficient flexibility in staff time to meet the increasing demands of the production department, whether such input is required in the form of training, or in an advisory or monitoring capacity.

6 REFERENCES

Anon. (1971) Microbial contamination of medicines administered to hospital patients: report by Public Health Laboratory Working Party. *Pharm. J.* **207** 96–99.

Anon. (1982) *The bacteriological examination of drinking water supplies.* HMSO, London.

Anon. (1986) *CTPA recommended microbiological limits and guidelines for microbiological quality control.* Cosmetic, Toiletry and Perfumery Association, London.

Anon. (1987) *Guideline on sterile drug products produced by aseptic processing.* Food and Drug Administration, Maryland, USA.

Baird, R. M. (1985) Microbial contamination of pharmaceutical products made in a hospital pharmacy: a nine year survey. *Pharm. J.* **231** 54–55.

Baird, R. M., Barnes, E. M., Corry, J. E. L., Curtis, G. D. W. and Mackey, B. M. (eds) (1985) Quality assurance and quality control of microbiological culture media. *Int. J. Food Microbiol.* **2** 1–136.

Baird, R. M., Corry, J. E. L. and Curtis, G. D. W. (eds) (1987) Pharmacopoeia of culture media for food microbiology. *Int. J. Food Microbiol.* **5** 187–300.

British Pharmacopoeia (1932) 6th edn, Appendix 16. Constable, London.

British Pharmacopoeia (1988) Vol. II, Appendix XVI. HMSO, London.

British Standard 6000 (1972) *The use of BS 6001, sampling procedures and tables for inspection by attributes.* British Standards Institution, London.

British Standard 6001 (1972) *Sampling procedures and tables for inspection by attributes.* British Standards Institution, London.

British Standard 6002 (1979) *Sampling procedures and charts for inspection by variables for per cent defective.* British Standards Institution, London.

British Standard 5295 (1989) *Environmental cleanliness in enclosed spaces.* British Standards Institution, London.

Brown, M. R. W. and Gilbert, P. (1977) Increasing the probability of sterility of medicinal products. *J. Pharm. Pharmacol.* **29** 517–523.

Cowan, S. T. (1974) *Cowan and Steel's manual for the identification of medical bacteria*, 2nd edn. Cambridge University Press, Cambridge.

European Pharmacopoeia (1980) Part I, Appendix VIII, Addendum 1986. Maison Neuve, Sainte Ruffine.

Friberger, P. (1987) A new method of endotoxin determination. *ICPR* July/August, 34–41.

Kallings, L. O., Ringertz, O., Silverstolpe, L. and Ernerfeldt, F. (1966) Microbiological contamination of medicinal preparations. *Acta Pharm. Suec.* **3** 219–230.

Kelsey, J. C. (1972) The myths of surgical sterility. *Lancet* **2** 1301–1303.

Meynell, G. G. and Meynell, E. (eds) (1970) In: *Theory and practice in experimental bacteriology*, 2nd edn. Cambridge University Press, Cambridge.

Miles, A. A., Misra, S. S. and Irwin, J. O. (1938) The examination of the bactericidal power of blood. *J. Hyg. (Camb.)* **38** 732–749.

Mossel, D. A. A. (1982) In: *Microbiology of foods. The ecological essentials of assurance and assessment of safety and quality*, 3rd edn. University of Utrecht, Utrecht, pp. 89–97.

Mossel, D. A. A., van Rossem, F., Koopmans, M., Henricks, M., Verouden, M. and Eelderink, I. (1980) Quality control of solid culture media: a comparison of the classical and the so-called ecographic technique. *J. Appl. Bact.* **49** 439–454.

Pearson, F. C. (1985) In: Robinson J. R. (ed), *Pyrogens*. Marcel Dekker, New York.

Russell, M. (1988) Microbiological control of raw materials. In: Bloomfield, S. F., Baird, R., Leak, R. E. and Leech, R. (eds), *Microbial quality assurance in pharmaceuticals, cosmetics and toiletries*, Ellis Horwood, Chichester, pp. 35–48.

Russell, M. P., Purdie, R. N., Goldsmith, J. A. and Phillips, I. (1984) Computer assisted evaluation of microbiological environmental control data *J. Parent. Sci. Technol.* **38** 98–102.

United States Pharmacopeia (1936) XI. Mack Printing Co., Easton, Pennsylvania.

United States Pharmacopeia (1990) XXII. US Pharmacopeial Convention, Rockville, Maryland.

Van Doorne, H., Baird, R. M., Hendriksz, D. T., van der Kreek, D. M. and Pauwels, H. P. (1981) Liquid modification of Baird-Parker's medium for the selective enrichment of *Staph. aureus. Ant. van Leeuwenhoek* **47** 267–278.

6B

Monitoring microbiological quality: application of rapid microbiological methods to pharmaceuticals

S. P. Denyer
Department of Pharmaceutical Sciences, University of Nottingham, University Park, Nottingham NG7 2RD, UK

1 INTRODUCTION

Traditional microbiological methods of detection and enumeration are generally time-consuming and labour-intensive. These practical considerations often limit the extent to which microbiological tests are routinely applied both at the formulation development level (i.e. preservative screening) and for microbiological quality assurance (MQA) in the manufacturing process. In the latter instance, the inevitable time delay associated with incubation often determines that MQA data are only of retrospecitve value. Considerable advantage would therefore be gained if suitable, more rapid methods of microbiological analysis could be available for application in the pharmaceutical sphere.

2 RAPID METHODS AVAILABLE

The development of rapid methods has been largely led by the food, dairy, water and medical industries, which has resulted in a diverse range of methods (Table 1) not all

Table 1 — A selection of rapid microbiological methods

Method	Detection principle	Level of development
DIRECT:		
Electronic particle counting	Direct determination of cell count and cell size	−
Filtration and microscopy; direct epifluorescent filter technique (DEFT)	Capture, staining (DEFT employs a fluorochrome stain) and direct enumeration of micro-organisms or micro-colonies on membrane filters, sometimes using image analysis	+
Photometry	Determination of microbial growth or changes in cell refractility by optical density measurements	+
INDIRECT:		
Bioluminescence:		
ATP	Light emission from microbial ATP by luciferin/luciferase reaction	+
in vivo	Generation of light by bioluminescent bacteria	−
Chromatography and spectrometry	Detection of microbial metabolites and cellular components	−
Dye reduction	Monitoring microbial metabolism by colour changes in redox dyes	(+)
Electrical resistance	Measurement of electrical changes (conductance, impedance) in specialized media due to microbial growth	+
Electrochemical	Metabolic reduction of a redox compound with generation of an electrode current	(+)
Enzyme monitoring	Detection of microbial enzymes	(+)
Limulus amoebocyte lysate (LAL)	Detection of (principally) Gram-negative bacterial lipopolysaccharide	+
Microcalorimetry	Generation of heat by micro-organisms	−
Radiometry	Monitoring of microbial metabolism using ^{14}C-radiolabelled substrate	(+)

+, highly developed; (+), moderate level of development; −, early stages of development or development limited to a narrow range of applications.

necessarily suited to pharmaceutical application. Their means of detection may be direct, in which individual micro-organisms or a population of organisms is directly observed, or indirect, whereby microbial metabolism, metabolites or components are monitored. Some methods may be highly developed with extensive equipment and information support while others can still be considered at the early stages of research or currently developed for only a narrow application range. Few have yet found their way to widespread acceptance (Jarvis and Easter 1987). It is also important to remember that the term 'rapid' is variously applied to techniques of 5 minutes to overnight duration, the definition often reflecting the expectations of the user. Furthermore, a method which may be deemed rapid in applications with high bioburden may require an extended enrichment period in situations of lower contamination.

Useful discussion and comparison of the principal methods can be found in the following works: general aspects (O'Toole 1983; McMurdo and Whyard, 1984; Balows *et al.* 1989; Stannard *et al.* 1989), bioluminescence (Jago *et al.* 1989; Stanley *et al.* 1989; Stewart *et al.* 1989; Stewart 1990), direct epifluorescent filter technique (DEFT) (Pettipher 1983; Manson *et al.* 1985; Hutcheson *et al.* 1988; Rodrigues and Kroll 1988, 1990), electrical resistance (Baynes *et al.* 1983; Firstenberg-Eden and Eden 1984; Owens and Wacher-Viveros 1986), electrochemical (Patchett *et al.* 1989), electronic particle counting (Kubitschek 1969), enzyme monitoring (Kroll and Rodrigues 1986), *Limulus* amoebycote lysate (LAL) (Jorgensen and Alexander 1981; Bussey and Tsuji 1984), microcalorimetry (Forrest 1972; Beezer 1980), photometry (Thomas *et al.* 1985) and radiometry (Cutler *et al.* 1989).

3   USE OF RAPID METHODS IN PHARMACEUTICALS

From a pharmaceutical perspective, the principal areas in which rapid methods have been considered for application are given in Table 2. A method may be required to

Table 2 — Principal areas of application for rapid microbiological methods in pharmaceuticals

Area	Application
Product quality assessment	Microbial limit tests for raw materials and final non-sterile products (includes total viable count and detection of pathogens)
	Sterility tests
Process hygiene	In-process samples
	Site hygiene
	Air quality
Preservative efficacy	Screening potential preservatives
	Examining the influence of formulation on preservative behaviour
	Challenge testing
Sterilizer testing	Biological indicators

provide either quantitative or qualitative evidence of microbial presence (survival), or alternatively to offer rapid confirmation of the absence of micro-organisms.

3.1   Product quality assessment

The pharmaceutical industry tends to be conservative in its approach to rapid methods for assessment of product quality, largely because of the regulatory constraints imposed upon these products. For this reason, much of the information accumulated in Table 3 is drawn from the cosmetic and toiletry industries, but using products comparable to non-sterile pharmaceuticals. This table clearly demonstrates the low probability that any single method will satisfy the requirements for all types of pharmaceutical product; it is a common misconception that a rapid method can be immediately applied in a wide range of situations without first undertaking extensive

Table 3 — Some examples of rapid methods applied to the detection of micro-organisms in pharmaceuticals and related products

Method	Sensitivity	Limitations	Applications	References
ATP bioluminescence	$>10^3$ bacteria; $>10^2$ yeasts	Interfering factors; luciferase inhibition	Cosmetics/toiletries; Intravenous fluids; Packaging materials; Sterility testing of suspensions; Surface hygiene; Water	Leech (1988); Bopp and Wachsmith (1981); Anderson et al. (1986); Senior et al. (1989); Bussey and Tsuji (1986); Blackburn et al. (1989); Webster (1986); Woolridge (1989)
DEFT[a]	Air, $>10^5$; liquid, generally 10^3–10^4 ml^{-1} down to 25 ml^{-1}; liquid (+enrichment), 6 organisms irrespective of sample volume	Cannot be applied to highly viscous or particulate materials	Air; Intravenous fluids; Surface hygiene; Water	Palmgren et al.(1986); Denyer and Ward (1983); Denyer and Lynn (1987); Denyer et al. (1989); Holah et al. (1988); Mittelman et al. (1983); Mittelman et al. (1985)
Electrical resistance[b]	Threshold for detection circa 10^6 ml^{-1}	Only narrow spectrum of detectable organisms without careful media selection	Cosmetics; Toiletries; Water	Kaiserman et al. (1989); Kahn and Firstenberg-Eden (1984); Leech (1988); Wilkins et al. (1980)
Electronic particle counting	See reference	Cannot be applied to particulate products	Shampoo	Leech (1988)
Limulus amoebocyte assay	10^4–10^5 ml^{-1}	Limited spectrum of detectable organisms; interfering substances	Intravenous fluids	Jorgensen and Smith (1973); Anderson et al. (1986)
Microcalorimetry[b]	Threshold for detection 10^4–10^5 ml^{-1}	Only applicable to low viscosity products; variable growth rate of contaminants affects end-point	Aqueous toiletries	Leech (1988)
Photometry[b]	$>10^1$ bacteria; $>10^2$ yeasts	Restricted to products of low opacity	Aqueous systems	Hunter, Ridgway Watt and Coleman (personal communication)

[a]Sensitivities influenced by volume filtered.
[b]Lower limit of sensitivity determined by incubation time.

protocol development. The sensitivity of all methods can be enhanced by sample enrichment but this will lead to an inevitable increase in analysis time; additionally, contaminants grow at different rates and this may result in a substantially different microbial flora from the original sampled product. In sterility testing, where the burden (if any) is likely to be low, samples inevitably require enrichment or extended incubation in order to reach the microbial levels required for detection by rapid methods.

3.2 Process hygiene
In general, examination of in-process product samples can utilize the same methods of rapid analysis as raw materials and final product (see Table 3). Surface hygiene assessment, using appropriate swabbing techniques, may require an enrichment period if low counts are expected; similarly, large volumes of process water or air may need to be sampled and concentrated by filtration to ensure a sufficient microbial burden before examination.

3.3 Preservative efficacy
The official preservative efficacy test methods (see Chapter 13A) require challenge periods of up to 28 days and the introduction of rapid methods in this situation would confer no meaningful benefit. Where rapid methodology can have an important role to play is in the rapid examination of several candidate preservative systems (and their possible permutations of concentration and combination) for use in new or developing formulations. Here, kinetic data from D-value determinations (see Chapter 13B) or estimation of growth-inhibitory concentrations can quickly provide a useful indication of preservative/formulation incompatibilities and can be used to compare the relative merits of potential preservative systems. Table 4 summarizes some published examples of preservative evaluation by rapid methods; it is important to distinguish between those methods used primarily to explore bacteriostatic behaviour and those able to examine bactericidal activity. In the latter instance, enrichment or extended incubation times may be necessary to detect low numbers of survivors thereby extending the overall detection time. The application of selected rapid methods in antibiotic sensitivity testing is well established (Coleman *et al.* 1983; Baynes *et al.* 1986; Balows *et al.* 1989) and the extension of these protocols to the assessment of model preservative systems is entirely feasible.

In a product challenge designed to explore the capacity of a preservative system to withstand repeated microbial insults or to study the ability of spoilage organisms to survive and grow, kinetic information is of less importance and the detection methods summarized in Table 3 are applicable.

3.4 Sterilizer testing
Sterilization protocols require regular microbiological validation; for some processes continual efficacy monitoring with biological indicators is necessary (see Chapter 9). In order to ensure that every reasonable opportunity is given for the recovery of stressed indicator spores a long incubation period, often in excess of one week, is allowed before assurance of sterilizer efficacy can be given; this provides little opportunity to detect partial sterilizer failure early. A recent publication has suggested a way forward in this respect where ATP bioluminescence methods are

Table 4 — Some published examples of preservative evaluation by rapid methods

Method	Organism	Comments	References
Bioluminescence:			
ATP	Bacteria	Estimation of bacteriostatic activity	Hussenet (1985); Denyer (1989)
in vivo	Bacteria	Bactericidal activity assessed by use of genetically engineered luminescent bacteria as challenge organisms	Stewart et al. (1989); Jassim et al. (1990); Stewart et al. (1990)
DEFT	Bacteria	Survivors of bactericidal action determined following enrichment	Denyer and Lynn (1987)
Dye reduction	Bacteria	Survivors of bactericidal action assessed by tetrazolium salt reduction	Hurwitz and McCarthy (1986); Mattila (1987); Hill et al. (1989)
Electronic particle counting	Bacterial spores	Used in size-analysis mode to follow changes in spore volume	Parker (1971)
Microcalorimetry	Bacteria and yeasts	Measurement of phenol coefficients; correlation with antimicrobial events	Beezer et al. (1981, 1987, 1988); Beezer (1990)
Photometry	Bacteria, yeasts and moulds	Growth inhibition followed by turbidity measurements	Brown (1966); Parker (1971); Magliano et al. (1989)
	Bacterial spores	Measurement of spore swelling	Parker (1969)

employed for the detection of spores surviving suboptimal sterilization processes (Webster *et al.* 1988); the opportunities for *in vivo* bioluminescence have also been addressed (Stewart *et al.* 1989).

4 OVERVIEW

There are several well-developed rapid microbiological methods now becoming available which may have useful application in pharmacy and these include DEFT, bioluminescence, electrical resistance methods and (bio)photometry. Some methods may require expensive equipment and offer full automation while others represent only a small investment in cost. Clearly in assessing the benefits of such methods the capital and running costs of these systems should be compared with traditional approaches. Inevitably, no single method is likely to satisfy all requirements, and many may need further development to adapt them to the specific demands of the pharmaceutical situation. Furthermore, once developed such methods may not always meet with early regulatory approval unless a clear relationship with traditional viable counting methods is demonstrated; for rapid methods to be valuable, however, such a relationship may perhaps not always be necessary or indeed possible (Sacree and Kilsby 1988) and greatest emphasis should be placed on their predictive benefit, proven through comparisons with traditional methods.

5 REFERENCES

Anderson, R. L., Highsmith, A. K. and Holland, B. W. (1986) Comparison of standard pour plate procedure and the ATP and *Limulus* amoebocyte lysate procedures for the detection of microbial contamination in intravenous fluids. *J. Clin. Microbiol.* **23** 465–468.

Balows, A., Tilton, R. C. and Turano, A. (1989) *Rapid methods and automation in microbiology and immunology.* Brixia Academic Press, Brescia.

Baynes, N. C., Comrie, J. and Prain, J. H. (1983) Detection of bacterial growth by the Malthus conductance meter. *Med. Lab. Sci.* **40** 149–158.

Baynes, N. C., Comrie, J. and Harper, I. A. (1986) Antimicrobial susceptibility determination by an automated conductance technique. *Med. Lab. Sci.* **43** 232–240.

Beezer, A. E. (1980) *Biological microcalorimetry.* Academic Press, London.

Beezer, A. E. (1990) Microcalorimetric methods for exploring mechanisms of antibacterial action. In: Denyer, S. P. and Hugo, W. B. (eds), *Mechanisms of action of chemical biocides: their study and exploitation, SAB Technical Series 27.* Blackwell Scientific Publications, Oxford (in press).

Beezer, A. E., Hunter, W. H. and Storey, D. E. (1981) The measurement of phenol coefficients by flow microcalorimetry. *J. Pharm. Pharmacol.* **33** 65–68.

Beezer, A. E., Gooch, C. A., Hunter, W. H., Lima, M. C. P. and Smith, B. V. (1987) Quantitative structure–activity relationships: a group additivity scheme for biological response of *E. coli* to the action of *o-*, *m-* and *p-*alkoxyphenol. *Int. J. Pharm.* **38** 251–254.

Beezer, A. E., Fox, C. G., Gooch, C. A., Hunter, W. H., Miles, R. J. and Smith, B.

V. (1988) Microcalorimetric studies of the interaction of *m*-hydroxybenzoates with *E. coli* and with *S. aureus*: demonstration of a Collander relationship for biological response. *Int. J. Pharm.* **45** 153–155.

Blackburn, C. de W., Gibbs, P. A., Roller, S. D. and Johal, S. (1989) Use of ATP in microbial adhesion studies. In: Stanley, P. E., McCarthy, B. J. and Smither, R. (eds) *ATP luminescence: rapid methods in microbiology, SAB Technical Series 26*. Blackwell Scientific Publications, Oxford, pp. 145–152.

Bopp, C. A. and Wachsmith, I. K. (1981) Luciferase assay to detect bacterial contamination of intravenous fluids. *Am. J. Hosp. Pharm.* **38** 1747–1750.

Brown, M. R. W. (1966) Turbidimetric method for the rapid evaluation of antimicrobial agents. *J. Soc. Cosmet. Chem.* **17** 185–192.

Bussey, D. M. and Tsuji, K. (1984) Optimization of chromogenic *Limulus* amebocyte lysate (LAL) assay for automated endotoxin detection. *J. Parent. Sci. Technol.* **38** 228–233.

Bussey, D. M. and Tsuji, K. (1986) Bioluminescence for USP sterility testing of pharmaceutical suspension products. *Appl. Environ., Microbiol.* **51** 349–355.

Coleman, K., Hunter, P. A. and Ridgway Watt, P. (1983) A novel multi-channel biophotometer and its use in determining antibiotic effects. In: Russell, A. D. and Quesnel, L. B. (eds), *Antibiotics: assessment of antimicrobial activity and resistance, SAB Technical Series 18*. Academic Press, London, pp. 317–330.

Cutler, R. R., Wilson, P. and Clarke, F. V. (1989) Evaluation of a radiometric method for studying bacterial activity in the presence of antimicrobial agents. *J. Appl. Bact.* **66** 515–521.

Denyer, S. P. (1989) ATP bioluminescence and biocide assessment: effect of bacteriostatic levels of biocide. In: Stanley, P. E., McCarthy, B. J. and Smither, R. (eds), *ATP luminescence: rapid methods in microbiology, SAB Technical Series 26*. Blackwell Scientific Publications, Oxford, pp. 189–195.

Denyer, S. P. and Lynn, R. (1987) A sensitive method for the rapid detection of bacterial contaminants in intravenous fluids. *J. Parent. Sci. Technol.* **41** 60–66.

Denyer, S. P. and Ward, K. H. (1983) A rapid method for the detection of bacterial contaminants in intravenous fluids using membrane filtration and epifluorescence microscopy. *J. Parent. Sci. Technol.* **37** 156–158.

Denyer, S. P., Lynn, R. A. P. and Pover, P. S. (1989) Medical and pharmaceutical applications of the direct epifluorescent filter technique (DEFT). In: Stannard, C. J., Petitt, S. B. and Skinner, F. A. (eds), *Rapid microbiological methods for foods, beveredges and pharmaceuticals, SAB Technical Series 25*. Blackwell Scientific Publications, Oxford, pp. 59–71.

Firstenberg-Eden, R. and Eden, G. (1984) *Impedance microbiology*. Research Studies Press, Letchworth.

Forrest, W. W. (1972) Microcalorimetry. In: Norris, J. R. and Ribbons, D. W. (eds), *Methods in microbiology*, Vol. 6B. Academic Press, London, pp. 285–318.

Hill, E. C., Hill, G. C. and Robbins, D. A. (1989) An informative and practical strategy for preventing spoilage and improving preservation using a simple assay for biocides and preservatives. *Int. Biodet.* **25** 245–252.

Holah, J. T., Betts, R. P. and Thorpe, R. H. (1988) The use of direct epifluorescent microscopy (DEM) and the direct epifluorescent filter technique (DEFT) to assess microbial populations on food contact surfaces. *J. Appl. Bacteriol.* **65** 215–221.

Hurwitz, S. J. and McCarthy, T. J. (1986) 2,3,5-Triphenyltetrazolium chloride as a novel tool in germicide dynamics. *J. Pharm. Sci.* **75** 912–916.

Hussenet, P. (1985) Applications récentes de la bioluminescence. *Parfums, Cosmétiques, Arômes* **61** 69–71.

Hutcheson, T. C., McKay, T., Farr, L. and Seddon, B. (1988) Evaluation of the stain Viablue for the rapid estimation of viable yeast cells. *Lett. Appl. Microbiol.* **6** 85–88.

Jago, P. H., Simpson, W. J., Denyer, S. P., Evans, A. W., Griffiths, M. W., Hammond, J. R. M., Ingram, T. P., Lacey, R. F., Macey, N. W., McCarthy, B. J., Salusbury, T. T., Senior, S. S., Sidorowicz, S., Smither, R., Stanfield, G. and Stanley, P. E. (1989) An evaluation of the performance of ten commercial luminometers. *J. Biolumin. Chemilumin.* **3** 131–145.

Jarvis, B. and Easter, M. C. (1987) Rapid methods in the assessment of microbiological quality: experiences and needs. *J. Appl. Bacteriol. Symposium Suppl.* **63** 115S–126S.

Jassim, S. A., Ellison, A., Denyer, S. P. and Stewart, G. S. A. B. (1990) *In vivo* bioluminescence: a cellular reporter for research and industry. *J. Biolumin. Chemilumin.* **5** 115–122.

Jorgensen, J. H. and Alexander, G. A. (1981) Automation of the *Limulus* amoebocyte lysate test by using the Abbott MS-2 microbiology system. *Appl. Environ. Microbiol.* **41** 1316–1320.

Jorgensen, J. H. and Smith, R. F. (1973) Rapid detection of contaminated intravenous infusion fluids using the *Limulus in vitro* endotoxin assay. *Appl. Microbiol.* **26** 521–524.

Kaiserman, J. M., Moral, J. and Wolf, B. A. (1989) A rapid impedimetric procedure to determine bacterial content in cosmetic formulations. *J. Soc. Cosmet. Chem.* **40** 21–31.

Khan, P. and Firstenberg-Eden, R. (1984) A new cosmetic sterility test. *Soap/Cosmetics/Chemical Specialities* **60** 46–48, 101.

Kroll, R. G. and Rodrigues, U. M. (1986) Prediction of the keeping quality of pasteurised milk by the detection of cytochrome *c* oxidase. *J. Appl. Bacteriol.* **60** 21–27.

Kubitschek, H. E. (1969) Counting and sizing micro-organisms with the Coulter Counter. In: Norris, J. R. and Ribbons, D. W. (eds), *Methods in microbiology*, Vol. 1. Academic Press, London, pp. 593–610.

Leech, R. (1988) New methodology for microbiological quality assurance. In: Bloomfield, S. F., Baird, R., Leak, R. E. and Leech, R. (eds), *Microbial quality assurance in pharmaceuticals, cosmetics and toiletries*. Ellis Horwood, Chichester, pp. 195–216.

Magliano, E. M., Colombo, R., Clerici, P., Pescatori, T. and Ocurti, C. (1989) Evaluation of antibacterial activity of antiseptics compounds with conventional method and automated system. In: Balows, A., Tilton, R. C. and Turano, A. (eds), *Rapid methods and automation in microbiology and immunology*. Brixia Academic Press, Brescia, pp. 616–618.

Manson, R., Scholefield, J., Johnston, R. J. and Scott, R. (1985) The screening of more than 2000 schoolgirls for bacteriuria using an automated fluorescence microscopy system. *Urol. Res.* **13** 143–148.

Mattila, T. (1987) A modified Kelsey–Sykes method for testing disinfectants with 2,3,5-triphenyltetrazolium chloride reduction as an indicator of bacterial growth. *J. Appl. Bacteriol.* **62** 551–554.

McMurdo, I. H. and Whyard, S. (1984) Suitability for rapid microbiological methods for the hygienic management of spray drier plant. *J. Soc. Dairy Technol.* **37** 4–9.

Mittelman, M. W., Geesey, G. G. and Hite, R. R. (1983) Epifluorescence micros-copy: a rapid method for enumerating viable and non-viable bacteria in ultra-pure-water systems. *Microcontamination* **1** 32–37, 52.

Mittleman, M. W., Geesey, G. G. and Platt, R. M. (1985) Rapid enumeration of bacteria in purified water systems. *Med. Dev. Diagnost. Ind.* **7** 144–149.

O'Toole, D. K. (1983) Methods for the direct and indirect assessment of the bacterial content of milk. *J. Appl. Bacteriol.* **55** 187–201.

Owens, J. D. and Wacher-Viveros, M. C. (1986) Selection of pH buffers for use in conductimetric microbiological assays. *J. Appl. Bacteriol.* **60** 395–400.

Palmgren, U., Ström, G., Blomquist, G. and Malmberg, P. (1986) Collection of airborne micro-organisms on Nucleopore filters, estimation and analysis — CAMNEA method. *J. Appl. Bacteriol.* **61** 401–406.

Parker, M. S. (1969) Some effects of preservatives on the development of bacterial spores. *J. Appl. Bacteriol.* **34** 322–328.

Parker, M. S. (1971) The rapid screening of preservatives for pharmaceutical and cosmetic preparations. *Int. Biodet. Bull.* **7** 47–53.

Patchett, R. A., Kelly, A. F. and Kroll, R. G. (1989) Investigation of a simple amperometric electrode system to rapidly quantify and detect bacteria in foods. *J. Appl. Bacteriol.* **66** 49–55.

Pettipher, G. L. (1983) *The direct epifluorescent filtration technique.* Research Studies Press, Letchworth.

Rodrigues, U. M. and Kroll, R. G. (1988) Rapid selective enumeration of bacteria in foods using a microcolony epifluorescence microscopy technique. *J. Appl. Bacteriol.* **64** 65–78.

Rodrigues, U. M. and Kroll, R. G. (1990) Rapid detection of salmonellas in raw meats using a fluorescent antibody–microcolony technique. *J. Appl. Bacteriol.* **68** 213–223.

Sacree, M. and Kilsby, D. C. (1988) The relevance of linear regression for assessing the performance of microbiological counting techniques. *Lett. Appl. Microbiol.* **7** 1–4.

Senior, P. S., Tyson, K. D., Parsons, B., White, R. and Wood, G. P. (1989) Bioluminescent assessment of microbial contamination on plastic packaging materials. In: Stanley, P. E., McCarthy, B. J. and Smither, R. (eds) *ATP luminescence: rapid methods in microbiology, SAB Technical Series 26.* Black-well Scientific Publications, Oxford, pp. 137–143.

Stanley, P. E., McCarthy, B. J. and Smither, R. (eds) (1989) *ATP luminescence: rapid methods in microbiology, SAB Technical Series 26.* Blackwell Scientific Publications, Oxford.

Stannard, C. J., Petitt, S. B. and Skinner, F. A. (eds) (1989) *Rapid microbiological methods for foods, beverages and pharmaceuticals, SAB Technical Series 25.* Blackwell Scientific Publications, Oxford.

Stewart, G. S. A. B. (1990) *In vivo* bioluminescence: new potentials for microbiology. *Lett. Appl. Microbiol.* **10** 1–8.

Stewart, G., Smith, T. and Denyer, S. (1989) Genetic engineering for bioluminescent bacteria: harnessing molecular genetics to provide revolutionary new methods for food microbiology. *Food Sci. Technol. Today* **3** 19–22.

Stewart, G. S. A. B., Jassim, S. and Denyer, S. P. (1990) Mechanisms of action and rapid biocide testing. In: Denyer, S. P. and Hugo, W., B. (eds), *Mechanisms of action of chemical biocides: their study and exploitation, SAB Technical Series 27* Blackwell Scientific Publications, Oxford (in press).

Thomas, D. S., Henschke, P. A., Garland, B. A. and Tucknott, O. G. (1985) A microprocessor-controlled photometer for monitoring microbial growth in multi-welled plates. *J. Appl. Bacteriol.* **59** 337–346.

Webster, W. A. (1986) cited in Olson, W. P. (1987) Sterility testing. In: Olsen, W. P. and Groves, M. J. (eds), *Aseptic pharmaceutical manufacturing: technology for the 1990's.* Interpharm Press, Illinois, pp. 315–354.

Webster, J. J., Walker, B. G., Ford, S. R. and Leach, F. R. (1988) Determination of sterilization effectiveness by measuring bacterial growth in a biological indicator through firefly luciferase determination of ATP. *J. Biolumin. Chemilum.* **2** 129–133.

Wilkins, J. R., Grana, D. C. and Fox, S. S. (1980) Combined membrane filtration-electrochemical microbial detection method. *Appl. Environ. Microbiol.* **40** 852–853.

Woolridge, C. A. (1989) ATP bioluminescence for microbial quality assurance of process water. In: Stanley, P. E., McCarthy, B. J. and Smither, R. (eds), *ATP luminescence: rapid methods in microbiology, SAB Technical Series 26.* Blackwell Scientific Publications, Oxford, pp. 93–97.

7

Principles of sterilization

C. J. Soper and D. J. G. Davies
Centre for Drug Formulation Studies, School of Pharmacy and Pharmacology,
University of Bath, Claverton Down, Bath BA2 7AY, UK

1 INTRODUCTION

Sterility is defined as the absence of all viable life forms. In pharmacy and medicine this relates especially to micro-organisms. The term is an absolute one and descriptions implying degrees of sterility are not only confusing, but erroneous. Sterilization is the process of achieving sterility, i.e. the process of destroying or removing all viable life forms. In practice this is achieved by exposure of the preparation to an inimical physical or chemical agent for a predetermined period. The agents used are elevated temperature, ionizing radiation, or chemicals in the gaseous state, generally together with elevated temperature. A fourth method that can be used with solutions and gases involves passing them through a micro-organism-proof filter.

In this context it is necessary to define death as it applies to micro-organisms. In practice a micro-organism is defined as dead when it cannot be detected in culture media in which it previously has been shown to proliferate. Detection requires the production of a colony on the surface of solid medium or turbidity in liquid medium. A single organism must be able to proliferate through many generations to be detected and an organism that cannot reproduce or can only reproduce through a few generations would be classified as dead by this criterion. We do not have media capable of culturing all known organisms. Furthermore, organisms that have survived a potentially lethal process may have specific metabolic requirements and if these are not known it will not be possible to recover them in standard culture media. The absence of all viable life forms is therefore a negative state that can never be practically proved. As a consequence the phrase 'free from demonstrable forms of life' has been suggested as an alternative to 'sterile'.

A further problem in achieving sterility is that organisms exposed to a lethal agent do not all die at the same time. To a first approximation the number of organisms decreases exponentially with the time of exposure and therefore the absence of all viable organisms will only occur after infinite exposure to the agent. After a particular exposure time, even when viable organisms can no longer be detected, there will always be a finite probability of finding a viable organism. This probability decreases as the exposure time is increased, but never in real terms reaches zero. Sterility, the absence of all viable life forms, is therefore an absolute state the achievement of which cannot be guaranteed. Even if it was theoretically possible to achieve this state it would not be possible to demonstrate its achievement practically. Nevertheless the careful design of sterilization processes enables sterility in the absolute sense to be approached with an increasing probability of success.

The problems associated with the strict definition of sterility have led to the development of practical or process definitions in which the adequacy of a sterilization process is expressed as the ability to meet a defined end-point specification. In practical terms sterility is expressed as a mathematical probability of a product item remaining contaminated with surviving micro-organisms after exposure to a sterilization process. For pharmaceutical products and medical devices the designation 'sterile' is generally applied to products which have been treated in such a manner that, on completion of the process, individual items have a probability of being non-sterile, or a sterility assurance level (SAL), equal to or better than 10^{-6}. This definition of sterility as a probability function does not, however, infer that one in one million products is allowed to be non-sterile.

Inactivation of micro-organisms by sterilizing agents involves the irreversible damage of essential molecules in the cell. Exposure to these agents is also likely to produce deleterious effects in the material to be sterilized. It is of particular importance with pharmaceutical dosage forms that the sterilization process should not produce changes in the formulation that would either reduce its therapeutic efficacy or render it unacceptable to the patient. As a consequence it is often necessary to reach a compromise between the maximum acceptable SAL and the maximum allowable concomitant adverse effect upon the material to be sterilized.

2   KINETICS OF MICROBIAL INACTIVATION

The design of a sterilization process that will achieve a defined probability of occurrence of survivors depends upon a knowledge of the initial population of micro-organisms in the product (the bioburden) and the kinetics of inactivation of micro-organisms when exposed to the lethal agent. A number of mathematical terms has been derived to describe microbial inactivation and to aid calculation of SAL.

2.1   Microbial inactivation rate constant (k)

When homogeneous populations of organisms are exposed to a lethal process they lose their viability in a regular manner. To a first approximation it is believed that the rate of inactivation is directly proportional to the number of organisms present at any given time and thus a constant proportion of the surviving population is inactivated for each increment of exposure to the lethal agent. Mathematically the inactivation process can be described in the same way as a first-order chemical reaction. A process where microbial inactivation is related to the time of exposure to a lethal agent can be described by the equation.

$$N_t = N_0 e^{-kt} \tag{1}$$

where N_t is the number of surviving organisms after time t, N_0 is the number of organisms at time zero, i.e. the bioburden, t is the exposure time and k is the microbial inactivation rate constant. If the logarithm of the fraction of survivors (N_t/N_0) is plotted against exposure time the resulting curve (survivor curve) will be linear with a negative slope (Fig. 1). The slope of the line is $k/2.303$, from which the microbial inactivation rate constant can be calculated.

2.2 D-Value

In sterilization microbiology the D-value is frequently used instead of k as a measure of the rate of microbial death. The D-value is the exposure time required for the number of survivors to change by a factor of 10 or the time for the microbial population to be reduced by 90%. This is the exposure time required to achieve a decrease of one log-cycle in the survivor curve. The D-value may be estimated graphically (Fig. 1) or mathematically from the equation

$$D = \frac{t}{\log N_0 - \log N_t} \tag{2}$$

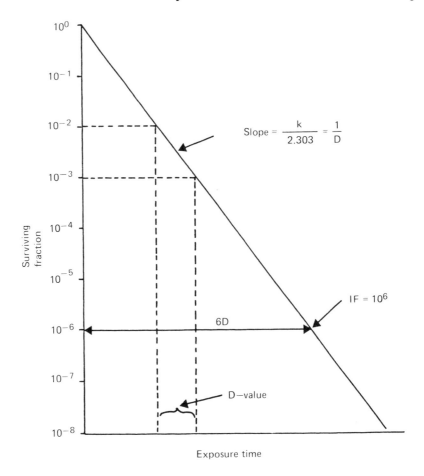

Fig. 1 — Microbial survivor curve: isothermal conditions.

The relationship between D-value and k for an exponential response is given by the equation

$$D = \frac{2.303}{k} \tag{3}$$

D-Value and k are specific for a particular inactivation process and when quoted the conditions under which they are determined must be stipulated. Thus with data for the heat inactivation of micro-organisms the temperature is shown as a subscript to the symbol, e.g. D_{121} is the D-value at 121°C. For radiation the D-value is stated in terms of absorbed dose (kGy). D-Value and k are measures of the resistance of an organism to the particular inactivation process; the smaller the D-value or the larger the value of k, the more sensitive is the organism.

    In the design of sterilization protocols the microbial inactivation required of the system is often expressed in terms of the D-value. An example is the use of the $12D$ end-point which defines that the sterilization process is required to produce 12 decimal reductions in the number of viable organisms or a decrease of 12 log-cycles in the survivor curve.

2.3   Inactivation factor (IF)

The total microbial inactivation of a sterilization process can also be a described by the inactivation factor (IF), which is defined as the reduction in the number of viable organisms brought about by the process. The inactivation factor is expressed in terms of the D-value as

$$IF = 10^{t/D} \tag{4}$$

where t is the exposure time and D is the D-value for the organism under the exposure conditions. A sterilization process that achieves $12D$ will therefore have an inactivation factor of 10^{12}.

3   EXPERIMENTAL DETERMINATION OF D-VALUE

Since the D-value is used extensively in the design of sterilization protocols it is necessary to be conversant with the methods that are used to determine it. These utilize direct enumeration and quantal data approaches.

3.1   Direct enumeration

In this method a known population of micro-organisms in a defined environment is exposed to the lethal agent and samples are withdrawn after different exposure times (for heat or chemical exposure) or after different absorbed doses (for radiation exposure). Alternatively, representative samples of the population can be exposed to different levels of inactivation. In both cases the number of surviving organisms is estimated by plating aliquots of the sample onto a suitable recovery medium, and counting the number of colonies formed after incubation.

The data can be used to generate a survivor curve and can be subjected to least-squares regression analysis to determine the value for the slope of the regression and its confidence limits. The D-value is calculated from the slope of the survivor curve using equation (3) given in section 2.2.

3.2   Quantal data

In this method replicate units each containing a known population of micro-organisms are exposed to different levels of inactivation. The contents of each unit are incubated under suitable recovery conditions and each unit is assessed as either showing growth or no growth. Exposure times or absorbed doses are selected so that at the first level all replicates show growth and at the last level all replicates show no growth. The intermediate levels then yield 'quantal' or 'fraction negative' data. When 20 or more replicate units are used the quantal range extends over about 2 log-cycles of microbial survival, from about 0.01 to 5 survivors per unit. The data can be analysed statistically by two methods.

3.2.1 The Stumbo–Murphy–Cochran method

This uses most probable number (MPN) analysis to estimate the probable number of survivors at the respective inactivation level:

$$N_U = 2.303 \log \frac{n}{r} \tag{5}$$

where N_U is the number of viable organisms per replicate unit after an exposure time or absorbed dose U, n is the number of replicate units treated and r is the number of replicate units showing no growth. The D-value is estimated from the equation

$$D = \frac{U}{\log N_0 - \log N_U} \tag{6}$$

where N_0 is the initial number of viable organisms per replicate unit.

3.2.2 The Spearman–Karber method

This method calculates the mean exposure time or dose until sterility, μ, using the equation

$$\mu = \sum_{i=1}^{k-1} \left(\frac{U_{i+1} + U_i}{2} \right) \left(\frac{r_{i+1}}{n_{i+1}} - \frac{r_i}{n_i} \right) \tag{7}$$

where U_i is the 'ith' exposure time or absorbed dose, r_i is the number of replicate units showing no growth out of n_i after an exposure time or absorbed dose U, and k is the first exposure time or absorbed dose that results in all replicate units showing no growth. If the initial number of viable organisms per replicate unit is N_0 the D-value can be calculated from the equation

$$D = \frac{\mu}{0.2507 + \log N_0} \tag{8}$$

There may be considerable difference between a D-value estimated from the regression line fitted to directly enumerated survivor data that extends over several log-cycles and the D-value estimated from quantal data where the value is calculated from N_0 and a point in the quantal region. For this reason D-values obtained by the different methods must not be used in combination, as, for example, in the calculation of z-values (see section 5.1.1.1).

4 RESISTANCE OF MICRO-ORGANISMS TO INACTIVATION

In sterilization processes the agents that are used to inactivate micro-organisms are elevated temperature, ionizing radiation and toxic gases. Although there is considerable variation in the resistance of micro-organisms to inactivation there is a general pattern in the degrees of resistance observed. Bacterial endospores are generally considered to be the most resistant forms, although there is a considerable range of resistance to individual agents within these spores. There is evidence that some of the 'slow viruses', e.g. Scrapie agent, may be considerably more resistant to certain lethal agents than bacterial spores and may present a major problem in the design of sterilization protocols. Non-sporing bacteria are the most sensitive to inactivation, along with the vegetative forms of yeasts and moulds. The larger viruses show similar resistance to vegetative bacteria. Spores formed by moulds and yeasts are generally more sensitive to inactivation than bacterial spores. In particular, the sexual spores of moulds are usually only marginally more resistant than the vegetative cells from which they are derived. In contrast, asexual spores e.g. chlamydospores produced by moulds, and the sexual ascospores formed by many yeasts, often shown enhanced resistance, intermediate between that of vegetative cells and bacterial spores. Small viruses such as poliovirus and hepatitis B virus also show enhanced resistance to inactivation.

Resistance to inactivation by a particular agent is a genetically determined charateristic of an organism and within the general pattern of microbial resistance there will often be considerable variation in the response of an organism to different agents. This is not surprising since the mechanisms by which each agent inactivates micro-organisms may be different. It should be noted that there may be considerable genetic variation in the resistance to a specific agent between different strains of the same species, and the development and selection of resistant mutants may present a particular problem. For this reason sterilization processes are often designed using, as the reference organism, resistant isolates that are characteristic of the bioburden of the particular product.

Microbial resistance to inactivation by a particular agent is affected by environmental influences during the formation and growth of the organism and during exposure of the organism to the agent. Environmental influences during the formation and growth of the organism include its growth phase and age, the growth temperature and conditions, and the nutrient composition of the growth medium (see Chapter 1). These influences become especially apparent when resistant strains isolated from a product bioburden are cultivated in the laboratory, whereupon they invariably show reduced resistance to the inactivating agent. For this reason it is usual to design sterilization protocols using, as the reference organism, a well-characterized resistant laboratory strain, usually a bacterial spore, which is maintained, grown and harvested under carefully controlled and defined conditions. Environmental influences during exposure of the organism to the lethal agent include pH, ionic strength, carbohydrate, protein and fat content of the menstruum and the presence of soluble organic and inorganic compounds. Microbial water content and gaseous atmosphere may also be important, for example, in respect to inactivation by dry heat or radiation. In pharmaceutical dosage forms the components may have considerable influence on the resistance of an organism to inactivation and it is necessary in the design of sterilization protocols to establish the resistance of the reference organism in the product to be sterilized, or a menstruum similar to it.

The apparent response of an organism to a lethal agent will depend upon the success with which organisms surviving the treatment can be recovered. In the determination of resistance charateristics used in the design of sterilization protocols it is essential that not only is a reference organism used and the environmental conditions carefully controlled, but also that standard, ideally optimal, recovery conditions, i.e. temperature, duration of incubation and medium composition, are stipulated.

5 MECHANISMS AND CHARACTERISTICS OF MICROBIAL INACTIVATION

5.1 Heat sterilization

Heat is the most reliable and widely employed method of sterilization. The efficiency with which heat is able to inactivate micro-organisms is dependent upon the degree of heat, the exposure time and the presence of water. Heat comprises a basic form of energy produced by the vibratory motion or activity of molecules. It is non-quantized and will act on every molecule in an organism. It would be unlikely therefore that any one factor or event would be responsible for heat-induced microbial inactivation. Provided that enough heat is supplied every site in the organism is likely to be damaged and death is probably due to an accumulation of irreparable damage to all of the organism's metabolic functions.

The action of heat will be due to induction of lethal chemical events mediated through the action of water and/or oxygen. In the presence of water much lower temperature–time exposures are needed to kill micro-organisms than in the absence of water. Coagulation of proteins also occurs at a lower temperature and in a shorter time in the presence of water. This observation has led to the hypothesis that, with moist heat, death results from denaturation and coagulation of essential proteinaceous sites, e.g. enzymes and structural proteins, within the organism. With dry heat, microbial inactivation is probably the result primarily of oxidative processes which require higher temperatures and longer exposure times.

While sensitive vegetative organisms show significant inactivation by moist heat at 60–70°C, resistant bacterial spores require temperatures in excess of 100°C. Moist heat sterilization is therefore carried out using saturated steam under pressure and is the method of choice for aqueous preparations and surgical materials. Dry heat sterilization employs temperatures between 150°C and 250°C and is used for non-aqueous preparations, powders and glassware (see Chapter 8).

Since heat-induced microbial inactivation probably results from irreversible damage to metabolic functions it would be expected that these reactions, like a number of other chemical reactions, would follow apparent first-order kinetics and result in linear survivor curves when the logarithm of the fraction of surviving organisms is plotted against exposure time. Although linear survivor curves have been determined experimentally there are many examples in the literature of survivor curves that show significant deviations from linearity. Fig. 2 illustrates the most common survivor curve shapes observed with heat inactivation of micro-organisms. Curve A is linear over the entire exposure time range, i.e. shows true logarithmic inactivation. Curve B is concave downward, having a low but increasing rate of inactivation during the initial exposure times, i.e. an initial shoulder, followed by logarithmic inactivation at longer exposure times. Curve C is concave upward having a very high but decreasing rate of inactivation during the initial exposure times follwed by logarithmic inactivation at longer exposure times. A fourth type of survivor curve, Curve D, is frequently obtained with bacterial spores of low growth index and shows an initial sharp increase in the number of viable organisms due to heat activation of dormant spores prior to heat inactivation at a logarithmic rate. Survivor curves that are entirely curvilinear or sigmoid in shape also occur occasionally.

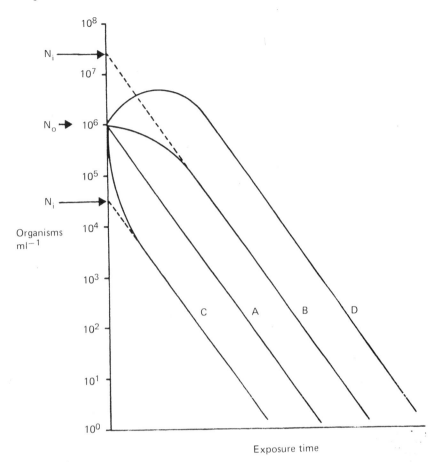

Fig. 2 — Heat survivor curve.

Type B curves have been explained as indicating the necessity for several critical events to occur in the organism before death occurs. Technical factors such as clumping of cells or a lag before the heat reaches the sensitive part of the organism could also result in this type of curve. It would also result if heat activation and inactivation occur concurrently, where the resulting number of viable organisms would never, unlike the type D curve, be greater than N_0. The initial shoulder of the type B curve may also be a measure of the capacity of the organism to repair heat-induced damage. The type C curve is usually attributed to differences in susceptibility of individual organisms, either as part of the natural distribution of resistance or as a result of cells being of different ages, or to the protective effect of the presence of dead cells. The non-linearity of survivor curves may also be attributed to the effects of components in the environment during heating, a factor to be considered when organisms are heated in complex pharmaceutical dosage forms.

Deviations from linearity of survivor curves can present a particular problem if the D-value is used as a measure of microbial resistance since the value is derived from logarithmic inactivation kinetics. It should be noted that D-value determinations based on quantal data take no account of survivor curve shape. If direct enumeration is used, corrections can be made if the D-value is calculated using only data from the logarithmic region of the survivor curve in the regression analysis. The y intercept of the regression line fitted to the survivor data, $\log N_i$, or the intercept ratio (IR), $\log N_i/\log N_0$, can then be used in conjunction with the D-value to describe the survivor curve.

A number of theoretical equations have been derived to describe non-linear survivor curves but these are inevitably complex and have not found favour in sterilization microbiology. Instead, sterilization protocols are designed using a reference organism, usually a bacterial spore, which has much greater resistance to the lethal agent than the organisms that comprise the normal bioburden, and shows reproducible logarithmic inactivation. In pharmaceutical applications the reference organism for moist heat sterilization is spores of *Bacillus stearothermophilus* and for dry heat sterilization is spores of *B. subtilus* var. *niger* (see Chapter 9).

5.1.1   Effect of temperature on microbial resistance

5.1.1.1   z-Value

Microbial resistance measurements and D-value determinations are carried out under isothermal conditions. The resistance of the organism will change with alteration in temperature. The change in the rate of microbial inactivation with a change in temperature is the temperature coefficient for the lethal process. If the logarithm of the D-value is plotted against temperature a linear relationship results (Fig. 3). The plot is called a thermal resistance (TR) curve. The negative reciprocal of the slope of this line is the z-value and represents the increase in temperature required to reduce the D-value of an organism by 90% or to produce a decrease of one log-cycle in the thermal resistance plot. The units of the z-value are degrees of temperature. The z-value can be estimated graphically (Fig. 3) or mathematically using the equation

$$z = \frac{T_2 - T_1}{\log D_1 - \log D_2} \tag{9}$$

where D_1 and D_2 are the D-values at temperatures T_1 and T_2, respectively.

The precision with which the z-value can be estimated is dependent upon the precision with which the individual D-values can be experimentally determined. In particular, if the data at the different temperatures are for different test conditions they cannot be combined to yield a meaningful z-value. Although the z-value is a fundamental characteristic of an organism it is not truly independent of temperature, and is constant only for small temperature differences of the order of $20 - 25°C$. However, since heat sterilization processes are usually carried out within a small temperature range, e.g. 110°–135°C for autoclaving, the z-value is considered constant for all practical purposes.

5.1.1.2 Q_{10} value

The Q_{10} value is also a measure of the change of microbial inactivation rate with temperature and is defined as the ratio of the microbial inactivation rate constants at two temperatures, 10°C apart. Thus

$$Q_{10} = \frac{k_1}{k_2} \tag{10}$$

when k_1 and k_2 are the microbial inactivation rate constants at temperatures $T°C$ and $T + 10°C$, respectively. The relationship of z-value to Q_{10} may be expressed as

$$z = \frac{10}{Q_{10}} \tag{11}$$

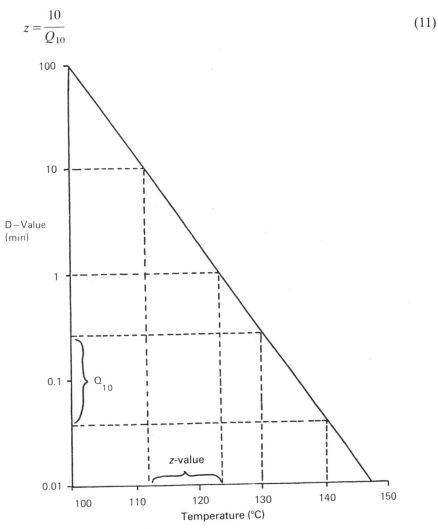

Fig. 3 — Thermal resistance curve.

5.1.1.3 Activation energy for microbial inactivation (E)
In nearly every known case the rate of a chemical reaction increases with increase in temperature. This increase in rate is reflected in a rise in the reaction rate constant.

The same applies to microbial inactivation where an increase in temperature results in an increase in the microbial inactivation rate constant. The Arrhenius rate theory used in chemical reaction kinetics can also be utilized to estimate the activation energy for the microbial inactivation. The relationship between the microbial inactivation rate constant (k) and absolute temperature (TK) is stated by

$$k = Ae^{-E/RT} \tag{12}$$

where A is the frequency factor, R is the universal gas constant and E is the activation energy for the microbial inactivation. When the logarithm of k is plotted against the reciprocal of absolute temperature a linear relationship is obtained where the slope is equal to $-E/2.303R$. The activation energy for microbial inactivation can also be calculated from the equation

$$\log\frac{k_2}{k_1} = \frac{E}{2.303R}\left(\frac{T_2 - T_1}{T_1 T_2}\right) \tag{13}$$

where k_1 and k_2 are the microbial inactivation rate constants at T_1 K and T_2 K, respectively. The precision with which E can be estimated will depend upon the quality of the survivor curve data and the precision with which the values of k can be experimentally determined.

The relationship between the z-values and the activation energy for microbial inactivation is represented by the equation

$$z = \left(\frac{2.303\, T_1 T_2}{E}\right) R \tag{14}$$

If microbial inactivation were a single chemical reaction or the result of a single event the Arrhenius equation should hold for all temperature ranges. In practice the plot of $\log k$ against $1/T$ over a wide temperature range often shows two straight portions of different slope joined by a curved section, indicating a change from one lethal reaction to another as the temperature changes. In sterilization microbiology this can have important significance if data obtained at low temperatures are used to predict the microbial inactivation at high process temperatures.

However, over the temperature range normally used for moist heat sterilization (110–135°C) there is generally obedience to the Arrhenius relationship, with bacterial spores having activation energies in the range 270–300 kJ per bacterium.

5.1.2   Measures of heat sterilization efficiency

Compendial heat sterilization protocols have evolved from custom and practice and a long history of use rather than being carefully designed on the basis of scientific principle and equivalence of lethality (see Chapter 8). The modern approach to the design of sterilization protocols is based on a quantitative approach using reliable microbial inactivation data. To be effective this requires a basis on which the equivalence of different sterilization processes can be established. The key terms for this are described below.

5.1.2.1   F-Value
The *F*-value is a 'unit of lethality' devised by the food industry and is a measure of the total lethality of a heat sterilization process with respect to a particular organism. It is defined as 'the equivalent in minutes at 250°F (121.1°C) of all heat considered with respect to its capacity to destroy spores or vegetative cells of a particular organism'. Since the *F*-value compares lethal effects at different temperatures the *z*-value of the organism should always be stated when an *F*-value is quoted. For the reference temperature of 121°C and a *z*-value of 10°C the *F*-value is referred to as F_0, the 'reference unit of lethality', and can be determined from the equation

$$F_0 = D_{121} (\log N_0 - \log N) \tag{15}$$

where D_{121} is the *D*-value at 121°C for the reference spores and N_0 and N are the initial and final numbers of viable spores, respectively. In pharmaceutical applications, *B. stearothermophilus* spores are usually used as the reference organism and *z*- and *D*-values of 10°C and 1.5 min respectively are generally assumed for aqueous solutions. For quantitative work however, these values must be accurately determined in the particular product to be sterilized.

F_0 can also be expressed in terms of the inactivation factor as

$$F_0 = D_{121} \, \text{IF} \tag{16}$$

Any process that is stated to have an F_0 of *x* will have the same lethality on the reference spore as *x* minutes at 121°C; a worked example is given in Chapter 9 (section 5.2.2). In practical terms the F_0-value of a sterilization process is the lethality delivered by that process to the product in its final container. If used to describe the lethal effect upon reference spores at the coolest location in the sterilizer the F_0-value represents the most conservative estimate of the lethality and thus the safest conditions for determining cycle times.

5.1.2.2   Lethality factor (F_i)
This is the time at any other temperature equivalent, in terms of lethality to a particular organism, to 1 minute at 121°C. This value will also be dependent on the *z*-value of the organism. For a reference organism with a *z*-value of 10°C, F_i is equal to the reciprocal of F_0.

5.1.2.3   Lethal rate (L)
The lethal rate *L* at a temperature *T* as a fraction of that at a reference temperature T_{ref} can be calculated from the equation

$$L = 10^{\left(\frac{T - T_{ref}}{z}\right)} \tag{17}$$

If the reference temperature is 121°C and the *z*-value of the reference organism is 10°C:

$$L = 10^{\left(\frac{T-121}{10}\right)} = \frac{F_0}{F_T} \tag{18}$$

where F_T is the F-value at temperature T. Tables of lethal rates for the reference temperature 121°C and a z-value of 10°C are available (Pflug 1973).

5.1.2.4 Nabla value (∇)
The Nabla value is the natural logarithm of the inactivation factor, i.e.

$$\nabla = \ln \frac{N_0}{N} \tag{19}$$

where N_0 and N are the initial and final numbers of viable organisms, respectively. The Nabla value is also directly related to the D-value, since the D-value is the exposure time which corresponds to a ∇ value of 2.303.

The Nabla value, at constant temperature, can also be derived from the inactivation rate constant, k, and the Arrhenius rate theory:

$$\nabla = kt = Ate^{-E/RT} \tag{20}$$

where t is the exposure time, A is the frequency factor, R is the universal gas constant, E is the activation energy for microbial inactivation and T is the process temperature in Kelvin units.

5.1.3 Integrated lethality determination
The compendial moist heat sterilization protocols specify a preferred combination of temperature and time, e.g. 121°C for 15 minutes. The measurement of time begins when the temperature of the material being sterilized reaches the defined temperature. It ignores the heating-up and cooling-down stages of the cycle which could be prolonged if the load has a large thermal capacity. The rate of heating and cooling of a product in a container is a function of container size, viscosity of the liquid and the size of the load. The resultant heating and cooling curves are usually exponential with respect to time.

It is usually considered that moist heat has very little lethal effect on bacterial spores at temperatures below 90°C. However, the heat imparted to the load during heating-up from 90°C to the holding temperature and during cooling-down from the holding temperature to 90°C can make a considerable contribution to the total lethality of the sterilization cycle. Reduction in energy consumption, processing time and product degradation can be achieved if this contribution is taken into account. The F_0 concept and the use of lethal rates facilitate integration of the lethality of the total heat process including the heating and cooling stages. The requirement is for accurate time–temperature data during the whole of the process, from that part of the product where heating is slowest. With these data the F_0 for the heating and cooling stages of the process can be determined and the holding time can then be reduced to that necessary to ensure that the predetermined F_0 for the process is attained. Two methods are commonly used to analyse time–temperature data.

5.1.3.1   Graphical method
This method involves plotting the time–temperature data on lethal rate or *F* reference paper, where the distance between each successive temperature line on the *y* (logarithmic) axis is a function of the lethality of that temperature compared to the lethality of the reference temperature. On the *x* axis time is plotted on a linear scale. The area under the curve is a measure of the *F*-value. This value can be calculated by multiplying the area by the appropriate scale factor. If the reference temperature is 121°C and the *z*-value is 10°C this gives the F_0 for the process.

   An alternative method calculates the lethal rate for each temperature *T* as a function of that at the reference temperature T_{ref}, i.e. minutes at T_{ref} per minute at *T*. The lethal rates are then plotted on a linear scale against time in minutes at *T*, and the area under the curve is the *F*-value for the process.

5.1.3.2   Summation methods
These methods eliminate the plotting of lethal rate graphs and the measuring of the area under the curve. One such method is based on the trapezoidal rule for evaluating the area under the lethal rate curve. This is written as

$$\text{area} = F = \Delta t \left(\frac{L_{T0}}{2} + L_{T1} + L_{T2} + \ldots + L_{Tn-1} + \frac{L_{Tn}}{2} \right) \quad (21)$$

where Δt is the constant time between measurements of *T* and *L* is the lethal rate at temperature *T*. If the time–temperature data for the total process is analysed, the data included in the analysis may be simplified so that the values of the first and last points, L_{T0} and L_{Tn} respectively, are zero. This simplifies the equation to

$$F = \Delta t \Sigma L \quad (22)$$

Interactive computer programs are available that evaluate the integral

$$F = \int_{t_1}^{t_2} L \, dt \quad (23)$$

according to the trapezoidal rule, directly from time–temperature data. These enable the F_0 value to be determined continuously and the process to be terminated when the predetermined F_0 for the process is attained. These form the basis of microprocessor controllers (temperature-integrating time controllers) for autoclaves.

   The Nabla value has also been used in the integration of the total lethality of heat sterilization processes particularly in continuous sterilization and in specialist sterilization applications such as fermenter mash sterilization. If the mathematical relationship between temperature and time is known for the heating or cooling curves then the equation

$$\nabla = A \int_0^t e^{-E/RT} \, dt \quad (24)$$

can be integrated over the whole heating or cooling period to obtain the ∇ value for each of these stages of the process. We have already seen previously in equation (20) that at constant temperature, e.g. during the holding stage of the process

$$\nabla = Ate^{-E/RT} \tag{25}$$

and so the holding time, t, can be adjusted to ensure that the total ∇ for the process attains the predetermined design value. The use of Nabla values requires the determination of E and A for the heat inactivation of the reference organism. For spores of *B. stearothermophilus* a frequency factor, A, of $1 \times 10^{36.2} \text{s}^{-1}$ and an activation energy for microbial inactivation, E, of 276 kJ per bacterium have been quoted (Hoskins and Diffey 1977).

5.1.4   *Design of optimum autoclaving protocols*
A knowledge of the activation energy both for the killing of bacteria and for inducing damage to the product to be sterilized together with use of the F_0 concept can lead to the design of an optimum time/temperature combination for particular applications.

BP 1988 prefers an autoclaving process for aqueous preparations consisting of a holding time of 15 minutes at 121°C together with the heating-up and cooling-down periods. It also accepts other time/temperature combinations and suggests an F_0-value of at least 8 if that concept is used. The two processes are likely to differ in lethal efficiency by at least a factor of two and it is difficult to see the logic of recommending two such different processes. However, if for example a decision to use an F_0 of 12 is made, which is approximately half-way between the two BP methods, then the times necessary for achieving this at different temperatures can be calculated and are shown in Table 1.

Table 1 — Different time/temperature combinations calculated to give an F_0 of 12 for reference *B. stearothermophilus* spores with a D_{121} of 1.5 min and z-value of 10°C

Temperature (°C)	Time (min)
115	48
118	24
121	12
124	6
127	3

The activation energy for killing spores is of the order 270–300 kJ per bacterium, while for inducing chemical change (hydrolytic or oxidative) in aqueous solution it is generally of the order of 70–100 kJ mole^{-1} for drugs which pose a stability problem to manufacturers. When such solutions need to be sterilized, in order to minimize the amount of chemical change, it is always preferable to use a combination of the highest temperature possible with the shortest time, rather than to use a low-temperature/longer-time combination with the same lethal efficiency.

This is illustrated in Fig. 4, which shows the Arrhenius plots for the killing of *B*.

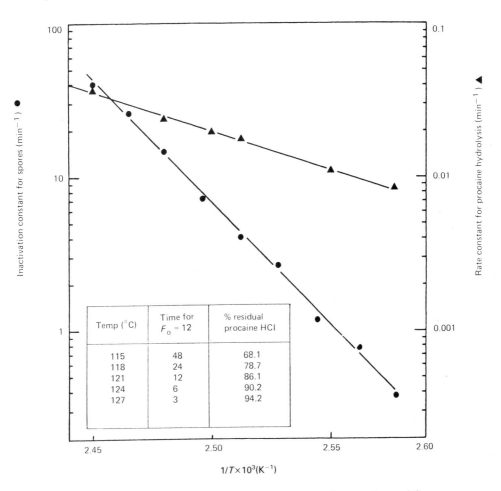

Fig. 4 — Arrhenius plots for moist heat inactivation of reference *B. stearothermophilus* spores
(●) and hydrolysis of procaine hydrochloride solution (▲).

Temp (°C)	Time for $F_0 = 12$	% residual procaine HCl
115	48	68.1
118	24	78.7
121	12	86.1
124	6	90.2
127	3	94.2

stearothermophilus spores, with an E of 285 kJ per bacterium and the hydrolysis of procaine hydrochloride at a pH of 6.2 with an E of 68 kJ mole^{-1}. The times necessary to achieve an F_0 of 12 at different temperatures are first calculated from the inactivation data for *B. stearothermophilus* spores, resulting in the data shown in Table 1. By substituting these values for t together with values for k for procaine hydrochloride hydrolysis, obtained from Fig. 4 for the $1/T$ values corresponding to the different required temperatures, into the equation

$$\log C_t = \log C_0 - \frac{k}{2.303} \cdot t \tag{26}$$

the percentage of procaine hydrochloride remaining (C_t) when the initial concentration $C_0 = 100\%$ can be calculated for each temperature (Fig. 4).

5.2 Radiation sterilization

Radiation sterilization is a low-temperature method that can be used in certain situations where heat sterilization would produce an unacceptable amount of damage to the product. However, because of the difficulties and costs of producing the radiations the method is only suitable for large-scale use. Radiations may be classified into two types: particulate, e.g. α-rays, β-rays, protons and neutrons; and electromagnetic, e.g. X-rays, γ-rays and ultraviolet (UV) light. In general particulate radiations are more difficult and costly to produce, have less penetrative power and are less efficient as sterilizing agents than electromagnetic radiations. Only fast electrons have found a practical use in sterilization and then only to a limited extent (see Chapter 8).

X-rays are emitted from an atom when there is a transition of an electron from an outer shell to a vacancy further within an inner shell. They are produced as secondary radiation by the bombardment of a heavy metal target with a beam of fast electrons in an accelerator. Power utilization in this process is low and X-ray production is consequently expensive, with the result that the electron beam itself has been used in preference as a sterilizing agent. γ-Radiation is identical to X-radiation in nature but is the result of a transition of an atomic nucleus from an excited state to a ground state in radioactive materials such as cobalt-60 (^{60}Co) and caesium-137 (^{137}Ce). Both X-rays and γ-rays are described as ionizing radiations since the principal means of energy dissipation in their passage through matter is the ejection of an electron with production of a positively-charged ion. In addition, ions produce free radicals and activated molecules in cells, some of which are lethal. The third type of electromagnetic radiation used as a sterilizing agent is UV radiation. This comprises that portion of the electromagnetic spectrum with wavelengths from about 190 nm to 390 nm. The high-emission wavelength of mercury (254 nm) is most frequently used for sterilization as being the wavelength closest to the absorption peak for DNA, the supposed chromophore and target. The quantum energies for UV are around 10^2 eV compared to values ranging from 10^6 eV to 10^9 eV for X-rays and γ-rays. As a consequence UV has very low penetrating power, being only useful for air and aqueous solution sterilization and producing only increased excitation and not ionization of molecules that absorb it. Furthermore, most organisms possess enzymatic processes that are capable of repairing UV-induced damage, resulting in the recovery of UV-irradiated cells under certain conditions. UV radiation is therefore a less efficient sterilizing agent than X- or γ-irradiation (see Chapter 8).

When a population of micro-organisms is exposed to increasing doses of radiation the plot of the logarithm of the surviving fraction against absorbed dose on a linear scale assumes one of three basic shapes (types A, B and C as illustrated in Fig. 2). The type A curve is represented by the equation

$$\frac{N_t}{N_0} = e^{-kD} \tag{27}$$

where N_t/N_0 is the surviving fraction after an absorbed dose of radiation D, and k is the microbial inactivation rate constant. This equation is comparable to that used to describe the linear heat survivor curve (equation (1) and section 2.1), but is derived on the basis that it represents the probability of a single randomly distributed radiation-induced lethal event or 'hit' occurring in a single 'target' within the cell, rather than on the basis of unimolecular chemical reaction kinetics. Although ionizing radiations can cause a wide variety of physical and biochemical effects in micro-organisms it is likely that DNA is the primary cell 'target' and that non-repaired strand breakage or cross-linkage caused by ionization of a molecule in the DNA is the lethal event.

The equation for the type B curve is derived on the basis that a single 'hit' is necessary on more than one 'target' to cause cell death. The equation is

$$\frac{N_t}{N_0} = 1 - (1 - e^{kD})^n \tag{28}$$

where n is the number of 'targets'. Below a surviving fraction of 0.1 this closely approximates to the equation

$$\frac{N_t}{N_0} = ne^{-kD} \tag{29}$$

which on log transformation is

$$\log\frac{N_t}{N_0} = \log n - \frac{kD}{2.303} \tag{30}$$

where n is the intercept with the log N_t/N_0 axis of the extrapolated linear portion of the survivor curve. Equations representing type B curves have also been derived on the basis that for cell death more than one 'hit' is necessary on a single 'target'. With radiation as with heat the type C curve cannot be readily explained and is often interpreted as being the result of non-homogeneous resistance in the microbial population. Most radiation sterilization protocols have been derived on the assumption that the type C curve is rare and atypical.

As with resistance to heat, unicellular organisms are more resistant to radiation than multicellular organisms. Bacterial spores are the most resistant to radiation, vegetative bacteria, particularly Gram-negative rods, the most sensitive and yeasts and fungi of intermediate resistance. There are exceptions, e.g. the Gram-positive *Micrococcus radiodurans* and the Gram-negative *Moraxella osloensis* are both extremely resistant to radiation. In general viruses are more resistant to radiation than bacteria. Resistance to one agent does not necesarily imply resistance to another. Spores of *B. stearothermophilus* and *B. subtilis*, which exhibit considerable heat resistance, are not especially resistant to radiation and thus *B. pumilus* spores with a *D*-value of 3 kGy are used as the reference organism for radiation sterilization.

Anoxic bacterial spores are more sensitive to radiation in the fully hydrated state than in the dry state due to the additional lethality induced by the radiolysis products of water. Resistance is also reduced when the organisms are irradiated in oxygen, particularly in the dry state. Radiation-induced degradation of materials is also greatest in the presence of water and this precludes the use of radiation as a method of sterilization for aqueous solutions of drugs. However, under dry anoxic conditions radiation induces less damage than heat with the same lethal efficiency and is the method of choice for some pharmaceuticals in the dry state and for medical devices.

The presence of protective or sensitizing agents in the environment will have a considerable influence on the radiation resistance of micro-organisms and ideally the resistance of organisms on and in the product to be sterilized should be taken into account when the radiation dose necessary for sterilization is being determined.

5.3 Gaseous sterilization

The search for a suitable chemical sterilization method was initiated by the need to sterilize items such as medical devices and plastics that cannot be subjected to heat or radiation sterilization. Although a great variety of chemicals are toxic to micro-organisms and are useful as disinfectants, very few are toxic to spores and are therefore of potential use as sterilizing agents. The complex structure of the materials requiring chemical sterilization invariably presents problems with the initial penetration and ultimate removal of the sterilizing agent, and these together with the requirement for terminal sterilization of items in their final packaging precludes the use of liquid antimicrobial chemicals. Toxic gases such as β-propiolactone, propylene oxide and methyl bromide have been used for specialized sterilization purposes but only ethylene oxide and formaldehyde have been extensively used in gaseous sterilization of medical and pharmaceutical products.

Both ethylene oxide and formaldehyde are potent alkylating agents and are considered to exert their lethal effect on micro-organisms by the alkylation of proteins, DNA and RNA. Comparison of the sensitivities of various micro-organisms to ethylene oxide and formaldehyde on the basis of published data is difficult due to the variations in exposure conditions and experimental methods employed. In general bacterial spores show the greatest resistance to these sterilizing agents, being five to ten times more resistant than vegetative bacteria. Moulds and yeasts show intermediate resistance to gaseous alkylating agents. Both ethylene oxide and formaldehyde have marked antiviral activity. In contrast to many antimicrobial chemicals, genetically determined resistance to alkylating agents has not been a practical problem to date.

Most antimicrobial chemicals induce non-linear inactivation kinetics in micro-organisms, resulting in sigmoid-shaped survivor curves, and ethylene oxide and formaldehyde are no exception. However, under carefully controlled conditions and in the high concentrations used in sterilization practice the survivor curves approximate to type A curves, enabling the realistic estimation of SALs (see section 2).

The activity of both gaseous ethylene oxide and gaseous formaldehyde is markedly influenced by the concentration of the gas, the temperature, the water content of the micro-organisms and the duration of exposure, and there is a complex interrelationship between these factors. Since the chemical must come into direct contact with the organism, the physical nature and penetrability of the material being treated are also of paramount importance when these chemicals are used as sterilizing agents. Although a concentration of ethylene oxide of $50 \, \text{mg} \, l^{-1}$ is sporicidal, higher concentrations are usually employed for gaseous sterilization to avoid prolonged exposure times. The relationship between ethylene oxide concentration and sporicidal activity is not a straightforward one. While doubling the gas concentration over the range $50–800 \, \text{mg} \, l^{-1}$ reduces the exposure time required to attain a given SAL by a factor of approximately 2, increasing the concentration above $1000 \, \text{mg} \, l^{-1}$ does not appreciably affect the exposure time.

Since the mechanism of action of alkylating agents involves chemical reaction with macromolecules it would be expected that the activity of these agents would increase with increase in temperature. Temperature coefficients (Q_{10} values) have been reported to vary with ethylene oxide concentration and with the temperature range. For the temperature range usually employed in sterilization cycles (40–60°C) and ethylene oxide concentrations above $400\,\mathrm{mg\,l^{-1}}$ the temperature coefficient for sporicidal activity is in the range 2–3.

Relative humidity (RH) has long been recognized as a critical factor in the antimicrobial activity of ethylene oxide. It has been generally accepted that RH levels of 20–40% are necessary for optimal sporicidal activity and that reduced activity occurs at levels below 20% RH and above 65% RH. Furthermore, efficient inactivation of micro-organisms by ethylene oxide requires that water molecules are present at the 'target site' within the organism before the ethylene oxide molecules reach that site. As a consequence organisms in the dehydrated state are much more resistant than when preconditioned in an atmosphere of high RH, usually regardless of the RH during exposure to the gas. Similarly, organisms on hygroscopic carrier materials such as paper or fabric exhibit a marked decrease in resistance to inactivation by ethylene oxide compared to organisms on non-hygroscopic materials such as metal or glass. Carefully controlled prehumidification of loads is therefore critical in gaseous sterilization processes using ethylene oxide.

Concentrations of formaldehyde gas of the order of $3.5\,\mathrm{mg\,l^{-1}}$ have been shown to be sporicidal at 25°C if the RH is above 50%. However, at temperatures below about 80°C formaldehyde gas polymerizes readily to form solid polymers, e.g. paraformaldehyde, and RH levels between 75% and 100% are generally considered to be desirable for rapid microbial inactivation. In order to provide the high RH and also to minimize polymerization while still enabling sterilization of heat-sensitive materials, formaldehyde gas is used in combination with low-temperature steam (LTS) at temperatures between 65°C and 80°C. Concentrations of formaldehyde gas between $3.3\,\mathrm{mg\,l^{-1}}$ and $100\,\mathrm{mg\,l^{-1}}$ have been used in low-temperature steam and formaldehyde (LTSF) sterilization and, since formaldehyde gas has high affinity for water, care is taken to ensure the absence of free water. A particular problem with formaldehyde gas is its low penetrability necessitating pre-evacuation of the sterilizer chamber and operation of the LTSF cycles at pressures between 100 mbar (10 kPa) and 400 mbar (40 kPa).

The efficiency of a gaseous sterilization process depends upon the interaction of a number of factors, including temperature, pressure, RH, time, gas concentration and distribution within the sterilizer chamber and moisture and gas penetration throughout the sterilizer load. For this reason any statement of the SAL achieved by a gaseous sterilization process must be qualified by a detailed definition of the sterilizing conditions. Since it is not yet practicable to reliably integrate all of the factors operating during the sterilization process by physical monitoring, parametric release of products subjected to gaseous sterilization is not currently feasible. Sterilization cycles must therefore be devised, validated and monitored with reference to their effect on reference micro-organisms on standardized biological test pieces distributed within the sterilizer load (see Chapter 9). The recommended reference organisms for ethylene oxide sterilization are spores of *B. subtilis* var. *niger*, and for LTSF sterilization spores of a *B. stearothermophilus* strain.

5.4   Filtration sterilization

Moist heat sterilization is the method of choice for liquid pharmaceutical products such as parenteral and ophthalmic solutions. For thermolabile solutions, where even the use of high-temperature/short-exposure-time protocols imparts unacceptable levels of product degradation, filtration provides an alternative sterilization method. Filtration is also used to remove micro-organisms and other particulate materials from gases as, for example, in the production of air with low particulate levels in aseptic production areas and operating theatres. This method differs from other sterilization methods in that micro-organisms are physically removed from the product and not inactivated.

The requirement that the filter should not shed fibres or leach undesired materials into the solution being filtered has restricted the types of filter that can be used for sterile filtration of pharmaceutical products to those made of sintered glass, metal or polymers. The polymeric membrane filters are the most universally used. Removal of particles by membrane filters is by combination of sieving out of particles larger than the rated pore size and by adsorption within the filter matrix. Sieving is a function of the pore size of the surface pores of the membrane and adsorption is influenced by the thickness of the filter. Membrane filters most commonly used to effect sterilization have a porosity of 0.2–0.22 μm. While the filter will have either a 'nominal' or an 'absolute' pore size rating, the pores in the membrane consist of a range of sizes characterized by its pore size distribution. There is always the probability, although very remote, that a micro-organism can pass through one of the few pores at the large pore size extreme of the pore size distribution. The absorption process in filtration also involves a degree of probability of retention. For these reasons sterile filtration is a probability function and cannot be regarded as absolute. Furthermore, in contrast to other sterilization methods, filtration is a unit operation where in-process validation is not practicable. Aseptic precautions during the process are therefore essential and validation of sterile filtration must include stringent tests for sterility. With sterile filtration, as with all sterilization methods, a high SAL is dependent upon good manufacturing practice and an initial low number of micro-organisms in the product (see Chapter 9).

6   COMPARISON OF THE EFFICACY OF STERILIZATION METHODS

Since there is no micro-organism that shows universal high resistance to all of the available sterilization methods it is difficult to obtain a direct comparison of the efficacy of the different sterilization processes. An indication of the expected antimicrobial efficacy of each of the processes can be obtained by examining the effect of the process on the reference organism for that process, i.e. the organism that is used to validate the process. In Table 2 the exposure time/absorbed dose required to achieve an inactivation factor of 10^6 is calculated for each sterilization method based on the highest acceptable D-value for the reference organism. The time/absorbed dose recommended for sterilization by each method is also recorded. It should be noted that for moist heat the D-values for the reference *B. stearothermophilus* strain at 115°C, 126°C and 134°C are calculated on the basis of a D_{121} of 1.5 minutes and a z-value of 10°C, and for dry heat the D-values for the reference *B.*

subtilis var. *niger* strain are calculated on the basis of a D_{160} of 10 minutes and a z-value of 20°C.

It is apparent from Table 2 that, with the exception of moist heat at 115°C, the

Table 2 — Comparison of microbial inactivation efficacy of sterilization methods

Method	Reference organism	*D*-Value	Time/dose to achieve an IF of 10^6	Recommended sterilization time/dose
Moist heat	*B. stearothermophilus*			
115°C	NCIB 8157	6 min	36 min	30 min
121°C	(NCTC 10007;	1.5 min	9 min	15 min[a]
126°C	ATCC 7953)	0.47 min	2.82 min	10 min
134°C	(z = 10°C)	0.075 min	0.45 min	3 min
Dry heat	*B. subtilis* var. *niger*			
160°C	NCIB 8058	10 min	60 min	120 min
170°C	(ATCC 9372)	3.2 min	19.2 min	60 min
180°C	(z = 20°C)	1 min	6 min	30 min
Radiation, γ- or X-ray	*B. pumilus* NCIB 8982 (NCTC 8241; ATCC 14884)	3 kGy	18 kGy	25 kGy
Ethylene oxide, $600\,mg\,l^{-1}$, 54°C, 60% RH	*B. subtilis* var. *niger* NCTC 10073 (ATCC 9372)	5.8 min	34.8 min	2–4 h +
Low-temperature steam and formaldehyde $12\,mg\,l^{-1}$, 73°C	*B. stearothermophilus* NCIB 8224	5 min	30 min	1–2 h +

[a] 8 min if an F_0 of 8 is used.

recommended sterilization protocols offer considerable margins of safety if the end-point specification is an inactivation factor of 10^6. It is worthy of note, however, that an F_0 of 8 would not achieve an inactivation factor of 10^6 against the reference organism for moist heat sterilization. The safety margin of each protocol will change depending upon the inactivation factor that is required. It must be remembered that these calculations are based on the response of carefully standardized organisms on selected carriers exposed to the sterilizing agent under ideal conditions. In practice the contaminating micro-organisms are not standardized and they are often exposed to the sterilizing agent under far from ideal conditions. To compensate for this the exposure times/absorbed doses are often extended and this is particularly the case in gaseous sterilization where the situation is further complicated by the multiplicity of component factors that are involved in the lethal process.

It seems clear, however, that even if the product to be sterilized is contaminated with an appreciable number of resistant spores, a high probability of achieving sterility can be assured by the choice of an efficient sterilizing protocol. In reality, in industry and hospitals far higher levels of sterility assurance will be sought by applying good manufacturing practices. It is particularly important in this regard to recognize that the sterilization procedure is merely the last stage in a carefully planned and controlled manufacturing process and that all stages of manufacture must be controlled and monitored. It is particularly important that the microbial contamination levels be controlled at all stages, from the new materials at acquisition to the final product (see Chapters 3 and 4). The manufacturing environment must also be controlled and personnel adequately trained and their performance monitored (see Chapters 4, 5 and 17). Only if all these aspects are carefully regulated can the health of the user be protected.

7   REFERENCES AND FURTHER READING

Dring, G. J., Ellar, D. J. and Gould, G. W. (1985) *Fundamental and applied aspects of bacterial spores*. Academic Press, London.

Gaughran, E. R. L. and Goudie, A. J. (1978) *Sterilization of medical products by ionizing radiation*. Multiscience Publications, Montreal.

Hoskins, H. T. and Diffey, B. L. (1977) Tables for assessing the efficiency of autoclaves. *Pharm. J.* **219** 218–219.

Johnson, E. and Brown, B. (1961) The Spearman estimator for serial dilution assays. *Biometrics* **17** 79–88.

Meltzer, T. H. (1987) *Advances in parenteral sciences: 3. Filtration in the pharmaceutical industry*. Marcel Dekker, New York.

Perkins, J. J. (1969) *Principles and methods of sterilization in health sciences*, 2nd edn. Charles C. Thomas, Springfield.

Pflug, I. J. (1973) Heat sterilization. In: Briggs Phillips, G. and Miller, W. S. (eds), *Industrial sterilization: the proceedings of the international symposium, Amsterdam, 1972*. Duke University Press, Durham, North Carolina, pp. 239–281.

Pflug, I. J. (1988) *Selected papers on the microbiology and engineering of sterilization processes*, 5th edn. Environmental Sterilization Laboratory, Minneapolis.

Pflug, I. J. and Holcomb, R. G. (1983) Principles of thermal destruction of microorganisms. In: Block, S. S. (ed.), *Disinfection, sterilization and preservation*, 3rd edn. Lea and Febiger, Philadelphia, pp. 751–810.

Phillips, C. R. (1977) Gaseous sterilization. In: Block, S. S. (ed.), *Disinfection, sterilization and preservation*, 2nd edn. Lea and Febiger, Philadelphia, pp. 592–611.

Richards, J. W. (1968) *Introduction to industrial sterilization*. Academic Press, London.

Russell, A. D., Hugo, W. B. and Ayliffe, G. A. J. (1982) *Principles and practice of disinfection, preservation and sterilization*. Blackwell Scientific Publications, Oxford.

Stumbo, C. R. (1973) *Thermobacteriology in food processing*, 2nd edn. Academic Press, New York.

Stumbo, C. R., Murphy, J. R. and Cochran, J. (1950). Nature of thermal death time curves for PA3679 and *Clostridium botulinum. Food Technol.* **4** 321–326.

8

Sterilization methods†

E. Dewhurst
Fisons Pharmaceuticals, Fisons plc, Pharmaceutical Division, London Road,
Holmes Chapel, Crewe, Cheshire, UK
and
E. V. Hoxey
NHS Procurement Directorate, Supplies Technology Division, 14 Russell Square,
London, UK

† The opinions expressed in this chapter are those of the authors and do not necessarily represent the views of their employers.

1   INTRODUCTION

Standards for quality-assurance systems recognize the importance of processes for which efficacy cannot be fully demonstrated by testing the finished product but has to be assured by the control and monitoring of the process itself. These are considered to be 'special processes' (British Standard 5750, 1987). Perhaps the best example of a 'special process' in the pharmaceutical or medical device industry is sterilization. With sterilization, the assurance of sterility is gained by demonstrating that conditions which are known to produce the required level of microbial inactivation have been attained. When the kinetics of microbial inactivation are understood and the critical variables can be accurately measured, sterility can be demonstrated by monitoring only the physical conditions of the sterilization process. A system of this type is termed 'parametric release', which has been defined as 'release of sterile product based on process compliance to physical specification' (Hoxey 1989). For sterilization processes such as steam, dry heat or irradiation, the physical conditions required are understood and can be directly monitored; therefore a system of parametric release is acceptable (Hurrell 1986). For gaseous sterilization or sterilization by liquid chemicals, however, parametric release is not yet accepted because the physical conditions cannot be readily and accurately measured. Therefore biological indicators must be incorporated into each sterilization batch. These indicators are removed after processing and cultured for surviving organisms, the growth of which shows a failure to sterilize (see Chapter 9).

Sterility testing is a statistical nightmare (Brown and Gilbert 1977) but may still be required by some regulatory authorities. A sterility test is defined in, for example, the British Pharmacopoeia (1988) although requirements for this test may vary in different countries.

For any sterilization method, the efficacy of the process must be demonstrated during validation studies (Chapter 9). Processes should be periodically revalidated to confirm that they continue to achieve the intended results (Department of Health 1983a). Sterilizers of all types should be regularly maintained in accordance with documented, planned preventative maintenance schedules (Department of Health 1980a) although requirements for maintenance will differ for different processes (Oates 1989). Sterilization instrumentation must be subject to routine calibration (Department of Health 1981).

Manufacturers often have sterilization processes carried out on their behalf by subcontractors. This may be for a number of reasons, including: lack of appropriate facilities; shortage of capacity for sterilization; or, limited expertise in sterilization. The most common sterilization processes to be performed by subcontractors are irradiation and ethylene oxide. Specialist subcontractors for both these processes are located throughout the world.

When sterilization is undertaken by a subcontractor, the manufacturer of the product retains overall responsibility. There should be a formal contract defining the limits of responsibility of both parties and detailing the technical requirements of the processing. The subcontractor should be subject to formal audit (Department of Health 1981, 1983a).

There are some essential requirements for product release following sterilization which are common to all the available sterilization methods. These general points include evidence that:

(a) the documented procedures relating to product handling had been followed;
(b) the process conformed to the sterilization specification;
(c) the sterilization facility had been correctly and routinely maintained, the process validated, and routine equipment tests performed in accordance with documented procedures;
(d) the load and its packaging were not damaged during transport or processing;
(e) the automatic sterilization process performed satisfactorily;
(f) any chemical indicators used to differentiate between processed and unprocessed products were satisfactory (Department of Health 1983a; see also Chapter 9);
(g) Sterilizer cycles were correctly and completely documented.

This chapter considers the types of sterilization methods available, their operational characteristics, equipment design, and any additional specific requirements for product release. The validation of these processes is considered in Chapter 9.

2 SELECTION OF STERILIZATION METHOD

The properties of the ideal sterilization method would include:

(a) high bactericidal, virucidal and fungicidal activity producing a high assurance of sterility;

(b) fully understood physical conditions necessary for microbial inactivation which are easily controllable and measurable;
(c) terminal sterilization in final packaging;
(d) compatibility with the range of materials to be sterilized;
(e) no hazard presented to operators;
(f) no toxic chemical residuals left in products;
(g) short processing time;
(h) low cost.

The selection of a method of sterilization therefore depends on balancing the advantages of the available methods against their disadvantages. Table 1 summarizes these advantages and disadvantages and indicates the suitability or otherwise of these sterilization methods to a range of products and packaging materials.

Two points need to be emphasized:

(a) Materials may be either physically or chemically incompatible with the sterilization conditions or a combination of materials may be incompatible, e.g. due to differential thermal expansion. Compatibility with an established method of sterilization can be designed into products by the initial selection of appropriate materials.
(b) The product itself should restrict the choice of sterilization method, not the chosen packaging material. If the packaging will not withstand a process but the product will, the packaging should be changed and not the sterilization method.

The methods of sterilization have been presented in what is considered to be a rank order of preference. There are considerable advantages in utilizing processes with established technology and regulatory requirements. It can be extremely expensive and time consuming to perform research and development into novel processes and to break new ground with regulatory authorities.

All sterilization methods have a finite capacity for destroying micro-organisms (Department of Health 1981). It is therefore necessary to control materials and processing prior to sterilization in order to reduce the pre-sterilization microbial level (bioburden) and hence reduce the challenge to the process (Department of Health 1981, 1983a). Whilst determination of bioburden is outside the scope of this section, it should be emphasized that the frequency of bioburden determinations will vary from different processes and be related to the capacity of the process for inactivation of micro-organisms. The selection of a process with a low inactivation factor based on a low product bioburden will require extensive validation and monitoring of that bioburden (Chapter 9). Such testing is invariably labour intensive and expensive.

3 TYPES OF STERILIZATION METHOD

Each method of sterilization places constraints and requirements on the design of the equipment used for the process. The majority of these requirements are special to the particular process but one feature is common to all sterilization methods. Each sterilizer is designed to control sterilization conditions within established limits and a

Table 1 — Selection of sterilization method: summary of advantages and disadvantages of the various processes together with examples of materials suitable and unsuitable for processing

Method of sterilization	Advantages	Materials suitable for processing	Materials unsuitable for processing	Other disadvantages and special requirements
1. Steam				
(a) Porous loads	Rapid cycle (1) Conditions required for sterilization known and documented (2) No requirement for biological indicators (3) Wrapped goods processed and suitable for storage (1) Automated equipment available	Heat-stable materials such as surgical instruments, dressings gowns and drapes, filters Temperature-resistant plastics such as high-density polypropylene Packaging materials to British standards (4–7) or permeable to steam and air	Temperature-, pressure- or moisture-sensitive materials Material combinations which will expand differentially and fracture on heating Packaging materials impermeable to air and/or steam Bottled fluids Materials which are a barrier to air removal	Will not depyrogenate
(b) Instrument and utensil	Rapid cycle (8) Conditions required for sterilization accepted (2) Automated equipment available including small portable models (8) No requirement for biological indicators (3)	Heat-stable materials such as unwrapped surgical instruments and utensils (8)	Wrapped goods (1, 8) Bottled fluids Temperature- or moisture-sensitive materials or combinations Porous loads from which air cannot be removed (8)	Products must be used immediately as they are unwrapped (8) Will not depyrogenate
(c) Bottled fluids	Conditions required for sterilization accepted and documented (1, 2) Biological indicators not required (3) Automated equipment available	Thermostable aqueous fluids Packaging in rigid polymer, glass or flexible polymer containers (1)	Non-aqueous fluids (1) Wrapped goods or porous loads (1) Temperature-sensitive products	Cycle times may be long (1) Heat-up times require determination for each load and configuration (1) Explosion risk if containers overfilled Will not depyrogenate Need to control period between filling and sterilization to minimize microbial growth

	Advantages	Suitable materials	Unsuitable materials	Limitations
2. Dry heat	Higher temperatures will also depyrogenate (2) Sterilizers available with simple design and installation requirements Sterilization conditions known and documented (9) No requirement for biological indicators (9)	Moisture-sensitive or steam-impermeable materials, e.g. powders, non-aqueous fluids, some surgical instruments such as sharps and powered drills (1) Aluminium foil preferred for packaging but glass or metal possible (1)	Aqueous fluids (1) Thermolabile materials	Long cycle times (1) Heat up times require determination for each load and configuration (1)
3. Irradiation	Product packaged in outer transit containers No need for biological indicators (13) Gamma irradiation: Highly penetrating Large-capacity sterilizers Electron beam: No radioactive source Less degradation to plastics materials (17) Rapid process	Range of plastic materials such as certain grades of polypropylene, styrene, acrylonitryl, polyethylene and natural materials such as latex Metallic products subject to limits on density (e.g. orthopaedic implants, scalpels)	Some plastics and glass undergo cross-linking leading to discolouration and embrittlement (10) Limited application to pharmaceutical products because of chemical alteration and breakdown products (11) Effect of radiation on packaging needs to be established (12)	High capital cost Equipment requirements extremely complex Will not depyrogenate Gamma irradiators: Control of radioactive material Localized heat generation (15) Slow process Electron beam: Low penetrating power (14) Product thickness crucial (14) Complex to control (16)
4. Gaseous sterilization (a) ethylene oxide	Cycle can be developed for particular products Can process product packaged in transit containers Automatic sterilizers available in variety of sizes from 1 m³ to 30 m³	Polymeric materials such as low-density polypropylene, polyvinyl chloride, polymethylmethacrylate and polyurethane Packaging materials must be permeable to air, water vapour and gas, e.g. sterilization-grade paper and spun-bonded polyolefin (Tyvek, Dupont)	External surfaces of ampoules or vials because of ingress of gas via microfractures (18) Impermeable packaging, e.g. glass, metal Products sensitive to high humidity present special problems Products which are not clean because gas may not penetrate organic or inorganic soil (19)	Biological indicators required (3, 16) No standard sterilization cycle available (20) Toxicity of gas Residual in processed goods Specialist expertise required Pre-chamber humidification usually required (21) Will not depyrogenate
(b) LTSF	Automated sterilizers available Can process some thermolabile materials	Materials which will withstand temperatures up to 80°C Packaging materials permeable to air, steam and formaldehyde	As ethylene oxide sterilization above	Biological indicators required Toxicity of gas Residuals in processed goods Specialist expertise required Will not depyrogenate

Method	Advantages	Applications	Disadvantages
5. Filtration	Operates at ambient temperature; Large volumes on semi-continuous basis; Also removes particles; Pyrogens not formed by processing; Choice of filter materials available which are compatible with even aggressive products	Fluids which cannot be terminally sterilized (11)	Aseptic processing after sterilization required; May not remove virus or mycoplasma; May not remove pyrogens from fluid stream; Sorption of some drugs, preservatives, etc.; Leaching of filter components
6. Liquid chemicals	Only method available for certain products	Products which cannot be sterilized by other means, e.g. materials of animal origin (heart valves, vascular prosthesis, tissue patches) and complex medical equipment, e.g. endoscopes (16)	Aseptic processing required after sterilization; Control of production of sterilizing solution required, including filtration sterilization of sterilant; Solution must contact all parts of product; Biological monitoring required; Residual chemicals in product (22); Processing times extended; Will not depyrogenate
7. Novel methods (see text)	May be less hazardous to operators; May not leave residues in products; Processing times may be short	May be compatible with items which cannot be processed in another way	Will depend upon method; Regulatory requirements not established; Need to demonstrate efficacy

1. Department of Health (1980a)
2. British Pharmacopoeia 1980 (Addendum 1983)
3. Eucomed (1988)
4. British Standard 6254 (1982)
5. British Standard 6255 (1982)
6. British Standard 6256 (1982)
7. British Standard 6871 (1987)
8. Department of Health (1988b)
9. Anon. (1962)
10. Chapiro (1974)
11. Department of Health (1983a)
12. Plester (1974)
13. Hurrell (1986)
14. Svendsen (1984)
15. Gardner and Peel (1986)
16. Department of Health (1981)
17. Bradbury (1974)
18. Crawford and George (1985)
19. Doyle and Ernst (1967)
20. Hoxey (1989)
21. Department of Health (1990a)
22. Osterberg (1978)

recording of the actual conditions produced during the process is required. The control and system of recording must be independent of each other and produced from the output of separate sensors to confirm that the required conditions have been achieved and maintained.

3.1 Steam sterilization

Steam is the method of choice for sterilization because it provides the majority of features of the ideal sterilization method. It is used either as a direct contact sterilant, e.g. in a porous load and 'instrument and utensil' sterilizer, or as a heat transfer medium to raise the temperature of the contents of containers, e.g. in a bottled fluids sterilizer. Heat transfer is achieved in steam sterilizers by the release of the latent heat from steam as it condenses (see Chapter 9).

A series of time–temperature relationships are accepted as providing satisfactory sterilizing conditions (Department of Health 1981). These conditions are illustrated in Table 2 but are not equipotent (see Table 4).

Table 2 — Time–temperature relationships for steam sterilization

Temperature range (°C)	Minimum holding time at temperature (min)
134–138	3
126–129	10
121–124	15
115–118	30

It is generally agreed that the highest temperature compatible with the product to be sterilized should be used as this combines the advantages of highest assurance of sterility with shortest cycle time. Steam sterilization can be monitored by physical measurement of the conditions because the kinetics of microbial inactivation by steam have been extensively studied (reviewed by Russell 1982; see also Chapter 7). The addition of biological indicators to steam sterilizers offers no advantages and does not increase the assurance of sterility (Eucomed 1988; Hoxey 1989).

3.1.1 Porous load sterilizers

Steam sterilizers used to process wrapped goods and porous materials are commonly referred to as 'porous load', 'high-vacuum' or 'pre-vacuum' sterilizers. In order to ensure that the cycle achieves sterilizing conditions, it is important that all the air is removed, permitting contact between product and steam (Anon. 1959). This can be achieved by a combination of evacuation and steam injection as a series of pulses which dilute and remove the air. Porous load sterilizers usually operate at the highest temperatures given in Table 2 (134–138°C) although machines operating at 126–129°C and 121–124°C are in use.

3.1.1.1 Equipment
British Standard 3970 (in press) details the requirements for porous load sterilizers
and the major aspects are summarized in Table 3. One of the most important factors

Table 3 — Principal features of porous load steam sterilizers

Feature	Rationale
Steam supply of suitable quality and quantity	To ensure correct functioning of sterilizer
Air removal system	To ensure rapid and even steam penetration throughout chamber and load
Air detector	To ensure adequate air removal is achieved
Automatic cycle controller	For reproducible cycle control
Time, temperature and pressure recorder	To provide batch/process record
Sterilization hold time initiated by drain temperature using separate sensor from that supplying recorder	To ensure coolest point of chamber (drain) reaches temperature prior to timing of hold period. Temperature record provides independent confirmation of attainment of correct conditions
Cycle counter	For maintenance and batch records
Door interlock and non-interruptable cycle	Operator safety and to prevent under-processing
Fault indication	To indicate incorrect function of sterilizer.
Leak test gauge of suitable scale range	For routine chamber integrity test when small changes in chamber pressure must be measured

for the correct operation of porous load sterilizers is the quality of the steam, the
ideal quality being represented by dry saturated steam. If the steam is too dry,
superheat may be created, while overly wet steam can produce a wet load at the end
of the sterilization cycle, and wet packaging is not an effective microbial barrier
(Placencia *et al.* 1986). Non-condensible gases in the steam supply, caused for
example by incorrect boiler feed water treatment, may affect sterilizer performance,
influence efficacy of the process, hinder steam penetration (see Bowie–Dick test,
section 3.1.1.3), cause chamber overheating, or result in inconsistent air detector
performance (Department of Health 1980a).
    Superheated steam is unsuitable for steam sterilization; it can be considered

equivalent to a dry gas and therefore dry heat sterilization time/temperature combinations would be required (see section 3.2). Superheat can be due to adiabatic expansion as a result of excessive reduction in pressure through a throttling device such as a reducing valve. The rehydration of exceptionally dry hygroscopic material is an exothermic reaction which can also cause superheating which may persist for the entire sterilization hold-time. For this reason textiles, particularly those containing cotton, should be allowed to air after laundering before they are sterilized (Department of Health 1980a).

Wet steam supply to the sterilizer is one cause of wet loads at the end of the sterilization process. This may be due to inadequate design or maintenance of the steam main, e.g. inadequate sloping and draining of the main, poor thermal insulation, incorrect installation of separators and steam traps or 'priming' in the boiler leading to carry-over of boiler water with the steam (Department of Health 1980a).

For these reasons the importance of correct installation and maintenance of steam boilers and distribution systems, together with the determination of the quality of steam provided at the sterilizer location, cannot be over-emphasized (Department of Health 1980a).

Incomplete air removal can cause a failure to sterilize (Anon. 1959). Air remaining in packages prior to the sterilization hold period will occur in random locations and may unpredictably delay or prevent steam from contacting surfaces over which air is present. Air removal is achieved by drawing a vacuum to between 40 and 60 mbar (4–6 kPa) absolute followed by dilution and removal of residual air by a series of steam injections and evacuations (see Fig. 1.). The correct function of the air removal portion of the sterilization cycle is monitored by the Bowie–Dick test on a daily basis and by the air detector for each sterilization cycle (see section 3.1.1.3).

3.1.1.2   The process
The essential features of a porous load steam sterilization cycle are illustrated in Fig. 1. The variables which can affect the efficacy of the process are time, temperature and pressure (because of its direct relationship with temperature of dry saturated steam). Factors such as steam quality (see section 3.1.1.1) and loading pattern will affect air removal and load dryness on cycle completion.

3.1.1.3   Routine tests of performance
(a) *Bowie–Dick test*. The Bowie–Dick test (Bowie *et al*. 1963) is the standard test for steam penetration which must be performed on porous load sterilizers each day of operation. The test consists of operating the cycle with a test pack containing a temperature-sensitive indicator as the only load. On completion of the cycle, the indicator is removed from the pack and examined for a uniform colour change. The basis of the test is that inadequate air removal will leave a pocket of air in the centre of the pack which will then act as a barrier to even steam penetration and result in an uneven colour change in the indicator. Traditionally this test was performed with a pack of 'Huckaback' linen towels and a test sheet with a cross of autoclave indicator tape. However, other materials for this test have been developed and performance requirements for

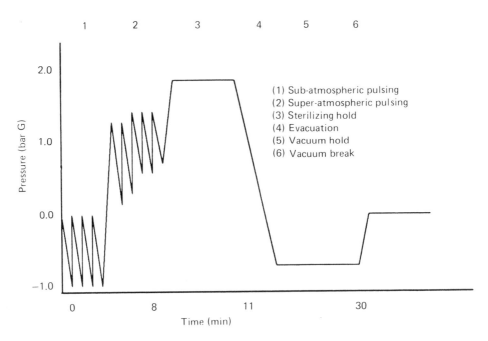

Fig. 1 — Schematic diagram of the stages of a steam sterilization cycle for porous loads.

materials used in the Bowie–Dick test have been detailed in published specifications (Department of Health 1983a, 1986, 1988a).

    This is generally considered a test of air removal based on detecting rapid and
even steam penetration into the pack. However, steam penetration may also be
affected by the steam quality, and in particular by superheat and the presence of
non-condensable gas in the steam supply. Failed Bowie–Dick tests therefore
require careful analysis of sterilizer performance.

(b) *Air detector*. Each porous load sterilization cycle should be monitored by an air
    detector (Department of Health 1980a). This device is part of the sterilizer
    control system and should be set to indicate a fault if there is sufficient air in the
    sterilizer to compromise the sterilization cycle (Pickerill *et al.* 1971). If the
    correct conditions are not established, this device should indicate a failure and
    the load be treated as non-sterile. The correct functioning of this device needs to
    be established at commissioning of the sterilizer and should be routinely
    confirmed.

(c) *Leak test*. The integrity of the sterilizer chamber should be routinely checked by
    performing a leak test (Department of Health 1980a). A vacuum is drawn in the
    chamber and the subsequent pressure rise monitored over a time period.

3.1.1.4 *Product release*
In addition to the general points described earlier (section 1), a complete sterilization
cycle record comprising time, temperature and pressure relationships is required to
support product release.

3.1.2   'Instrument and utensil' steam sterilizers

'Instrument and utensil' steam sterilizers are also referred to as 'bowl and instrument', 'dropped instrument', 'gravity displacement' or 'downward displacement'. The descriptions 'gravity displacement' and 'downward displacement' are, in fact, often incorrect as many sterilizers of this type generate steam within the sterilizer chamber and rely on upward displacement of air by steam. Like porous load sterilizers their efficiency relies on direct contact between steam and the surface to be sterilized. However, in these machines, air is directly displaced by steam either admitted from a separate steam source or generated within the chamber; there is no evacuation either to aid air removal or to help dry the load at the end of the cycle. These machines are therefore unsuitable for sterilizing wrapped goods or porous loads (Department of Health 1980a, 1988b).

Sterilizers of this type include the common portable machines which require a simple connection to an electrical power supply. They often operate at the highest temperatures given in Table 2, although machines operating over the range of conditions specified are available.

3.1.2.1   Equipment

Forthcoming British Standards outline the detailed requirements for this type of sterilizer (British Standard 3970, in press). The requirements for portable sterilizers have also been summarized in Department of Health Comparative Evaluation Reports (Department of Health 1988b, 1990b).

Most machines are portable and are not equipped with temperature recorders. A monitoring sensor, separate from the control sensor, should be incorporated into the automatic control system to indicate a failed cycle should the required temperature not be maintained for the designated time. Temperature and pressure gauges should be provided to allow the operation of the equipment to be checked.

3.1.2.2   The process

The essential features of an 'instrument and utensil' sterilization cycle are air displacement, sterilization and cooling, and these are summarized in Fig. 2.

3.1.2.3   Product release

In addition to the general points described earlier (see section 1), a complete sterilization cycle record of time and temperature is required when a temperature recorder is installed with the sterilizer. If a temperature recorder is not fitted, the operator should confirm the attainment of the correct conditions by checking the temperature and pressure indicated by the sterilizer instrumentation during the sterilization stage.

3.1.3   Bottled fluids sterilizers

Unlike porous load and 'instrument and utensil' steam sterilizers, bottled fluids machines do not rely on contact between the steam and the product to effect sterilization. The steam is a transfer medium which heats the container; the actual sterilization occurs in the product fluid. Steam is used because it is an efficient heat

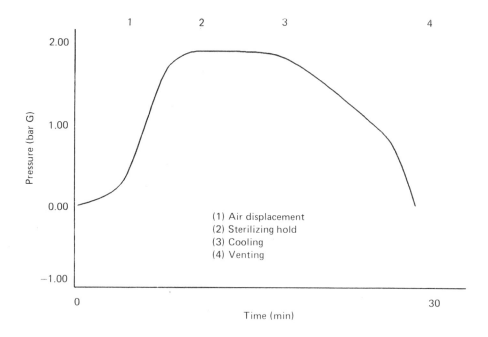

Fig. 2 — Schematic diagram of the stages of a steam sterilization cycle for instruments and utensils.

transfer medium and the pressure associated with steam will help counteract the pressure rise within a heated sealed container.

The lower temperature treatments quoted in Table 2 are used for fluids loads because of the lower associated pressure employed, i.e. 121–124°C for 15 minutes or 115–118°C for 30 minutes. The F-value may be used as an alternative to defining the sterilization process as a minimum hold-time at a given temperature (Chapters 7 and 9). The lethality of a process includes the effects of the heating and cooling periods as well as the sterilization hold-time. In a large fluids load the heat-up and cool-down times may be long and have a considerable microbiocidal effect. The F_0 value expresses the lethality of the whole process as an equivalent hold-time at 121°C and its calculation has been extensively reviewed (Deindoerfer and Humphrey 1959; Stumbo 1973; De Santis and Rudo 1986). It is generally accepted that an F_0 value greater than 8 should be delivered to every container in the load (British Pharmacopoeia 1988). For heat-labile products F_0 values of less than 8 may be acceptable if the level and heat resistance of the product bioburden are known and are closely monitored (Chapter 9).

It should be noted that lower temperature processes impart significantly less lethal effect than those operating at higher temperatures. This is demonstrated in Table 4 where the lethal (F_0) effects of the sterilization hold periods of accepted standard conditions are compared.

Table 4 — F_0 of the hold period of standard sterilizing
cycles previously specified in Table 2

Temperature (°C)	Sterilization hold time (min)	F_0 Value
134	3	59
126	10	31
121	15	15
115	30	8.1

Based on reference spores of *Bacillus stearothermophilus* with specified
D- and z-values of 1.5 min and 10°C respectively.

3.1.3.1 *Equipment*

The basic requirements for bottled fluids sterilizers are outlined in Table 5. The British Standard 3970, 1966) for this type of equipment is somewhat aged and is currently under revision. The revised standard will provide more detailed information when published (British Standard 3970, in press).

As shown in Table 5, the design of a bottled fluids sterilizer has to consider many factors; certain special features merit detailed consideration.

(a) The heating of a sealed container of aqueous fluid will raise the pressure within that container. The steam pressure in the sterilizer chamber and the strength of the container itself will each counteract this pressure rise to some degree. However, the sterilizer chamber pressure is often increased with the addition of sterile air to above that associated with dry saturated steam at the sterilizing temperature; this prevents bottle breakage or deformation of polymeric containers and is known as air ballasting. Additional pressurization with air could introduce problems of temperature variations within the sterilizer chamber unless the air/stream mixture is homogeneous. Forced circulation of the air/stream mixture is usually employed to provide this homogeneity.

(b) The cooling times for large loads may be extremely long. In order to decrease the total cycle time, a cooling system may be employed in which the load temperature is reduced by spraying with water. Contamination of the contents of containers with spray-cooling water has occurred and therefore water used for this purpose is usually sterile, but the provision of sterile cooling water is not an alternative to ensuring effective sealing of the containers being sterilized (Department of Health 1980a).

(c) Serious explosions have resulted from the transfer of loads of hot sterile fluids from the sterilizer into rooms at ambient temperature. Therefore, a door interlock should be installed to prevent removal of the load until the contents of all containers are below 80°C for glass or rigid polymer or 90°C for flexible polymer containers. This interlock should operate through a load simulator, rather than a temperature sensor in an actual load container, in case the latter breaks during the process.

Table 5 — Features of bottled fluids steam sterilizers

Feature	Rationale
Steam supply of suitable quality and quantity	To ensure correct functioning of the sterilizer
Automatic cycle controller	For reproducible cycle control
Time, temperature and pressure recorder	To provide batch process records
Sterilization hold period time, or F_0 integration, taken from load simulator using separate sensor from that supplying the recorder	To ensure that coolest point of load controls the cycle and that the temperature record is an independent confirmation of the attainment of correct conditions
Temperature control from a drain sensor during sterilization hold period	More sensitive to temperature fluctuations in the chamber than a load stimulator
Cycle counter	For maintenance and batch records
If temperature is monitored and/or controlled from a load bottle this must not control door opening	If the load bottle breaks, the probe will cool more rapidly than the load bottles and door opening may lead to explosion
Chamber over-pressure (air ballasting)	To prevent bottle breakage or distortion of flexible containers especially during cooling cycle
Assisted cooling either by fan circulation of air or spraying load with recycled condensate	To reduce the time for load to cool to below 80°C
Door interlock and non-interruptable cycle. Door must not open until entire load is below 80°C	Operator safety. Serious accidents have occurred due to load explosion when sterlizer door opened with load above 80°C

3.1.3.2   The process

The essential features of a bottled fluids steam sterilization cycle are heat-up combined with air displacement, sterilization and cooling; these are illustrated in Fig. 3.

The efficacy of the process is determined by the time at sterilizing temperature. The size of the load and the size of the individual containers within the load will significantly affect heat-up and cool-down times and hence total cycle time.

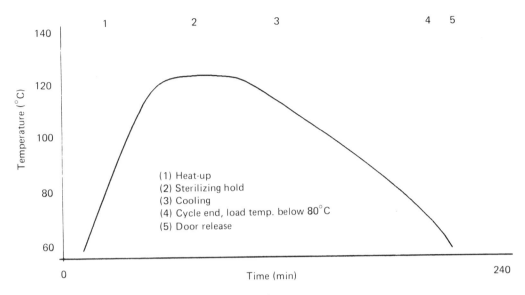

Fig. 3 — Schematic diagram of the stages of a steam sterilization cycle for fluids in sealed containers.

3.1.3.3   Product release
In addition to the general points described earlier (section 1), the following are required to support product release following a bottled fluids steam sterilization cycle: sterilization cycle temperature/time records and/or confirmation, where appropriate, of attainment of required F_0 value; where appropriate, sterility test result.

3.2   Dry-heat sterilization
Dry-heat sterilization is the method of choice for heat-stable but moisture-sensitive items. The evolution of the physical conditions proposed for dry-heat sterilization is outlined in Table 6. It should be noted that the temperatures and times required are significantly greater than for steam sterilization.

Dry heat at higher temperatures than those specified for sterilization may also be used for depyrogenation of some materials, and the British Pharmacopoeia (1988) in its Test for Pyrogens recommends time/temperature combinations of 250°C for 30 minutes or 200°C for 1 hour for depyrogenation.

3.2.1   Equipment
A somewhat dated standard exists for the performance of dry-heat sterilizers (British Standard 3421, 1961) and further details are given in Health Technical Memorandum 10 (Department of Health 1980a). Table 7 illustrates the features of a hot-air sterilizer; Chapter 9 details the differences between forced-convection batch sterilizers and dry-heat sterilizing tunnels.

Table 6 — Comparison of time–temperature relationships for dry heat sterilization

Temp. (°C)	Time (min)			
	Anon. (1962)	PC (1979)	DH (1980a)	BP (1980) Addendum 1983 and BP (1988)
150	—	60[a]	60[a]	—
160	45	60	60	120
170	18	—	40	60
180	7.5	11	20	30

[a]Note: only for fixed oils, ethyl oleate, liquid paraffin, glycerol.
PC, Pharmaceutical Codex; BP, British Pharmacopoeia; DH, Department of Health.

Table 7 — Features of hot-air sterilizers

Feature	Rationale
Open-mesh shelving and adequate circulating fan	To allow even heat distribution and maximum heating
Temperature recorder with no control function	To provide independent batch/process history
Overheat cut-out	Safety and product protection
Thermally insulated chamber	Efficiency and operator safety/comfort
Cycle counter	Maintenance records (batch recording)
Forced cooling and filtered air	Increased turn-round/shortened cycle
Thermocouple inlet	Validation purposes
Door interlock and automatic non-interruptable cycle	Prevent inadvertent under-processing
Sterilization hold period timer initiated by chamber temperature (separate sensor from chart recorder)	Timing of sterilization period
Fault indication	To indicate incorrect function of sterlizer

3.2.2 The process

The essential features of a hot-air sterilization cycle are heating, sterilizing and cooling and are illustrated in Fig. 4.

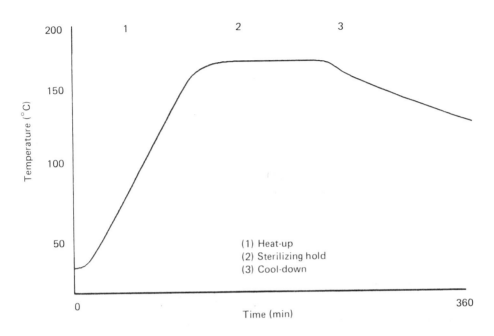

Fig. 4 — Schematic diagram of the stages of a dry-heat sterilization process.

The heating of the contents of a hot-air sterilizer relies on sensible heat transfer. An even temperature distribution throughout the load is essential and design features are incorporated into the sterilizer to minimize temperature variations (see Table 7). However, the distribution of the load within the chamber can also dramatically effect the performance of the sterilizer. Variation from the established loading pattern may seriously affect the heat distribuition and sterilization conditions may not be attained throughout the load (Department of Health 1980a). The loading pattern must therefore be controlled and hot-air sterilizers must not be overfilled.

3.2.3 *Product release*
Product release following a dry-heat sterilization process requires complete sterilization records (e.g. time, temperature) in addition to the general points outlined earlier (section 1).

3.3 Irradiation sterilization
The use of ionizing radiation is the method of choice for the sterilization of heat-labile materials which will withstand the high levels of radiation involved. The two methods currently available use either γ-rays from a radioactive source or accelerated electrons (β-particles) from an electron beam sterilizer, although the use of X-rays for sterilization is under investigation (see section 3.7.6). Ultraviolet (UV) light is not recommended for product sterilization due to its extremely low penetrating

power, which means that only organisms directly exposed to the UV light will be affected and those lying in shadows will be protected (Gardner and Peel 1986). The uses of UV light for sanitation purposes in glove boxes or water streams (Zinnbauer 1985) are outside the scope of this chapter (but see Chapter 3). The nature and mechanism of action of sterilizing radiations is discussed in Chapter 7.

The γ-irradiation process utilizes a cobalt-60 (or less commonly, caesium-137) source. Cobalt-60 emits radiation at two levels, 1.33 and 1.17 MeV (Denyer 1987). The γ-rays bombard the material, resulting in the emission of lower-energy photons and electrons. These electrons undergo further reactions which cause ionization of molecules within any micro-organisms. Accelerated electron processes are essentially equivalent to the second stage of the γ-process, the high-speed electrons causing direct ionization of molecules within the micro-organism. There are two types of accelerator, producing electrons with maximum energies of 5 MeV and 10 MeV (Denyer 1987).

The accepted radiation dose for sterilization varies throughout the world. UK regulatory authorities currently require a minimum dose of 25 kGy (Department of Health 1981, 1983a) as confirmed by studies of microbial resistance using *Bacillus pumilus* (Ley and Tallentire 1964; Ley 1984). In Scandinavia, doses as high as 32 kGy are specified following studies on highly radiation-resistant organisms under protected conditions (Christensen and Sehested 1964). In the USA, the Association for the Advancement of Medical Instrumentation (AAMI 1981) have published guidelines on dose-setting methods dependent upon the numbers and radiation resistance of products' pre-sterilization microbial contamination. Other dose-setting methods have also been described (Dorpema 1984; Darbord and Laizier 1987). All such methods allow the use of lower irradiation doses in circumstances where the pre-sterilization microbial contamination is low. Such an approach may be beneficial where higher doses of 25 kGy may cause product damage but these dose-setting methods require considerable microbiological input and are not universally accepted (UK Panel on Gamma and Electron Irradiation 1987).

3.3.1 Equipment
Currently the use of γ-irradiators far outweighs the use of electron beam sterilizers (Svendsen 1984).

There are two types of plants used for γ-irradiation: batch or continuous. Both have similar source arrangments. Within the irradiation cell an array of cobalt-60 rods (or caesium-137), with up to 1 MCi (3.7×10^{16} Bq) of activity, is contained in a deep pit filled with water to a depth of about 4 m. In a continuous process, the cobalt source is raised from the water and product passes into the cell along a conveyor which tracks a zig-zag path around the cell to ensure all sides of the load receive equal exposure. The dose delivered to the load is dependent on source strength and exposure time. A typical dwell time may be up to 20 hours. In a batch process the load is manually placed in a static position in the cell before the source is raised. In this batch approach, some variation will exist in the dose absorbed by product items in different locations within the load (Eucomed 1988).

The basic principle of an electron beam sterilizer is that electrons from a hot filament or cathode source are emitted into a vacuum, accelerated by passage through high-voltage electrodes and concentrated into a beam. The maximum energy for sterilizing is around 10 mega-electron volts (MeV) although many machines operate at 3–4 MeV. The product passes on a conveyor under the beam, which scans from side to side across the product. The dose delivered to the product is determined by the speed of the conveyor, the width of beam and the speed at which it sweeps across the conveyor. As penetrating power is low, the dose received by product at the bottom of the container is influenced by its thickness and density (Svendsen 1984). In contrast to γ-irradiation, the dwell time of product in an electron beam sterilizer is usually only a few seconds or minutes.

3.3.2 The process

For cobalt-60, the only process variable is the source exposure time. For a load of given density and a source of given activity, the time of exposure to the source (dwell time) is adjusted to ensure the minimum required dose at the lowest dose point. The dose received at any point can be measured by the use of dosimeters (Chapter 9). National standard traceable 'red perspex' dosimeters such as those prepared by the UK Atomic Energy Authority at Harwell give a reproducible change in absorbance for a given dose of irradiation. Each batch of product should routinely contain at least two dosimeters in the first and last container in the batch located at a point which can be related to the minimum dose position by the validation data.

Routine control of a γ-sterilizer is relatively straightforward. A chart record should show the position of the source (up or down) and the product dwell time.

Electron beam sterilizers are more difficult to control, as several factors affect the dose received by the product. These factors are the electron voltage, the beam current, width of the beam scan, the conveyor speed and product density. Dose to product is moitored with dosimeters usually in the form of PVC film. Routine controls on an electron beam sterilizer consist of continuous measurement of the characteristics of the beam and the conveyor speed (Department of Health 1981).

The dose delivered to each batch of product must be determined whichever method of irradiation is used. Colour change monitors are attached to each container of product to indicate that it has been processed, and products arriving at the irradiation facility are physically segregated from processed goods. For products sterilized by a contractor, all the above may be carried out by the contractor who provides documentary evidence of the dose delivered to the product. Alternatively the manufacturer may supply product boxes containing dosimeters to be returned with the load.

3.3.3 Product release

Following an irradiation sterilization process, evidence that the required dose has been delivered to the product must be available in addition to the general points for product release discussed earlier (see section 1). Evidence of dose delivered may be the actual dosimeter results or a certificate giving the dose delivered.

3.4 Gaseous sterilization

Many chemicals which can be generated in a gaseous phase have microbiocidal activity, including ethylene oxide (Phillips and Kaye 1949), formaldehyde (Nordgren 1939), propylene oxide (Bruch 1961), methyl bromide (Kolb and Schneiter 1950), β-propiolactone (Allen and Murphy 1960), peracetic acid (Portner and Hoffman

1968), chlorine dioxide (Knapp *et al.* 1986) and ozone (Hoffman 1971). The use of all these agents as sterilants or disinfectants has been proposed at some time but ethylene oxide is the most widely used gaseous sterilant in the medical device and pharmaceutical industry (Hoxey 1989). Formaldehyde gas has been used for fumigation in a number of areas (Ackland *et al.* 1980), and gaseous formaldehyde has been combined with steam at sub-atmospheric pressure in the low-temperature steam and formaldehyde (LTSF) sterilization process used in hospitals in northern Europe for processing multiple-use, heat-sensitive items (Hurrell 1987).

This section will consider only the established technology of ethylene oxide and LTSF. Other methods will be discussed in the later section on new sterilization technology (see section 3.7).

3.4.1 Ethylene oxide

Ethylene oxide gas is used to sterilize heat-sensitive materials, principally plastics, which will not withstand irradiation. There is no standard set of conditions for ethylene oxide sterilization. Each cycle in use is individually developed and microbiologically validated for the particular product to be processed (Hoxey 1989; Department of Health 1990a). The efficacy of the process is affected by a number of variables, including time of exposure, temperature, humidity, gas concentration and pressure, gas penetration and distribution (see Chapter 7), and all must be carefully controlled (Hoxey 1989). The range of conditions in use are illustrated in Table 8.

Table 8 — The range of conditions used for ethylene oxide sterilization (from Hoxey 1989)

Factor	Conditions
Concentration of ethylene oxide	250–1500 mg l^{-1}
Temperature	30–65°C
Exposure time	1–30 h
Humidity	30–99%

Ethylene oxide sterilization cycles in use vary enormously because each product presents distinct problems for cycle development. Whilst the interrelationship of factors which affect microbial inactivation by ethylene oxide have been extensively studied (reviewed by Hoffman 1971; Russell 1982), the product characteristics constrain the choice of conditions used such that an optimum cycle suitable for any product does not exist.

Ethylene oxide is inflammable and toxic and its use is controlled to protect the health and safety of workers. The maximum exposure level to ethylene oxide in the UK has been set by the Health and Safety Executive at a time-weighted average over 8 hours of 5 p.p.m. (Health and Safety Executive 1989). The operation of an ethylene oxide sterilization process requires specialist knowledge and preferably microbiological facilities at the site of the operation (Department of Health 1981).

3.4.1.1 Equipment

The development of a European Standard specification for ethylene oxide sterilizers has just started. Some guidance on technical requirements for the sterilizer are currently available (Department of Health 1990a) and a basic summary of equipment features for a sterilizer utilizing ethylene oxide is given in Table 9.

Table 9 — Features of ethylene oxide sterilizers

Feature	Rationale
Pre-chamber humidification with temperature control and steam injection	To increase efficacy of process and reduce cycle time in the chamber
Automatically controlled sterilization process	To avoid variations between cycles inherent in manual control
Evacuation cycle	To remove air and ensure penetration of ethylene oxide
In-chamber humidification by steam injection	To replace moisture removed by evacuation stage of cycle
Jacketed chamber	To control cycle temperature
Time–temperature, pressure and humidity recorders, separate to sterilizer controller	To provide independent batch process history
Over-temperature cut-out	To protect product
Heated gas vapourizer	To prevent admission of liquid ethylene oxide to sterilizer chamber
Cycle counter	Maintenance records (batch records)
Forced gas circulation in chamber	To minimize variations in conditions throughout sterilizer chamber
Thermocouple inlet	Validation purposes
Door lock and non-interruptable cycle	Product and operator protection
Ethylene oxide concentration in chamber controlled by pressure rise; independent monitor system such as weight loss from gas cylinder or in-chamber concentration measurement	Check of in-chamber concentration
Fault indication system	To indicate incorrect functioning of sterilizer
Degassing area with forced circulation and exhaust to safe place	Reduce gas residuals in product and operator safety

Ethylene oxide gas may be supplied to a sterilizer either as the pure gas or mixed with an inert carrier such as a chlorofluorocarbon, carbon dioxide or nitrogen. As a result of the environmental effects of chlorofluorocarbons, alternative carrier gases are under investigation (Reich 1989). The quality of this gas supply will affect the efficacy of the sterilization process. Supplies of ethylene oxide should be purchased to comply with a formal specification agreed with an appropriate supplier. Ethylene oxide should be treated as any other raw material and undergo documented incoming inspection. A certificate of analysis, which may be provided by the gas supplier, should be available for each batch of sterilant and this should demonstrate conformance with the purchasing specification.

3.4.1.2 *The process*
The principal stages of an ethylene oxide sterilization cycle are illustrated in Fig. 5.

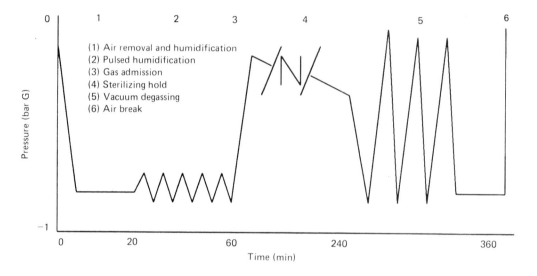

Fig. 5 — Schematic diagram of the stages of an ethylene oxide sterilization cycle, using 100% ethylene oxide.

The development of an ethylene oxide sterilization cycle allows selection of a suitable combination of factors, including ethylene oxide gas supply (pure or mixed with an inert carrier gas), ethylene oxide concentration, temperature, pressure (dependent on required gas concentration and type of gas mixture used), humidity, exposure time, pre-conditioning and degassing conditions. Once the process has been selected and validated, the variables within the cycle which have to be controlled and monitored are temperature, pressure, relative humidity, gas concentration, exposure time, load configuration and load density.

Each sterilization batch is monitored by including biological indicators in each sterilizer load (Department of Health 1981; 1990a; see also Chapter 9). These are generally spores of *Bacillus subtilis* var. *niger* deposited onto a suitable carrier material (Dadd *et al*. 1983). Specifications for these monitors are available (Department of Health 1983a) although requirements may vary in different countries. Biological indicators should be distributed throughout the sterilizer load prior to any pre-humidification and removed as soon as possible after the sterilization process. Positioning of biological indicators should be selected on the basis of the validation studies and include those sites found most difficult to sterilize. The recommended number of biological indicators per sterilizer load varies in different countries; the UK recommends a minimum of ten indicators for sterilizers with a capacity up to 5000 litres, with additional indicators added for larger chambers (Department of Health 1981, 1990a).

3.4.1.3 Product release
In addition to the general points described earlier (section 1), the following release data are required for a product sterilized by an ethylene oxide process:

(a) pre-conditioning records (time, temperature, relative humidity);
(b) time elapsed between pre-conditioning and sterilization;
(c) sterilization cycle records (time, temperature, pressure, relative humidity, measure of gas concentration, e.g. weight of gas used);
(d) incoming inspection records of ethylene oxide supply;
(e) results of biological indicator incubation;
(f) degassing records (time, temperature).

3.4.2 Low-temperature steam and formaldehyde (LTSF)
The LTSF process generally operates in the temperature range between 70 and 80°C, with a formaldehyde concentration of approximately 14 mg l^{-1} of chamber volume. Like ethylene oxide, formaldehyde is a toxic gas and maximum exposure levels in air have been established in the UK by the Health and Safety Executive at a time-weighted average over 8 hours of 2 p.p.m. (Health and Safety Executive 1989). Each sterilization cycle requires monitoring with a biological indicator and spores of *Bacillus stearothermophilus* deposited on a suitable carrier are generally used for this purpose (Department of Health 1980b).

3.4.2.1 Equipment
An LTSF sterilizer can in some ways be considered as similar to a porous load steam sterilizer but operating at sub-atmospheric pressure with injection of formaldehyde gas (Hurrell 1987). A British Standard specification (BS 3970, in press) for this type of equipment is currently in preparation. A steam supply of suitable quality is important to the satisfactory operation of an LTSF sterilizer for the same reasons as it is critical in porous load sterilizers (see section 3.1.1).

3.4.2.2 The process
The features of an LTSF sterilization cycle are illustrated in Fig. 6. The cycle consists of a series of pulses in which formaldehyde is admitted to the evacuated chamber and allowed to diffuse through the load for approximately 2 minutes. This is followed by

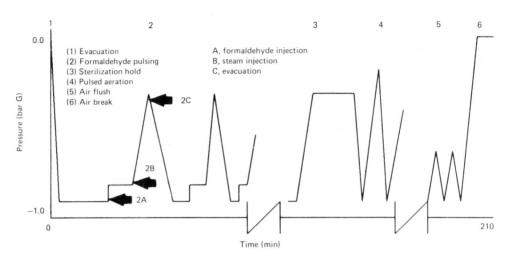

Fig. 6 — Schematic diagram of the stages of a low-temperature steam and formaldehyde sterilization cycle.

an injection of steam to the operating temperature and re-evacuation. These stages are repeated to produce up to twenty pulses which may be followed by a hold period (Hoxey, in press). The value of the hold period has been questioned as the chamber formaldehyde concentration decreases rapidly in static conditions due to polymerization and dissolution (Marcos and Wiseman 1979). Aeration prior to cycle completion is achieved by a series of pulses in which air admission through a bacteria-retentive filter is alternated with evacuation of the chamber.

The variables within an LTSF cycle are the same as the variables within an ethylene oxide sterilization cycle (Hoxey *et al.* 1984). Temperature, formaldehyde concentration and pressure, sterilant penetration and distribution all affect the efficacy of the process (see Chapter 7). Humidity also affects the rate of microbial inactivation by gaseous formaldehyde (Nordgren 1939) but in the LTSF process a constant high humidity is provided by the steam injection.

The physical conditions in each sterilization cycle should be monitored and recorded. In addition, each sterilizer load should contain a biological indicator. In order to test gas penetration, this is placed in a Line–Pickerill helix (Line and Pickerill 1973), which is a stainless steel tube in a helical configuration attached to a small chamber into which the biological indicator is placed. The length : bore ratio of the tube makes the helix a rigorous challenge to the process.

3.4.2.3   *Product release*
In addition to the general points described earlier (section 1), the release of product following LTSF sterilization requires the following:

(a) sterilization cycle records (time, temperature, pressure);
(b) results of biological indicator incubation;
(c) record to confirm that validated degassing procedures have been followed.

3.5 Filtration sterilization

Filtration has a number of fundamental differences when compared with other sterilization processes. Filtration sterilization during aseptic filling is not a terminal sterilization step as the product undergoes further processing under aseptic conditions which potentially can compromise product sterility. Although very high levels of sterility assurance can be demonstrated in the product immediately after passing through the filter, final product sterility assurance is dependent upon the subsequent aseptic processing and is therefore variable and difficult to quantify. Aseptic filling is the method of choice only for the production of sterile pharmaceuticals which cannot be terminally sterilized in their final containers. The selection of aseptic filling because of its low cost or due to choice of heat-labile packaging materials for heat-stable products is not readily acceptable to regulatory authorities (Department of Health 1983a; Cooper 1989).

The requirements for aseptic filling of pharmaceutical materials are extensive and this section will concentrate only on the use of filters to sterilize fluids.

Filtration physically removes viable and non-viable organisms from the process stream rather than inactivating them. Filters suitable for sterilization of pharmaceutical products should have a nominal rated pore size of 0.22 μm or less, or have at least equivalent micro-organism-retaining properties (Department of Health 1983a). Such filters have a finite capacity for the retention of micro-organisms.

Guidelines in the USA specify a minimum challenge of 10^7 *Pseudomonas diminuta* per square centimetre with no passage into the effluent (HIMA 1982). Thus if the process stream has a low bioburden there is a very low probability that a filter will pass organisms because of the level of challenge. Furthermore, two sterilizing filters are often operated in line to increase protection.

A vast range of types of filter materials and configurations are available (Denyer *et al.* 1982). Most of the major filter manufacturers offer technical services and prospective users are advised to discuss particular process requirements with them. A brief discussion of filter characteristics is given in Chapter 7.

3.5.1 Equipment

Requirements of the filter medium and the filtration equipment have to be considered separately. The essential features of both are summarized in Table 10. For satisfactory aseptic filling, it is important to remember that the filters and downstream pipework must be readily sterilizable and must be designed so that they may be maintained in a clean condition.

3.5.2 The process

Variables which may affect the efficacy and rate of filtration sterilization are filter surface area, nominal pore size and microbial challenge.

The microbial contamination level should be maintained as low as possible prior to filtration sterilization (Department of Health 1983a). A maximum time interval should be specified between solution preparation and filtration to prevent microbial growth. Ideally, product should be filled into final containers and sealed immediately following filtration.

Filter integrity testing should be carried out at least after each batch and ideally before and after each batch (Department of Health 1983a). The system *in situ* and

Table 10 — Features of filter media and equipment used for filtration sterilization

Feature	Rationale
1. Filter medium	
Acceptable flow rate	Product must flow through the filter at an acceptable rate within pressure drop limitations
Biological capacity (10^7 *Ps. diminuta* cm^{-2})	Ideally the filter should block before passing organisms. In order to give a 10^{-6} sterility assurance level (SAL) for the process filter capacity should be $10^6 \times$ maximum total process challenge
Strength	The filter should be capable of steam sterilization without affecting any properties and should have significant strength when wet
Inertness	The filter must not shed particles or leach chemical substances into the process stream. This is particularly important with 'aggressive' products
Sorption	Must not strongly sorb substances
2. Filtration equipment	
Steam sterilizable in position	This avoids the need for aseptic assembly operations for pre-sterilized filtration equipment
Integrity test carried out in place before and after use	Integrity test before use prevents expensive processing through incorrectly fitted or damaged filters and after use ensures filter integrity maintained throughout the batch.
Equipment can be easily and effectively cleaned	As product contact occurs all process equipment must be cleanable

not the filter in isolation should be tested. A number of different methods are available and these include bubble point, pressure hold and forward flow tests (Errico 1986; Chapter 9). The nature of the process stream will affect the values recorded in integrity tests (Errico 1986). Most major manufacturers produce automatic integrity-testing equipment for their filtration units and offer assistance in selecting suitable integrity test procedures for particular applications and products.

Each filter type has a finite capacity for retaining micro-organisms, which is tested by the filter manufacturer. Nevertheless, the user has a responsibility to ensure that the filter will be effective with his product, although evidence exists that if the pore diameter of the filter is smaller than the minimum diameter of the challenging organism the suspending liquid does not affect bacterial retention (Levy 1986).

It has been documented that some organisms naturally occurring in water supplies or cultured under specific conditions may pass through 0.2-μm filters over extended time periods (Wallhaeusser 1979; Howard and Duberstein 1980). Whilst such organisms are uncommon in the pharmaceutical manufacturing environment, the long-term use of filters in water systems requires careful consideration.

Traditional aseptic filling is required to be carried out under environmental conditions controlled to Class F (British Standard 5295 1989; see also Chapter 5) to prevent post-filtration contamination (Department of Health 1983a). Guidance on environmental contamination control in such areas has recently been published (Parenteral Society 1989). There is currently debate over the environmental requirements for recent technologies such as blow–fill–seal in which a single piece of production equipment sterilizes the product by filtration and fills it into a blow-moulded container which is immediately sealed. A working group has been set up in the UK to discuss the particular environmental requirements for this type of process. A review of current blow–fill–seal technology is given by Leo (1987).

3.5.3 *Product release*
In addition to the general requirements for compliance with documented procedures (see section 1), the following are required for product release following aseptic filling operations.

Filtration system:

(a) identification of filter type in use;
(b) details of sterilization of filter system;
(c) acceptable filter integrity test;
(d) acceptable pre-filtration bioburden data;
(e) sterile post-filtration sample.

Aseptic process:

(a) details of sterilization of components;
(b) environmental monitoring data from aseptic filling area;
(c) sterility test results;
(d) operator test procedure results (broth fill data).

Further detailed consideration of filtration is given by Errico (1986) and Olson (1987).

3.6 **Liquid chemical sterilants**
Liquid chemicals, predominantly alkylating agents such as glutaraldehyde or formaldehyde solutions, are used as a last resort to sterilize items which cannot be processed in any other way. For example, prostheses made from material of animal origin

(heart valves, vascular prostheses and tissue patches) (Bruch, in press) and complex items of medical equipment such as flexible fibre-optic endoscopes may be sterilized in this way. For processing endoscopes, 2% glutaraldehyde solution is the most commonly used sterilant, but other chemicals such as formaldehyde or succinaldehyde alone or in combination with phenates or alcohols may also be employed. The efficacy of the process will be affected by chemical concentration and temperature (Russell 1982) and these factors should be controlled.

As these chemicals are toxic, their use must be carefully controlled. Maximum atmospheric exposure limits for formaldehyde have been set in the UK at a time-weighted average over 8 hours of 2 p.p.m. (Health and Safety Executive 1989). The approved occupational exposure standard for atmospheric glutaraldehyde over the same period is 0.2 p.p.m. (Health and Safety Executive 1989). Incidents of allergic responses in personnel exposed to liquid chemical sterilants and their vapours have been reported (Ballantyne and Berman 1984; Corrado *et al.* 1986).

The use of liquid chemical sterilants for reprocessing medical equipment in clinical areas is not considered further in this chapter.

3.6.1 Equipment
The equipment requirements for liquid chemical sterilization are essentially simple: a closed container to hold the solution and product and a means to control and monitor the temperature of exposure.

3.6.2 The process
The main variables in a liquid chemical sterilization process which must be controlled and monitored are chemical concentration and exposure temperature. In addition, the pH of glutaraldehyde solutions affects their efficacy (reviewed by Russell 1982). The sterilant solution must be carefully prepared and the concentration of active ingredient is generally determined by assay, as is the pH. Solutions are often sterilized by filtration prior to use to reduce the microbial challenge. Additionally, liquid chemical sterilization processes are generally monitored using biological indicators. However, these indicators are not exposed to the sterilant with the device being processed, but are used to test the solution after the device has been removed. Furthermore, a sterility test is often performed on samples, because of the aseptic processing necessary after removal from the sterilant.

3.6.3 Product release
In addition to the general requirements (see section 1), the following information is required in order to release a product as sterile following a liquid sterilization process:

(a) records of manufacture and test of sterilant solution (including records of preparation of solution, assay results, pH, records of sterilant filtration);
(b) records of sterilization conditions (temperature, time);
(c) details of sterilization of packaging components;
(d) environmental monitoring data of area used for aseptic packaging;
(e) sterility test results.

3.7   New technologies for sterilization

Consideration of Table 1 shows that no single sterilization method satisfies all the criteria of an ideal process. Steam sterilization is accepted as the method of choice because it comes closest to meeting the ideal criteria but investigations into alternatives continue, particularly alternatives to chemical sterilants (either gaseous or liquid). Current interest centres on materials which can be used in the vapour phase but which will break down to form non-toxic residues. Such developments are academically interesting but present many problems in routine use. The regulatory requirements for novel sterilization methods are not established and use of established technologies remains the most straightforward route to product acceptance.

A potential user of a new method for sterilization would be expected to demonstrate:

(a)   that established methods of sterilization are not practical or that the new method demonstrates a clear advantage over established methods;
(b)   efficacy of the propsed method against a range of micro-organisms;
(c)   the range and number of micro-organisms likely to contaminate the product and activity of the proposed sterilization method against these organisms;
(d)   the critical variables of the process and their means of control;
(e)   reproducibility of effectiveness for the proposed sterilization method;
(f)   the critical variables attained with physical records;
(g)   an appropriate standard organism for biological monitoring.

3.7.1   Sterilization by free radicals

The synergistic effects of combined UV irradiation and hydrogen peroxide in inactivating bacterial spores has been demonstrated (Bayliss and Waites 1979b). This synergism may be due to the production of hydroxyl radicals (Russell 1982) but this does not appear to have been developed into a sterilization method. It has recently been suggested that synergism between radio waves and hydrogen peroxide vapour produces sterilizing conditions. The system consists of chamber evacuation, injection and diffusion of very small amounts of hydrogen peroxide vapour, followed by the creation of a strong electromagnetic field to ionize the gas partially (i.e. generate a 'gas plasma'). The system operates at low temperature, approximately 40°C, and is claimed to be suitable for a range of materials, with the exception of fabrics (Hardie 1989).

The generation of a 'gas plasma' which is not seeded with hydrogen peroxide has also been reported as producing sterilizing conditions suitable for glass containers (Tensmeyer et al. 1981; Peebles and Anderson 1985).

3.7.2   Chlorine dioxide

Chlorine dioxide has been used in solution as a bactericide and virucide in the treatment of water for some years (Staquet 1969; Aieta and Roberts 1983) and as a general disinfectant in the food industry (Masschelein 1979).

The antimicrobial activity of chlorine dioxide has been reviewed by Knapp et al. (1986). These workers investigated sporicidal activity and suggested that exposure to chlorine dioxide gas at concentrations above 40 mg l^{-1} for 1–2 hours could be an effective sterilization method. However, no data on the kinetics of sporicidal activity were presented.

3.7.3   Ozone
Whilst the microbiocidal properties of ozone have long been established, it has previously been considered that the instability, toxicity and corrosive nature of the agent made it unsuitable for disinfection or sterilization (Hoffman 1971). Methods of sterilization utilizing ozone are, however, now being investigated (Karlson 1989; Stoddart 1989).

3.7.4   Peracetic acid
The sporicidal activity of peracetic acid in liquid (Jones *et al.* 1967) and gaseous (Portner and Hoffman 1968) forms has been demonstrated. The use of peracetic acid vapour for sterilization of equipment used in aseptic production has been reported (Hoet and Thorogood 1986). Evaporation of 0.35% peracetic acid at the rate of 42.5 ml per hour was shown to inactivate 10^6 *B. subtilis* var. *niger* spores on an aluminium carrier in 90 minutes.

3.7.5   Vapour-phase hydrogen peroxide
In addition to the combination of hydrogen peroxide and radiowaves (see section 3.7.1), vapour-phase hydrogen peroxide alone has also been proposed as a sterilant. Inactivation of 10^6 spores of *B. stearothermophilus* in 2 minutes has been reported using 2 mg l^{-1} hydrogen peroxide in the vapour phase at 35°C (Rickloff and Graham 1989). As with the combined hydrogen peroxide/radio wave system, compatibility has been claimed with a range of materials, with the exception of cellulosics and nylon (Rickloff and Graham 1989).

3.7.6   X-ray irradiation
The use of machine-generated X-rays for the sterilization of medical products is currently under investigation. The system operates with a linear accelerator producing a scan of electrons (see section 3.3). A 'target', a film of high atomic number, is placed in front of the scan to absorb electrons and emit X-ray photons (Bremsstahlung effect). A major problem is dissipating the heat generated within the target since 70% of the input energy is lost as heat.

The advantages of such a system are seen as: high penetrating power of X-ray photons; no radioactive material; dual-mode operation as X-ray and electron beam using a movable 'target'; continuous plant operation; extension of established irradiation technology and quality-assurance systems. The major problems are the enormous capital cost and the current lack of a dosimetry system designed to operate at these energy levels (Saylor, in press).

3.7.7   Other agents
Propylene oxide has been suggested as a possible sterilizing agent with advantages over ethylene oxide in terms of toxicity of breakdown products despite possessing lower microbiocidal activity (Bruch 1961). Liquid propylene oxide has been proposed for the sterilization of immunoadsorbents because it decomposes rapidly, reducing residual toxicity without affecting the performance of the product (Sato *et al.* 1985).

The use of microwave heating has been proposed for the sterilization of empty vials (Lohmann and Manique 1986) and hydrophilic contact lenses (Rohrer *et al.*

1986). The perceived advantage in this method is that there may be more intensive heating of organic materials such as micro-organisms than the product to be sterilized; naturally this is dependent upon the materials of construction of the product (Lohmann and Manique 1986). However, the level of control provided by domestic microwave equipment used in these studies is unlikely to be adequate for large-scale sterilization in industry.

4 REFERENCES

Ackland, N. R., Hinton, M. R. and Denmeade, K. R. (1980) Controlled formaldehyde fumigation system. *Appl. Environ. Microbiol.* **39** 480–487.

Aieta, E. M. and Roberts, P. V. (1983) Disinfection with chlorine and chlorine dioxide. *J. Environ. Eng.* **109** 783–799.

Allen, H. F. and Murphy, J. T. (1960) Sterilization of instruments and materials with beta-propiolactone. *JAMA* **172** 1759–1763.

Anon. (1959) Sterilization by steam under increased pressure. *Lancet* **i** 425–435.

Anon. (1962) The sterilization, use and care of syringes. *Medical Research Council Memorandum No. 41.* HMSO, London.

Association for the Advancement of Medical Instrumentation (AAMI) (1981) *Process control guidelines for radiation sterilization of medical devices.* AAMI, Arlington, VA.

Ballantyne, B. and Berman, B. (1984) Dermal sensitizing potential of glutaraldehyde: a review and recent observations. *J. Toxicol. Cut. Ocular Toxicol.* **3** 251–262.

Bayliss, C. E. and Waites, W. M. (1979a) The combined effect of hydrogen peroxide and ultraviolet irradiation on bacterial spores. *J. Appl. Bact.* **47** 263–268.

Bayliss, C. E. and Waites, W. M. (1979b) The synergistic killing of spores of *Bacillus subtilis* by hydrogen peroxide and ultra-violet light irradiation. *FEMS Microbiol. Lett.* **5** 331–333.

Bowie, J. H., Kelsey, J. C. and Thompson, R. (1963) The Bowie and Dick autoclave tape test. *Lancet* **i** 586–587.

Bradbury, W. C. (1974) Physical and chemical effects of ionizing radiations on cellulosic systems. In: Gaughran, E. R. L. and Goudie, A. J. (eds), *Sterilization by ionizing radiations.* MultiScience, Montreal, pp. 387–402.

British Pharmacopoeia (1980) Addendum 1983. HMSO, London.

British Pharmacopoeia (1988) HMSO, London.

British Standard 3421 (1961) *Specification for performance of electrically heated sterilizing ovens.* British Standards Institution, London.

British Standard 3970 (1966) *Specification of steam sterilizers, Part 2. Sterilizers for bottled fluids.* British Standards Institution, London.

British Standard 6254 (1982) *Specification for creped sterilization paper for medical use.* British Standards Institution, London.

British Standard 6255 (1982) *Specification for plain sterilization paper for medical use.* British Standards Institution, London.

British Standard 6256 (1982) *Specification for steam sterilization paper bags for medical use.* British Standards Institution, London.

British Standard 5750 (1987) *Part 1. Quality Systems. Specification of design/ development, production, installation and servicing.* British Standards Institution, London.

British Standard 6871 (1987) *Specification for heat sealable pouches and tube material converted from transparent plastics film and paper for steam sterilization for medical use.* British Standards Institution, London.

British Standard 5295 (1989) *Environmental cleanliness in enclosed spaces.* British Standards Institution, London.

British Standard 3970 (in press). *Specifications for sterilizers and disinfectors for medical purposes.* British Standards Institution, London.

Brown, M. R. W. and Gilbert, P. (1977) Increasing the probability of sterility of medicinal products. *J. Pharm. Pharmacol.* **29** 517–523.

Bruch, C. W. (1961) Gaseous sterilization. *Ann. Rev. Microbiol.* **15**, 245–262.

Bruch, C. W. (in press) Role of glutaraldehyde and other liquid chemical sterilants in the processing of new medical devices. *Proceedings of the Kilmer Memorial Conference on the Sterilization of Medical Products,* Moscow, 1989.

Chapiro, A. (1974) Physical and chemical effects of ionizing radiations on polymeric systems. In: Gaughran, E. R. L. and Goudie, A. J. (eds), *Sterilization by ionizing radiations.* Multiscience, Montreal, pp. 367–374.

Christensen, E. A. and Sehested, K. (1964) Radiation resistance of *Streptococcus faecium* and spores of *Bacillus subtilis* dried on various media. *Acta Pathol. Microbiol. Scand.* **62** 448.

Cooper, M. S. (1989) Sterilization: microbiological and aseptic processing. *Update* **89** 6–11.

Corrado, O. J., Osman, J. and Davies, R. J. (1986) Asthma and rhinitis after exposure to glutaraldehyde in endoscopy units. *Human Toxicol.* **5** 325–327.

Crawford, J. S. and George, R. H. (1985). On sterilization of ampoules of local anaesthetic solution. *Anaesthesia* **40** 1235.

Dadd, A. H., Stewart, C. M. and Town, M. M. (1983) A standard monitor for the control of ethylene oxide sterilization cycles. *J. Hyg. Camb.* **91** 93–100.

Darbord, J. C. and Laizier, J. (1987) A theoretical basis for choosing the dose in radiation sterilization of medical supplies. *Int. J. Pharm.* **37** 1–10.

Darmody, E. M., Hughes, K. E. A., Jones, J. D., Prince, D. and Tuke, W. (1961) Sterilization by dry heat. *J. Clin. Pathol.* **14** 38–44.

Deindoerfer, F. H. and Humphrey, A. E. (1959) Analytical method for calculating heat sterilization times. *Appl. Microbiol.* **7** 256–264.

Denyer, S. P. (1987) Principles and practice of sterilization. In: Hugo, W. B. and Russell, A. D. (eds), *Pharmaceutical microbiology* 4th edn. Blackwell Scientific Publications, Oxford, pp. 417–432.

Denyer, S. P., Russell, A. D. and Hugo, W. B. (1982) Filtration sterilization. In: Russell, A. D., Hugo, W. B. and Ayliffe, G. A. J. (eds), *Principles and practice of disinfection, preservation and sterilization.* Blackwell Scientific Publications, Oxford, pp. 569–608.

Department of Health (1980a) *Sterilizers.* Health Technical Memorandum No. 10. HMSO, London.

Department of Health (1980b) *Departmental guidance on some aspects of steriliza-*

tion and disinfection. Health Equipment Information No. 88 (95/80), Department of Health, London.

Department of Health (1981) *Guide to good manufacturing practice for sterile medical devices and surgical products.* HMSO, London.

Department of Health (1983a) *Guide to good pharmaceutical manufacturing practice.* HMSO, London.

Department of Health (1983b) *Specification for performance indicator tapes for porous load steam sterilizers and for packaging tapes for materials to be autoclaved.* TSS/S/330.013. Department of Health, London.

Department of Health (1985) *Specification for biological monitors for ethylene oxide sterilization.* TSS/S/330.012. Department of Health, London.

Department of Health (1986) *Specification for indicator test sheets for use in the Bowie and Dick test (for porous load steam sterilizers).* TSS/S/330/014. Department of Health, London.

Department of Health (1988a) *Specification for total pack systems for use in the Bowie and Dick test (for porous load steam sterilizers).* TSS/S/330.17. Department of Health, London.

Department of Health (1988b) *Evaluation of portable steam sterilizers.* Health Equipment Information 185. Department of Health, London.

Department of Health (1990a) *Guidance on ethylene oxide sterilization.* HMSO, London.

Department of Health (1990b) *Evaluation of transportable steam sterilizers.* Health Equipment Information 196. Department of Health, London.

De Santis, P. and Rudo, V. S. (1986) Validation of steam sterilization in autoclaves. In: Carleton, F. J. and Agalloco, J. P. (eds), *Validation of aseptic pharmaceutical processes.* Marcel Dekker, New York, pp. 279–317.

Dorpema, J. W. (1984) IMO-Gamma. A bioburden based sterilization dose. In: *Proceedings of the Eucomed Conference on Sterilization Validation of Medical Devices and Surgical Products*, 16–17 May, Copenhagen. Eucomed, London, Abstract No. 18.

Doyle, J. E. and Ernst, R. R. (1967) Resistance of *Bacillus subtilis* var *niger* spores occluded in water insoluble crystals to three sterilizing agents. *Appl. Microbiol.* **15** 726–730.

Errico, J. J. (1986) Validation of aseptic processing filters. In: Carleton, F. J. and Agalloco, J. P. (eds), *Validation of aseptic pharmaceutical processes.* Marcel Dekker, New York, pp. 427–472.

Eucomed (1988) *Recommendations for the sterilization of medical devices and surgical products*, revised edn. Eucomed, London.

Gardner, J. and Peel, M. (1986) Sterilization by ionizing radiation. In: *Introduction to sterilization and disinfection.* Churchill Livingstone, Edinburgh, pp. 99–115.

Hardie, I. (1989) A new technology for instrument and equipment sterilization. Proceedings of the Central Sterilizing Club Conference. *J. Institute Sterile Supply Management* (in press).

Health and Safety Executive (1989). Occupational exposure limits. *Guidance Note EH40.* HMSO, London.

HIMA (1982). Microbiological evaluation of filters for sterilizing liquids. *HIMA*

Document No. 3, Vol. 14. Health Industry Manufacturers Association, Washington, DC.

Hoet, P. and Thorogood, D. (1986) Biological monitoring of peracetic acid sterilization. In: *Proceedings of the Eucomed Workshop on Biological Monitoring of Sterilization,* 21–23 April 1986, Kerkrade, The Netherlands. Eucomed, London, pp. 95–99.

Hoffman, R. K. (1971) Toxic gases. In: Hugo, W. B. (ed.) *Inhibition and destruction of the microbial cell.* Academic Press, London, pp. 225–258.

Howard, B. A. and Duberstein, R. (1980) A case of penetration of 0.2 micron rated membrane filters by bacteria. *J. Parent. Drug Assoc.* **34** 95–102.

Hoxey, E. V. (1989) The case for parametric release. In *Proceedings of the Eucomed Conference on Ethylene Oxide Sterilization,* 21–22 April 1989, Paris. Eucomed, London, pp. 25–32.

Hoxey, E. V. (in press) Low temperature steam formaldehyde sterilization. In: *Proceedings of the Kilmer Memorial Conference on the Sterilization of Medical Products,* Moscow, 1989.

Hoxey, E. V., Soper, C. J. and Davies, D. J. G. (1984) The effect of temperature and formaldehyde concentration on the inactivation of *Bacillus stearothermophilis* spores by LTSF, *J. Pharm. Pharmacol.* **36** 60P.

Hurrell, D. J. (1986) UK regulatory standards for monitoring LTSF and EO sterilization. *Proceedings of the Eucomed Workshop on Biological Monitoring of Sterlization,* 21–23 April, Kerkrade, The Netherlands. Eucomed, London, pp. 45–47.

Hurrell, D. J. (1987) Low temperature steam and formaldehyde sterilization (LTSF): its effectiveness and merits. *J. Sterile Services Management* June 40–43.

Jones, L. A., Hoffman, R. K. and Phillips, C. R. (1967) Sporicidal activity of peracetic acid and betapropriolactone at subzero temperatures. *Appl. Microbiol.* **15** 357–362.

Karlson, E. L. (1989) Ozone sterilization. *J. Healthcare Mat. Man.* **7** 42–45.

Knapp, J. E., Rosenblatt, D. H. and Rosenblatt, A. A. (1986) Chlorine dioxide as a gaseous sterilant. *Med. Dev. Diagn. Ind.* **8** 48–50.

Kolb, R. W. and Schneiter, R. (1950) The germicidal and sporicidal efficacy of methyl bromide for *Bacillus anthracis. J. Bacteriol.* **59** 401–411.

Leemhorst, J. G. (1984) Industrial applications of the gamma sterilization process. In: *Proceedings of the Eucomed Conference on Sterilization Validation of Medical Devices and Surgical Products,* 16–17 May 1984, Copenhagen. Eucomed, London, Abstract No. 16.

Leo, F. (1987) Blow–fill–seal aseptic packaging technology. In: Olson, W. P. and Groves, M. J. (eds), *Aseptic pharmaceutical manufacturing technology for the 1990s.* Interpharm Press, Prairie View, IL, pp. 195–218.

Levy, R. V. (1986) Fluid filtration: In: Johnson, P. R. and Scroeder, H. G. (eds), *Liquid Vol. II, ASTM STP 975.* Am. Soc. Testing and Materials, Philadelphia, PA, pp. 80–89.

Ley, F. J. (1984) Radiation sterilization: microbiological aspects. In: *Proceedings of the Eucomed Conference on Sterilization Validation of Medical Devices and*

Surgical Products, 16–17 May 1984, Copenhagen. Eucomed, London, Abstract No. 15.

Ley, F. J. and Tallentire, A. (1964) Sterilization by radiation or heat: some microbiological considerations. *Pharm. J.* **193** 59–61.

Line, S. J. and Pickerill, K. I. (1973) Testing a steam formaldehyde sterilizer for gas penetration efficiency. *J. Clin. Pathol.* **26** 716–720.

Lohmann, S. and Manique, F. (1986) Microwave sterilization of vials. *J. Parent. Sci. Technol.* **40** 25–30.

Marcos, D. and Wiseman, D. (1979). Measurement of formaldehyde concentrations in a subatmospheric steam–formaldehyde autoclave. *J. Clin. Pathol.* **32** 567–575.

Masschelein, W. J. (1979) Industrial applications of chlorine dioxide and sodium chlorite. In: Rice, R. G. (ed.), *Chlorine dioxide, chemistry and environmental impact of oxychlorine compounds*. Ann Arbor Sciences, Ann Arbor, MI, pp. 147–183.

Nordgren, G. (1939) Investigations on the sterilization efficacy of gaseous formaldehyde. *Acta Pathol. Microbiol. Scand.* Suppl. XL 1–165.

Oates, K. (1989). Equipment maintenance. In: *Proceedings of the Eucomed Conference on Ethylene Oxide Sterilization*, 21–22 April 1989, Paris. Eucomed, London, pp. 119–128.

Olson, W. P. (1987) Sterilization of small volume parenterals and therapeutic proteins by filtration. In: Olson, W. P. and Groves, M. J. (eds), *Aseptic pharmaceutical manufacturing technology for the 1990s*. Interpharm Press, Prairie View, IL, pp. 101–150.

Osterberg, B. (1978) Residual glutaraldehyde in plastics and rubbers after exposure to alkalinised glutaraldehyde solution and its importance on blood cell toxicity. *Arch. Pharm. Chem. Sci. Ed.* **6** 241–248.

Parenteral Society (1989) Environmental contamination control practice. *Technical Monograph No. 2*. Parenteral Society, Swindon.

Peebles, R. E., and Anderson, N. R. (1985) Microwave coupled plasma sterilization and depyrogenation. I. System Characteristics. *J. Parent. Sci. Technol.* **39** 2–8.

Pharmaceutical Codex (1979) 11th edn. Pharmaceutical Press, London.

Phillips, C. R. and Kaye, S. (1949) The sterilizing action of gaseous ethylene oxide. *Am. J. Hyg.* **50** 270–279.

Pickerill, J. K., Perera, R., and Knox, R. (1971) Air detection in dressings steam sterilizers. *Lab. Pract.* **20** 406–413.

Placencia, A. M., Oxborrow, G. S. and Peeler, J. T. (1986) Package integrity methodology for testing biobarrier properties of porous packaging. Part 1. Membrane agar plate strike-through method. *Med. Dev. Diag. Ind.* **8** 61–65.

Plester, D. W. (1972) The effects of radiation sterilization on plastics. In: Briggs Phillips, G. and Miller, W. (eds), *Industrial sterilization*. Duke University press, Durham, NC, pp. 375–386.

Plester, D. W. (1974) Physical and chemical effects of ionizing radiations on plastic films, laminates and packaging materials. In: Gaughran, E. R. L. and Goudie, A. J. (eds), *Technical developments and prospects of sterilization by ionizing radiation*. Multiscience, Montreal, pp. 375–402.

Portner, D. M. and Hoffman, R. K. (1968) Sporicidal effect of peracetic acid vapour. *Appl. Microbiol.* **16** 1782–1785.

Reich, R. R. (1989) CFC Control: more than air conditioners and styrofoam cups. *Med. Dev. Diag. Ind.* **11** 10–13.

Rickloff, J. R. and Graham, G. S. (1989) Vapour phase hydrogen peroxide sterilization. *J. Healthcare Mat. Man.* **7** 45–49.

Rohrer, M. D., Terry, M. A., Bulard, R. A., Graves, D. C. and Taylor, E. M. (1986) Microwave sterilization of hydrophilic contact lenses. *Am. J. Ophthalmol.* **101** 49–57.

Russell, A. D. (1982) *The destruction of bacterial spores.* Academic Press, London.

Sato, H., Kidaka, T. and Hori, M. (1985) Sterilization of therapeutic immunoadsorbents with aqueous propylene oxide solution. *Int. J. Artif. Organs* **8** 109–114.

Saylor, M. C. (in press) Developments in radiation equipment including the application of machine-generated X-rays to medical product sterilization. In: *Proceedings of the Kilmer Memorial Conference on the Sterilization of Medical Products*, Moscow, 1989.

Staquet, M. (1969) Water sterilization and chlorine dioxide. *Tech. Eau Assainissement* **276** 35–44.

Stoddart, G. M. (1989) Ozone as a sterilizing agent. *J. Healthcare Mat. Man.* **7** 42–43.

Stumbo, C. R. (1973). *Thermobacteriology in food processing*, 2nd edn. Academic Press, New York.

Svendsen, E. B. (1984) Radiation sterilization by accelerators and their process control. In: *Proceedings of the Eucomed Conference on Sterilization Validation of Medical Devices and Surgical Products*, 16–17 May, Copenhagen. Eucomed, London, Abstract No. 17.

Tensmeyer, L., Wright, P. E., Fegenbush, D. O. and Snapp, S. W. (1981) Sterilization of glass containers by laser initiated plasmas. *J. Parent. Sci. Technol.* **35** 93–96.

UK Panel on Gamma and Electron Irradiation (1987) Radiation sterilization dose. *Radiat. Phys. Chem.* **29** 87–88.

Wallhaeusser, K.-H. (1979) Is removal of microorganisms by filtration really a sterilizing method? *J. Parent. Drug Assoc.* **33** 156–170.

Wallhaeusser, K.-H. (1983) Durchwachs- und durchblasseffekte bei langzeit-steril-filtrationsprozessen. *Pharm. Ind.* **45** 527–531.

Zinnbauer, F. E. (1985) Ultraviolet water disinfection comes of age. *Pharm. Eng.* Mar/April 36–43.

9

Assurance of sterility by validation of the sterilization process

K. Haberer
Hoechst AG, 6230 Frankfurt am Main 80, Postfach 80–03–20, West Germany, and
K.-H. Wallhaeusser
6238 Hofheim a.Ts., Lessingstrasse 20, West Germany

1   STERILITY AND ASSURANCE OF STERILITY

Sterility, the absence of any micro-organism capable of reproduction, is an absolute requirement which cannot be compromised. For the purpose of sterility assurance, however, a maximum acceptable number of unsterile units is usually defined to describe the required safety of the sterilization process. For pharmaceuticals sterilized within their final container, the following definition is given by major pharmacopoeiae: the procedures and precautions employed should be such as to give a theoretical level of not more than one living micro-organism in 1×10^6 sterilized units of the final product (European Pharmacopoeia 1980). It is generally accepted that terminally sterilized injectable articles or critical devices purporting to be sterile, when processed in the autoclave, attain at least a 10^{-6} microbial survivor probability (United States Pharmacopeia 1990).

Such a level of sterility assurance can only be derived from theoretical calculations. Even though the definition for sterile products given in the European Pharmacopoeia (1980) asks for compliance with the test for sterility this test cannot, for statistical reasons, contribute in any significant way to the assurance of sterility at the required safety level (Spicher and Peters 1975). Three million units of an article would have to be tested with not more than one positive result to demonstrate sterility in 1×10^6 units with 95% confidence (Fig. 1).

Furthermore the test for sterility in itself consitutes an added source of error. For testing sterile articles the protective sealed container has to be penetrated with the inherent risk of introducing contamination. The uncertainity as to whether a contaminant detected during a sterility test resulted from a true lack of sterility or was introduced during the test led to the formulation of detailed retesting procedures in various pharmacopoeiae (European Pharmacopoeia 1980; British Pharmacopoeia 1988; United States Pharmacopeia 1990).

Such retesting procedures further reduce the statistical significance of the sterility test and are therefore questionable. The Food and Drug Association of the USA (FDA 1987) accepts sterility retests only if it can be shown during a comprehensive review of all circumstances of production and testing that the first positive test was not related to the product itself.

In consequence, for disposable plastic material, sterilized by irradiation, a sterility test is no longer considered mandatory in the UK (Bishop 1973). Further, 'no reliance can be placed on sterility tests performed on a small number of randomly obtained samples by personnel not routinely engaged in this form of testing. The

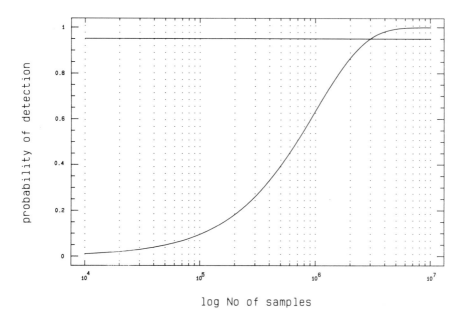

Fig. 1 — Theoretical number of samples required to detect one unsterile unit per 10^6 units purporting to be sterile. The figure is based on the expression

$$p = 1 - (1-q)^n$$

where
p = probability of detection
q = relative frequency of contaminated units (10^{-6})
n = number of samples used in the test.

errors in the test will greatly outweigh the probability of detecting an unsterile article' (White 1973).

There is no good reason why these arguments should only be applied to articles sterilized by irradiation. For all other forms of sterilized products at the expected safety level of one unsterile article in a total of 10^6, errors of even well-trained personnel will certainly be far more frequent than the probability of detecting an unsterile article. Thus, meaningful sterility assurance cannot be based solely on sterility testing. Instead, any process designed to manufacture sterile goods has to be meticulously validated. Manufacturing area, equipment, raw materials, operators and process conditions have to be kept under careful surveillance. Validation of sterilization methods employed should be part of a comprehensive validation programme.

2   REGULATORY REQUIREMENTS

Validation of sterilization methods today is an absolute requirement in numerous official texts: 'Each sterilization process should be validated' (European Pharmaco-poeia 1980). Similarly, the FDA (1988) states in the text of *Good manufacturing practice* (cGMP) regulations: 'Appropriate written procedures designed to prevent microbiological contamination of drug products purporting to be sterile, shall be established and followed. Such procedures shall include validation of any sterilization process.'

The measures to be taken for validation are clearly and comprehensively summarized in the British Pharmacopoeia (1988).

> 'In establishing any process of sterilization that is applied to a product in its final container it is essential to take into account the non-uniformity of the physical and, where relevant, chemical condition within the sterilizing chamber. The location within the sterilizing chamber that is least accessible to the sterilizing agent must be determined for each loading configuration of each type and size of container or package (for example the coolest location in an autoclave). The minimum lethality delivered by the sterilizing cycle and its reproducibility must also be determined in order to ensure that all loads will consistently receive the specified treatment.
>
> Having established a process, knowledge of its performance in routine use should, wherever possible, be gained by monitoring and suitably recording the physical and, where relevant, chemical conditions achieved within the load in the chamber throughout each sterilizing cycle.'

Thus, wherever validation requirements are given in regulatory tests, the same goals are to be met:

(a) *Suitability of the process*
   — The process must be compatible with the items to be sterilized.
   — The process must be effective to inactivate or remove all micro-organisms to the required safety level.
(b) *Uniformity of the process*
   — All parts of the item to be sterilized must receive the specified minimal treatment.
   — No part must receive a treatment destructive to the item.
(c) *Reproducibility of the process*
   — Measurements and recordings of suitable parameters must fully document the reproducibility of the process.
   — Any conditions rendering the process ineffective must be recognized, and procedures established to prevent the release of product so affected.

3   GENERAL PRINCIPLES OF VALIDATION

In order to demonstrate the correct performance of sterilization processes, two concepts are used which yield different types of information:

(a) Measurement and recording of the required physical or chemical conditions reached throughout the sterilization cycle within every part of the load.
(b) Observation of the effect exhibited by a chosen sterilization cycle on indicator organisms or indicator substances.

Both principles are often applied simultaneously, and the combined information obtained can be condensed into a comprehensive scheme of validation. This section reviews the main pharmacopoeial sterilization methods and highlights those features which need to be considered in a validation programme; a detailed discussion of sterilizer design and operation can be found in Chapter 8.

3.1 Sterilization by heating in an autoclave

Sterilization in an autoclave is based upon highly efficient heat transfer from saturated steam to autoclave load, combined in some cases with a hydrating effect caused by condensate which is formed during the process. Heat transfer is maximum if steam is kept along the phase separation line of the water–steam phase diagram (Fig. 2). Neither unsaturated steam–air mixtures nor overheated steam exhibit the same favourable conditions (see Chapter 8).

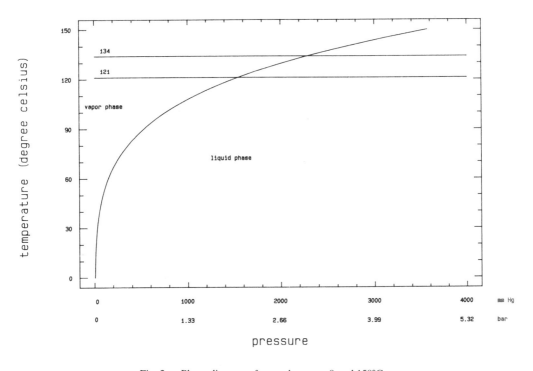

Fig. 2 — Phase diagram of water between 0 and 150°C.

It is, therefore, critical to maintain water–steam equilibrium conditions at every point in the autoclave chamber throughout the sterilization cycle. For the empty autoclave chamber, this can be easily demonstrated by recording temperature curves at various points within the chamber throughout a test cycle by means of thermal sensors such as thermocouples or resistance temperature devices (RTD). Frequently, depending on the type of equipment used, the pressure within the chamber is also recorded (e.g. autoclaves with vacuum cycles or gravity displacement cycles). Usually, the coldest point in the unloaded autoclave should be within the pipe leading to the steam trap.

3.1.1 Types of autoclave used

For validation of loaded autoclaves it can be far more difficult to demonstrate homogeneous conditions. Depending on the type of the load different types of autoclaves employing different types of cycles can be used. The correct choice of a suitable autoclave cycle constitutes an important part of validation.

3.1.1.1 Gravity displacement cycle

For autoclave loads with non-porous materials of simple geometry the classical gravity displacement principle may be used. Steam is injected at the top of the chamber and displaces the cold air which, due to its heavier specific weight, remains at the bottom of the chamber and exits through the trap.

The steam injection rate is critical in this type of process because turbulence may lead to trapped air pockets within the load. Conversely, if displacement is too slow the air will be heated and, by losing specific weight, will then diffuse into the steam, leading to less efficient air–steam mixtures.

For all loads with complicated geometry or porous surfaces where air can easily be trapped, complete air displacement is very difficult to achieve.

Validation must rely on a large number of individual measurements distributed within the load. Material and geometry for every type of autoclave load must be stated in written procedures and strictly adhered to, in order to assure reproducible conditions between validation runs and during routine operation.

3.1.1.2 Pre-vacuum cycles

Penetration of the load by saturated steam can be more effectively secured by pre-vacuum or fractionated pre-vacuum cycles. Before saturated steam is injected into the chamber, air is removed by a vacuum pump. A vacuum as low as 55 mbar (5.5 kPa) applied for 8–10 minutes may be needed for some porous loads in order to remove effectively about 95% of the air from the chamber (Wallhaeusser 1988); fractionated vacuum cycles have therefore been developed to remove air by successive vacuum cycles and steam pulses.

Pre-vacuum systems are especially suited for porous material and loads of complicated geometry which are not sensitive to vacuum treatment (e.g. surgical dressings). Liquids may evaporate during the vacuum cycles and are therefore less suited or even unsuited for treatment in pre-vacuum cycles.

For validation it is important that pressure along with temperature be recorded. Except for highly porous loads, steam distribution presents less of a problem. Nevertheless the temperature at several points within the load should be measured, and a fixed loading pattern established.

3.1.1.3 Air–steam mixture cycles

Whenever liquids, sealed in their final container, are to be sterilized a situation quite different from other autoclave cycles arises. The headspace within every unit forms a gas pocket which cannot be displaced or otherwise removed. If the autoclave is operated with saturated steam, a differential pressure between the outside and inside of the individual containers may be generated, with a risk of bursting containers (Wallhaeusser 1988). Therefore, for sterilizing a liquid in sealed containers steam–air mixtures are often used to generate a higher chamber pressure, a technique known as air ballasting (Chapter 8). For the purpose of sterilization the autoclave chamber merely serves as a steam jacket. Temperature recordings thus have to be taken from reference containers of the same size and configuration as the actual containers of the load. Such reference containers should be distributed throughout the load to check for temperature differences, which can easily arise if the air–steam mixture in the chamber is not sufficiently mixed.

3.2 Sterilization by dry heat

Sterilization by dry heat must overcome the poor heat transfer capacity and conductivity of air. Therefore, higher temperatures and/or longer sterilization times are required as compared to the more efficient autoclave process. For heat-resistant articles sensitive to moisture, dry heat is nevertheless the method of choice. If the dry-heat sterilizer is operated at temperatures above 250°C, bacterial lipopolysaccharides (pyrogens) are destroyed under highly effective sterilization conditions (Wegel 1973; Wallhaeusser 1988).

Several types of sterilizer are used in the pharmaceutical industry which require different considerations for validation.

3.2.1 Forced-convection batch sterilizers

For batch sterilizers, homogeneous heat distribution within the chamber is difficult to achieve. Heated air should be blown through a high-efficiency particulate air (HEPA) filter to minimize particle contamination and distributed into the chamber via a baffle system. For validation studies, a large number of thermal sensors have to be distributed within the chamber and throughout the load to identify cold points. Usually several patterns of thermal sensor distribution should be used during validation in order to characterize heat distribution in a load as precisely as possible. Thermal sensors must be placed within each type of container to be sterilized in order to demonstrate sufficient heat transfer under all circumstances.

Rearrangement of the load may alter convection patterns of the air considerably. Therefore exact loading patterns must be established, validated and strictly adhered to.

3.2.2 Dry-heat sterilizing tunnels

Dry-heat sterilizing tunnels usually operate at temperatures well above 250°C. Items to be sterilized are placed on a conveyor belt. During passage through the heating zone high temperatures of usually more than 300°C are reached for a few minutes in every item. Heat transfer is achieved by radiation in infrared tunnels or by forced convection in HEPA-filtered laminar-flow tunnels (Wegel 1973). Ventilation with HEPA-filtered air is employed in most sterilizers to cool the sterilized goods.

In addition to temperature probes which should be placed all across the conveyor belt, reproducibility of belt speed and integrity of HEPA filters are considered critical parameters for validation.

3.3   Gaseous sterilization

The use of toxic gases to sterilize heat-sensitive goods is an attractive concept from a technological point of view, although there are concerns over their safety in use (Chapter 8).

For validation of gas sterilizers loading patterns have to be established and strictly adhered to. Temperature and relative humidity should be measured at various geometrical positions within the load. The measurement of gas concentration within the load is, however, difficult, although in theory it should be possible to install valved tubes for withdrawal of gas from within the load. Withdrawal of gas, however, creates a pressure differential within the chamber, thus leading to unrealistic conditions during validation as compared to routine operation.

For the validation of gas sterilizers, bioindicators are still the most effective and widely used method and their use is considered mandatory in the European Pharmacopoeia (1980).

3.4   Sterilization by ionizing radiation

Radiation is a highly effective means of sterilization and is used with increasing frequency. However, chemical changes are caused in many products by reaction with free radicals generated by the ionizing radiation. In order to avoid such radiation damage, radiation sterilization can only be used if all parts of the product have been demonstrated to be compatible with this kind of treatment at the required energy level. A standard sterilizing dose of 2.5 Mrad (25 kGy) has been widely accepted.

For operational qualification loading patterns have to be established and radiation penetration determined by use of dosimeters distributed within the articles. Configuration of the load should be such that a minimal dose of 2.5 Mrad (or another suitable dose established by bioburden studies) is delivered to every point in the load while the maximum dose is still compatible with the product to be sterilized.

Bioindicators should only be used to determine inactivation characteristics in a product newly validated for radiation sterilization. For operational validation or revalidation, dosimetry is a much more reliable method.

3.5   Sterilization by membrane filtration

Sterilization by passage through a micro-organism-retentive filter is a commonly used method for heat-sensitive fluids. In contrast to all other sterilization methods which inactivate living micro-organisms within their environment, filtration is a physical process, removing contaminants from the fluid (see Chapter 7).

For validation purposes, the retentive capacity of the filter, the accuracy of pore size during all conditions employed in the process, and integrity of the filter assembly are key factors with respect to sterilization (Wallhaeusser 1979, 1982, 1988). Inertness of the filter and its housing toward the processed fluid and flow rate are other important considerations.

4   METHODS USED FOR VALIDATION

4.1   Physical methods for validation

4.1.1   Measuring devices for heat

For heat sterilizers, including autoclaves and dry-heat sterilizers, determination and recording of heat distribution within the chamber is of prime importance. The most commonly used equipment consists of resistance temperature detectors (RTD) or thermocouple measuring systems.

RTDs are most commonly used as temperature standards for calibration studies, while thermocouple systems connected to multichannel electronic recording instruments are best suited for heat penetration studies. With thermocouple elements, care should be taken to use only high-grade thermocouple wire, if possible from the same production lot, in order to avoid errors due to non-interchangeable elements. The entire system should be calibrated before each run to ensure a measurement accuracy of at least ±0.1°C at 120°C, ±0.2°C at 200°C and ±0.4°C at 300°C. Calibration should be repeated at the process temperature after each use to verify proper operation during the validation. A detailed description of thermocouple installation and calibration has been given by Kemper (1986).

4.1.2 Pressure sensors

Pressure sensors should be chosen to fit the purpose of the instrument. For autoclaves it is specified in Deutsche Industrie Norm (1986): 'Pressure gauges should show zero pressure at atmospheric pressure with a meter range beween −1 and +5 bar (−100 and +500 kPa), the scale being not wider than 0.2 bar (20 kPa).' The precision of recording should be better than ±5% at a working pressure of 2 bar (200 kPa).

4.1.3 Physical methods for determining filter integrity

Filter integrity is usually determined by suitable methods such as bubble point, pressure hold, or diffusion rate procedures. Measurement of bubble point determines at which differential pressure the liquid contained in the weakest point (i.e. largest pore) of the matrix of a wetted filter is driven out. Besides the nominal pore size, the bubble point is also dependent on the filter material, the wetting fluid and temperature. Diffusional flow measurements determine the flow of a test gas through a wetted filter at lower differential pressure than in the bubble point test. Results are dependent on the thickness and structure of the filter, the temperature, and interactions between test gas and test fluid (Wallhaeusser 1988).

If the data obtained from these tests are in accordance with the known characteristics of the filter type used, the filter assembly can be assumed to be integral and correctly assembled. Integrity data should be obtained for every filter assembly before and after a filtration process is performed (Wallhaeusser 1982, 1988).

4.1.4 Dosimeters for radiation sterilization

Perspex (polymethacrylate) strips 1–3 mm thick are most frequently used as dosimeters. Perspex shows dose-dependent colouration when exposed to γ-radiation. The dose can then be deduced from photometric determination of the colour.

Dosimetry for radiation processing is discussed in detail by McLaughlin et al. (1989).

4.2 Bioindicators for the validation of sterilizers

Bioindicators are preparations of micro-organisms inoculated into the product, adsorbed onto paper strips or glass beads, or suspended in liquid medium and sealed in ampoules for steam sterilization. The bacteria chosen are specifically selected for their high resistance against particular sterilization principles (Table 1; see also Chapter 7).

If a specified high concentration of these organisms is inactivated or eliminated, the sterilization process has been demonstrated to be effective. While this procedure seems to be very convincing at first sight, many questions arise if the approach is considered in detail.

Table 1 — Bioindicators for sterilization procedures

Procedure	Species	Strain	Required by
Steam	B. stearothermophilus	ATCC 7953	EP 1980
			BP 1988
			USP 1990
		ATCC 12980	USP 1990
	Cl. sporogenes	ATCC 7955	BP 1988
Dry heat	B. subtilis var. niger	ATCC 9372	EP 1980
			USP 1990
			BP 1988
Gas	B. subtilis var. niger	ATCC 9372	EP 1980
			USP 1990
			BP 1988
	B. stearothermophilus	ATCC 9753	BP 1988
Radiation	B. pumilus	ATCC 14884	EP 1980
			BP 1988
	B. cereus	SSI C 1/1	BP 1988
	B. sphaericus	SSI C_1 A	BP 1988
Membrane filtration	Pseudomonas diminuta	ATCC 19146	HIMA (1982)

Abbreviations
ATCC: American Type Culture Collection. EP 1980:European Pharmacopoeia (1980). USP 1990: United States Pharmacopeia (1990). BP 1988: British Pharmacopoeia (1988). HIMA: Health Industry Manufacturers Association.

4.2.1 Bioindicators for steam sterilization
Bioindicators for steam sterilization are spores of *Bacillus stearothermophilus*. For these spores, a decimal reduction time at 121°C (D_{121}-value) of about 1.5 minutes is usually given in textbooks, and the temperature difference leading to a tenfold change in the *D*-value (*z*-value; Pflug 1973) may be taken as 6°C (Wallhaeuser 1988)†.

Inactivation of spores by heat is considered to follow first-order kinetics (Chapter 7). Thus for a bioindicator containing 10^6 of the above reference *B. stearothermophilus* spores, after 9 minutes of treatment at 121°C, the average indicator would be assumed to contain $10^0 = 1$ surviving organism. If a statistical distribution of survivors is assumed, according to Poisson's distribution (equation 1) 37% of all indicators are expected to be sterile, 37% to contain just 1 survivor, 18% to contain 2 survivors and 8% to contain more than 2 survivors. After 10.5 minutes of treatment the respective expectations are: 90% sterile and 10% non-sterile, containing 1 or more survivors (Lorenz 1988).

---

† A range of *D*- and *z*-values have been described for *B. stearothermophilus* (e.g. Molin 1982), the values being dependent upon the strain and status of the organism, its environment, and the temperature range employed.

$$P_{(x=k)} = e^{-\mu} \cdot \frac{\mu^k}{k!} \tag{1}$$

where

e = base of natural logarithm

k = expected value

μ = median value

$P_{(x=k)}$ = probability of occurrence of units containing the expected number of $x = k$ viable cells.

The distribution of survivors within the autoclave is expected to be random if homogeneous conditions exist within the chamber. In order to demonstrate homogeneous conditions within the autoclave, at least ten indicators would have to be located at each measuring point to ensure that statistical distribution could be differentiated from true deviations.

In theory, for *B. stearothermophilus* with a z-value of 6°C, a 1°C drop of temperature to 120°C would lead to a D-value of 2.2 minutes, and thus after 9 minutes of autoclaving to a median survivor probability of $10^{1.9}$ within every indicator. The probability of detecting a bioindicator without surviving spores would be highly unlikely ($P_0 = 3.2 \times 10^{-34}$). At 10.5 minutes $10^{0.8}$ survivors would be expected with a probability $P_0 = 1.8 \times 10^{-3}$ to detect a negative one. These figures can clearly be contrasted with the expectations at the correct temperature. However, it should be kept in mind that bioindicators are not precision instruments. Actual spore numbers and D-values as well as z-values vary with pretreatment or storage conditions of the indicators. For *B. stearothermophilus*, D_{120}/D_{121}-values have been reported to vary between 1 and 5.8 (Molin 1982). Since determination of these values is only possible by destructive treatment for any individual indicator, the uniformity of these critical parameters can only be determined by statistical studies to be conducted on every lot of indicators and for every validation experiment, which is tedious and time consuming.

For these reasons, it is far easier and at least as reliable to determine the performance of a sterilizer by carefully designed and recorded physical measurements, compared with bioindicator studies. Bioindicators should only be used to determine autoclave performance where physical measurements are not feasible, for example in equipment not designed to allow access to thermal sensors. When bioindicators are employed, data should not be over-emphasized.

However, D-values of bioindicators are strongly influenced by the environment in which they are sterilized. Valuable information for establishing a suitable sterilization cycle can be gained with bioindicators by comparing inactivation rates of the indicator organisms in a new product with those in water. If the D-value in the product as derived from such studies is different from the D-value found in water the sterilization time may have to be adjusted. In this situation, either longer or shorter sterilization times may be required when compared to standard recommendations. Requalification of a sterilization procedure in this way would only become necessary should the product formulation be subject to change.

4.2.2 Bioindicators for dry-heat sterilization

The use of bioindicators for validation of dry-heat sterilizers is limited to forced-convection batch sterilizers. Other types of dry-heat sterilizers usually operate at such high temperatures that bacterial inactivation kinetics become practically impossible to follow due to the very fast inactivation of bioindicators (Wallhaeusser 1988).

An alternative biologically based method of validation has been developed for these high temperatures which yields more useful information. Bacterial lipopoly-saccharides (endotoxins) are inactivated by dry heat at temperatures above 200°C (Wegel 1973; Wallhaeusser 1988) and their inactivation kinetics have been described by Tsuji and Harrison (1978). Glassware can be impregnated with endotoxins and their inactivation rate used as a measure of the correct performance of a dry-heat sterilizer. It is important, however, to standardize carefully both the amount of endotoxin adsorbed as well as the procedures for desorption and recovery (Jensch *et al.* 1987).

For forced-convection batch sterilizers operating at 160–200°C bioindicators can be applied (Table 1) but the same factors as for steam sterilization should be taken into consideration.

4.2.3 Bioindicators for gaseous sterilization

For gaseous sterilization, physical measurements of gas concentrations within a given load are difficult to perform. Therefore, the use of bioindicators (Table 1) is prescribed by the European Pharmacopoeia (1980) and United States Pharmacopeia (1990) for every cycle and their use should be regarded more favourably than in the more easily and precisely monitored heat sterilizers. It is clear, however, that the same statistical considerations apply as in all other cases. Mapping of the exact conditions in the sterilizer is difficult by means of bioindicator exposure.

4.2.4 Bioindicators for radiation sterilization

Radiation is easily and precisely monitored by exposure of dosimeters within the load. Bioindicator validation should only be used for initial characterization of inactivation rates within a given product.

4.2.5 Bioindicators for micro-organism-retentive filters

The micro-organism-retentive capacity of a filter can only be determined by destructive testing. *Pseudomonas diminuta*, a Gram-negative rod-shaped bacterium, is generally employed as the bioindicator test organism for filters with a nominal pore size of 0.2 μm (Table 1). It has been chosen because of its relatively small dimensions of 0.5 × 1.0–4.0 μm (Palleroni 1984). The dimensions of bacteria are, however, strongly dependent on their growth conditions (Wallhaeusser 1979, 1982); fast-growing forms differ in appearance from slower-growing or starved forms. When validating filters, it is necessary to verify by microscopy that the challenge used predominantly consists of single cells with dimensions at the lower end of the ones given above. For the validation of 0.45-μm filters, *Serratia marcescens* ATCC 14756 is used.

A detailed arrangement for a bacterial challenge test is described by Health Industry Manufacturers Association (HIMA) (1982). In principle, filters are challenged with about 10^7 organisms per square centimetre of effective filter area. The filtrate is then analysed for bacteria passing through the filter (Wallhaeusser 1982, 1988). Once a filter is loaded with 10^7 organisms per square centimetre of effective filter area the test should be considered complete. While it is usually possible to retain some flow after depositing further organisms on the filter, such multiple layers of cells on the surface do not provide significant information on the additional retentive capacity of the filter.

4.3 Chemical methods for monitoring sterilizers

Chemical monitoring of sterilization processes is based on the ability of heat, steam, sterilant gases and ionizing radiation to alter the chemical and/or physical characteristics of a variety of chemical substances (Denyer 1987). Ideally this change should not occur until the sterilization cycle has been satisfactorily completed, but in practice this condition is rarely met. Thus, with the exception of radiation dosimeters (section 4.1.4), these devices should never be used as sole monitors of a sterilization process although they may be used in conjunction with other physical or biological methods. Again with the exception of radiation dosimeters, such devices would not be used for the validation of sterilizer efficacy since the changes recorded do not necessarily correspond to microbiocidal activity. Nevertheless, they do serve as useful indicators of the conditions prevailing at the coolest or most inaccessible points of a sterilizer or load, and also offer a mechanism to differentiate between processed and unprocessed products (see section 1, Chapter 8).

5 VALIDATION PLANS FOR STERILIZERS

For all sterilization procedures a coherent validation plan should be developed. This plan should include:

Qualification of the sterilizer

(a) installation qualification;
(b) operation qualification.

Product validation

(a) compatibility of the sterilization process with a given product;
(b) development of the sterilization cycle.

Process validation

(a) specification of data to be routinely collected and evaluated;
(b) revalidation, i.e. specification of frequency and types of operation qualification to be repeated at regular intervals.

5.1 Qualification of sterilizers

Before any sterilizer is taken into routine use in a production process, correct functioning of the equipment has to be verified.

5.1.1 *Installation qualification*

After installation of any sterilizer correct installation of all parts, calibration of all measuring instruments, and compliance of equipment performance with equipment specifications has to be demonstrated and certified. This is usually done by the supplier in collaboration with the user of the equipment.

Installation qualification has to be repeated, in part at least, whenever significant technical manipulations occur during maintenance or modification of the equipment.

5.1.2 *Operation qualification*

For any given type of load, the reliable performance of the equipment has to be demonstrated in at least three consecutive runs. It must also be shown that the expected sterilizing activity is reached within every part of the load, and that no conditions are attained which are incompatible with the article to be sterilized.

For autoclaves and other heat sterilizers, this is done by heat penetration studies with thermocouples placed at suitable positions within chamber and load. The number and position of the thermocouples is determined by type and configuration of the load as well as by the type of instrument and sterilization cycle used. For gas sterilizers, relative humidity and temperature should be measured by physical sensors distributed at suitable positions within chamber and load. Bioindicators distributed in the load must be used to verify sterilizing conditions at all positions within the load (European Pharmacopoeia 1980). Penetration of ionizing radiation within a load is most reliably monitored by the distribution of sufficient dosimeters within the load.

Operation qualification of sterlizing filters is usually based on integrity testing, pressure differential and flow rate measurements (Wallhaeusser 1982, 1988). It should be noted that fluids sterilized by passing through a membrane filter are usually exposed to the environment during further processing. In such cases, environmental control and proper validation of the aseptic handling area should be considered as an integral part of the sterile filtration process (Wallhaeusser 1988).

5.2 Product validation

5.2.1 *Compatibility of the sterilization process*

For each product to be sterilized, careful consideration should be given to the suitability of the proposed sterilization method. For heat-stable products, processing in the autoclave within the final container usually will be the method of choice. However, it must be confirmed that all parts of the container are equally resistant to the autoclave conditions and that product stability is not impaired. Also, as mentioned earlier, the type of autoclave cycle must be considered, depending on whether the product is sealed in the final container, its penetrability by steam, and its resistance to vacuum. The suitability of the autoclaving process should be demonstrated in experiments conducted during product development. These experiments should also include inactivation studies of bioindicators in the product itself, to elucidate possible influences (positive or negative) of the product on inactivation rates.

For the highly reactive sterilizing gases, careful consideration should be given to possible damage to the product due to reactions with the sterilant. Another concern lies in the retention of the toxic gases or degradation products thereof within the product. Degassing procedures must be validated and carefully adhered to.

In radiation sterilization, possible radiolysis products caused by reactions with highly reactive free radicals have to be carefully investigated. While some radiolysis products themselves may present a risk to the consumer, others, like those causing discolouration, may be merely aesthetic in nature, but may still lead to the decision that the sterilization method cannot be used.

The main consideration with filtration processes will be one of practicality with flow rates, filter fouling rates and longevity being the main issues. Product interations with the filter (and housings) may, however, become a problem, for example with some of the recently available charged filter materials (Wallhaeusser 1988). Also, if non-aqueous systems are to be filtered, filter compatibility with the solvent must be considered.

5.2.2 Development of the sterilization cycle

Three different types of approach can be chosen to develop a sterilization procedure.

(a) If the product is resistant towards the chosen conditions of sterilization by a wide margin a standard overkill method will normally be chosen. Standard overkill methods are designed to kill highly resistant test organisms by at least 8–10 orders of magnitude. For example, *B. stearothermophilus* has a theoretical logarithmic reduction time (*D*-value) of 1.5 minutes at 121°C. After application of standard autoclave conditions of 15 minutes at 121°C in saturated steam a theoretical reduction of *B. stearothermophilus* spores of 10 orders of magnitude should be achieved. If this overkill method is used, no further biological validation is required once the initial inactivation rates of *B. stearothermophilus* in the product have been investigated.

(b) For a heat-sensitive product, however, heat exposure has to be minimized, and non-standard conditions may have to be chosen. Under these circumstances, an attempt will usually be made to achieve an equivalent level of kill from the new conditions as from a standard procedure.

Equivalent sterilization conditions can only be calculated for a given micro-organism with known *D*- and *z*-values. Usually, the formula (2) is used for equivalence calculations:

$$F_T^z = \frac{F_{121}^z}{10^{(T-121)/z}} \ (\text{min}) \tag{2}$$

where
F = effectiveness
T = process temperature.

For *B. stearothermophilus* with a *z*-value of 6°C (see section 4.2.1) and an inactivation of 10 decades at 121°C (*D*-value of 1.5 min) an equivalence calculation for 118°C would be as follows:

$$F_{118}^6 = \frac{15}{10^{(118-121)/6}} = \frac{15}{10^{-1/2}} = 47.43 \text{ (min)} \tag{3}$$

In some cases, a short exposure of the product to higher temperatures, e.g. 1.5 minutes at 127°C, while having an equivalent sterilizing effect, may be less destructive to the product when compared with a standard treatment. This is the basis of ultra-high-temperature (UHT) treatment of milk. A further comparison of time–temperature relationships is given in section 5.1.4 of Chapter 7, and the non-equivalence of standard autoclaving protocols is shown in Chapter 8 (section 3.1.3).

(c) Alternative cycles, based on product bioburden determinations, constitute a further possibility to reduce the input of heat. For a given product, the maximum number and heat resistance of micro-organisms are determined on a number of lots. These bioburden data are then used to calculate the sterilization conditions required to reach the safety level of 1×10^{-6} unsterile units.

For example, if it is shown that the maximum number of heat-resistant spores is one in 10 ml of a parenteral solution of 10 ml volume, only six decimal reductions are required to reach the necessary safety level. A conservative approach would be to assume that all spores might be *B. stearothermophilus*. Sterilization time at standard conditions would then be 9 minutes. If an alternative cycle like that described is chosen, the pre-sterilization bioburden of each lot has to be determined retrospectively to demonstrate the validity of the chosen sterilization process.

For liquids sterilized in large volumes, it may be useful to calculate a total effective sterilization time by summing the sterilizing effect of the temperatures reached during heating and cooling down of the product. The mathematical expression used for such calculations is given in formula (4) and is discussed in Chapter 7 (section 5.1.3).

$$F_T^z \int_{t=0}^{t=x} 10^{(T-121)/z} \, dt \tag{4}$$

where

$t = 0 = $ beginning of sterilization time
$t = x = $ end of sterilization time.

Calculations can be based on temperature readouts taken every minute as described by Patashnik (1953), or else automatic F calculators can be used to do the integration.

5.3 Process validation: computerized control and monitoring of sterilization methods

Computerized multichannel recording systems are capable of handling a wealth of data and using these systems it is possible to map exactly the development of relevant conditions at various locations within the sterilizer. Figure 3 shows temperature recordings at 12 different locations within an autoclave during a validation cycle of the loaded chamber. Temperature deviations can easily be detected as demonstrated in a load of complicated geometry with an unsuitable sterilization cycle (gravity displacement) in validation experiments (Fig. 4). If measuring sensors are correctly placed within the sterilizer data are automatically processed and recorded; this can be of great value in demonstrating the safety and reliability of a sterilization procedure.

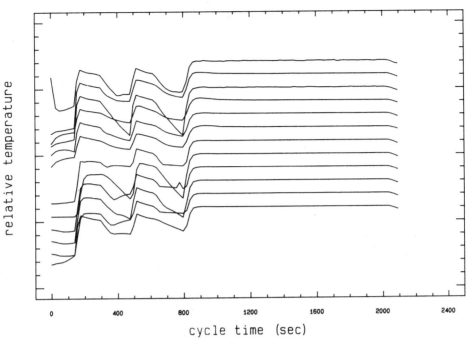

Fig. 3 — Temperature distribution in an autoclave operated with a fractionated pre-vacuum cycle. Continuous temperature recordings were taken from 12 different thermocouples within the loaded chamber. To allow comparison of the individual curves in the plot, a 10°C increment was added to the values registered by thermocouple 2, a 20°C increment to the values registered by thermocouple 3 and so on.

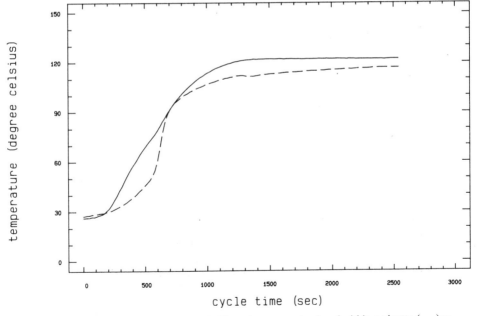

Fig. 4 — Temperature deviation recorded by a thermocouple placed within a pipette (- - -) as compared to the correct sterilization temperature recorded in the autoclave chamber (——). The gravity displacement cycle used in the experiment was demonstrated to be unable to displace the air trapped in a geometrically complicated load.

6 GENERAL VALIDATION PROGRAMME

Validation of a sterilization cycle should not be seen as an isolated exercise but always as an integral part of a general validation programme. An example of such a programme for a standard product (steam-sterilizable aqueous solution in 10 ml ampoules) is given in Table 2. A programme which is developed to the specific requirements of the product is thus to be recommended as the basis of validated production.

Table 2 — General validation plan (microbiology)

Product: aqueous solution, ampoules 10 ml, sterile
Sterilization: steam 121°C

1. Qualification

Item	Parameter	Requirements	Frequency
Raw materials	Bioburden	$<10^3$ c.f.u. g^{-1} or ml^{-1} $<10^2$ c.f.u. g^{-1} or ml^{-1} (in some countries) Absence of specific pathogens	5 lots initially, then random samples
First cycle rinsing water	Bioburden	$<10^2$ c.f.u. ml^{-1} Absence of specific pathogens	Weekly
Process water and final cycle rinsing water	Bioburden	<10 c.f.u. per 100 ml Bacterial endotoxins <0.25 EU ml^{-1}	Weekly
Production area Set-up	Air-locks	Separate area for preparation and filling Entry of personnel only via air locks Entry of goods via air locks or sterilizers	
Air supply	Ventilation	Enough air changes to provide short clean-up phase	Every 6 months
	Filters	All air passed through HEPA filters Filters integrity tested	
Air quality at rest	Air particle count	>5 μm diameter, <2000 m^{-3} >0.5 μm diameter, $<350\,000$ m^{-3}	Every 6 months
	Air viable micro-organisms	<100 m^{-3}	
Maintenance	Maintenance plan	Maintenance plan containing; scope, frequency of cleaning and disinfection, required measures, responsibilities Effectiveness of measures validated	Yearly
Construction	Floor	Even, smooth surface, resistant towards specified disinfectants, seams sealed, edges rounded and sealed	
	Walls	Smooth surface, washable, resistant towards specified disinfectants	
	Sewers, sinks, water taps	No open sewers, sinks or water taps present	

Table 2 — Continued

Product: aqueous solution, ampoules 10 ml, sterile
Sterilization: steam 121°C

1. Qualification

Item	Parameter	Requirements	Frequency
Ampoule washer and sterilizer qualification	Calibration of measuring equipment	Correct values indicated with predetermined accuracy	Yearly
	Belt speed	Conform with specification	
	Temperature distribution	Required temperature reached for specified time at each point across the belt	
	Filter integrity	No leaks detected	
	Particle count	>5 μm diameter, <3500 particles	
	Endotoxin inactivation (only in high-temperature sterilizers >220°C)	>3 log-cycle inactivation of endotoxins adsorbed on 20-ml ampoules (USP 1990)	
Autoclave qualification	Calibration of measuring equipment for temperature and pressure	Correct values indicated with predetermined accuracy, $\pm 2°C$ and ± 10 kPa according to European Pharmacopoeia (1980)	2–4 times/year
	Temperature distribution, empty chamber	Correct temperature distribution with predetermined accuracy	After major modifications
	Cycle time	Correct cycle time with predetermined accuracy	Yearly
	Air filter	Passed integrity test	Twice a year
	Direct cooling water	<1 c.f.u. ml^{-1}	Monthly
Personnel	Hygiene training	Passed training programme with detailed instruction in: Basic hygiene, correct behaviour in clean room, correct wear of garments, correct use of disinfectants	Every 6 months
	Clean-room garments	Hair and where appropriate beard cover, single or two-piece trousers suit, gathered at wrists and with high neck. Gloves permanently covering the sleeves; mask; goggles. Appropriate shoes or overshoes	

2. Validation

Item	Parameter	Requirements	Frequency
Preparation of solution	Raw material	Integrity and orderly appearance of individual containers	Every container
	Process time	Specified process times, minimized waiting time between preparation, filling and sterilization	Process development
	Pre-sterilization bioburden	<10^2 c.f.u. ml^{-1} Bacterial endotoxins <15 EU ml^{-1}	3 lots initially, then random samples

Table 2 — Continued

Product: aqueous solution, ampoules 10 ml, sterile
Sterilization: steam 121°C

2. Validation

Item	Parameter	Requirements	Frequency
Production hygiene	Air viable micro-organisms	<100 m^{-3} during work	Monthly active sampling
	Surface viable micro-organisms	<40 per 100 cm^2	Monthly
	Gloves of personnel, viable micro-organisms (contact plates)	<10 c.f.u./plate	Weekly
Sterilization cycle	Temperature sensitivity of product	No deterioration at 121°C for 15 min detectable	Cycle development
	Sterilization efficacy	Bioindicators as effectively inactivated as in water	Cycle development
	Autoclave loading pattern	Written description of autoclave loading pattern	Cycle development
	Temperature distribution within load	Determination of hot and cold points within the load Fixation of measuring points for measurement during routine run	Cycle development
Methylene blue bath	Bioburden	<1 c.f.u. ml^{-1}	Weekly
Test on final product	Sterility test area	Class A (GMP 1989) environment validated	
	Sterility test	Complies with pharmacopoeial requirement	Every lot unless parametrical release agreed by authorities
	Pyrogen test	Negative on 3 rabbits	Every lot unless endotoxin test permissible
	Endotoxin test	Bacterial endotoxins per hourly human dose <5 EU kg^{-1}	Every lot
Documentation	Bioburden of raw materials, water intermediate	Trends recognizable	Continuously recorded
	Production hygiene Hygiene training	Trends recognizable Frequency, subjects and attending personnel documented	Continuously recorded
	Sterilizers: temperature and pressure recordings	Available for every lot	Every lot
	Test for sterility	Performance: retest rate $<0.5\%$	Continuously monitored

This table is based on current requirements put forward by EEC authorities (GMP 1989), FDA (1987) and the European Pharmacopoeia (1980) and United States Pharmacopeia (1990), also in part on industrial standards (Deutsche Industrie Norm 1986). The example applies only for the production of the stated product. Aseptic preparations would require different standards.

Abbreviations
c.f.u.	colony-forming units
USP	United States Pharmacopeia
EU	endotoxin units
HEPA	high-efficiency particulate air
Pa	Pascal
FDA	Food and Drug Administration (USA)

7 REFERENCES

Bishop, A. (1973) Control of the manufacture and sale of disposable plastics in the United Kingdom. In: Briggs Phillips G. and Miller W. S. (eds), *Industrial sterilization*. Duke University Press, Durham, NC, pp. 125–130.

British Pharmacopoeia (1988) HMSO, London.

Deutsche Industrie Norm (1986) *Dampf-Sterilisatoren für Pharmazeutische Sterilisiergüter, DIN 58 950 Teil 3 Abnahmeprüfungen*. Beuth Verlag, Berlin.

European Pharmacopoeia (1980) 2nd edn. Mainsonneuve SA, 57-Sainte Ruffine, France.

Food and Drug Administration (1987) *Guidelines on sterile drug products produced by aseptic processing*. Center for Drugs and Biologics Food and Drug Administration, Rockville, MD.

GMP (1989) *EEC guide to good manufacturing practice for medicinal products*, Document III/2244/87-EN, Rev. 3. Commission of the European Communities.

Health Industry Manufacturers Association (1982) *Microbiological evaluation of filters for sterilizing liquids*. HIMA Document No. 3, Vol. 14, Washington, DC.

Denyer, S. P. (1987) Sterilisation control and sterility testing. In: Hugo, W. B. and Russell, A. D. (eds), *Pharmaceutical microbiology*, 4th edn. Blackwell Scientific Publications, Oxford, pp. 446–458.

Jensch, U.-E., Gail, L. and Klavehn, M. (1987) Fixing and removing of bacterial endotoxins from glass surfaces for validation of dry heat sterilization. In: Watson, S. W., Levin, J. and Novitsky, T. J. (eds), *Detection of bacterial endotoxins with the limulus amoebocyte lysate test*. Alan R. Liss, New York, pp. 273–281.

Kemper, C. A. (1986) Design, installation and calibration of thermocouple measuring systems. In: Carleton, F. J. and Agallaco, J. P. (eds), *Validation of aseptic pharmaceutical processes*. Marcel Dekker, New York, pp. 93–124.

Lorenz, R. J. (1988) *Grundbegriffe der Biometrie*. G. Fischer Verlag, Stuttgart, p. 207.

McLaughlin, W. L., Boyd, A. W., Chadwick, K. H., McDonald, J. C. and Miller, A. (1989) *Dosimetry for radiation processing*. Taylor and Francis, London, pp. 66–79.

Molin, G. (1982) Destruction of bacterial spores by thermal methods. In: Russel, A. D., Hugo, W. B. and Ayliffe, G. A. J. (eds), *Principles and practice of disinfection, preservation and sterilization*. Blackwell Scientific Publications, Oxford, pp. 454–468.

Palleroni, N. J. (1984) Pseudomonadaceae. In: Krieg, N. R. and Holt, J. G. (eds), *Bergey's manual of systematic bacteriology*, Vol. 1. Williams and Wilkins, Baltimore/London, pp. 140–199.

Patashnik, M. (1953) A simplified procedure for thermal process evaluation. *Food Technol.* **7** 1–6.

Pflug, J. J. (1973) Heat sterilization. In: Briggs Phillips, G. and Miller, W. S. (eds), *Industrial sterilization*. Duke University Press, Durham, NC, pp. 239–282.

Spicher, G. and Peters, J. (1975) Mathematische Grundlagen der Sterilitatsprüfung. *Zbl. Bakt. Hyg. I. Abt. Orig. A* **230** 112–138.

Tsuji, K. and Harrison, S. J. (1978) Dry heat destruction of lipopolysaccharide: dry heat destruction kinetics. *Appl. Environ. Microbiol.* **36** 710–714.

United States Pharmacopeia (1990) 22nd revision. US Pharmacopeial Convention, Rockville, MD.

Wallhaeusser, K.-H. (1979) Is the removal of micro-organisms by filtration really a sterilization method? *Bull. Parenteral Drug Ass.* **33** 156–170.

Wallhaeusser, K.-H. (1982) Germ removal filtration. In: Bean, H. S., Beckett, A. H. and Carless, J. E. (eds), *Advances in pharmaceutical sciences.* Academic Press, London, pp. 1–116.

Wallhaeusser, K.-H. (1988) In: *Praxis der Sterilisation — Desinfektion — Konservierung,* 4th edn. Thieme, Stuttgart/New York.

Wegel, S. (1973) Kurzzeit-Sterilisationsverfahren nach dem Laminar-Flow-Prinzip. *Pharm. Ind.* **35** 809–814.

White, J. D. M. (1973) Biological control of industrial gamma radiation sterilization. In: Briggs Phillips, G. and Miller, W. S. (eds), *Industrial sterilization.* Duke University Press, Durham, NC, pp. 101–116.

10

Principles of preservation

D. S. Orth
Neutrogena Corporation, 5755 West 96th Street, Los Angeles, CA 90045, USA

1   INTRODUCTION

Pharmaceutical products are subject to microbiological contamination and spoilage. Antimicrobial preservatives are used to reduce the likelihood of microbial growth in aqueous products and to reduce the chance of microbial survival in anhydrous products that may be contaminated and/or moistened during use. Sterile products, including parenterals, irrigating and ophthalmic solutions, must remain sterile until they are used by the consumer. If these products become contaminated before use, they are in violation of the US Food, Drug, and Cosmetic Act, as amended, because they are both adulterated and mislabelled (Federal Food, Drug, and Cosmetic Act 1976).

Sterile drugs in multiple-dose containers must have a preservative system that is capable of self-sterilizing these products should contamination occur. Non-sterile aqueous products need preservative systems that are capable of reducing the microbial bioburden to an acceptable level in a reasonable time (Orth 1979).

The object of pharmaceutical product preservation is to ensure that the product is microbiologically safe and stable. Preservative efficacy testing is performed to determine the type and minimum effective concentration of preservative required to preserve the product during manufacture and throughout its use by the consumer. This testing is an essential part of documenting the safety and stability of pharmaceutical products.

2   OBJECTIVES OF PRESERVATION

2.1   The need for preservation of pharmaceutical products

Bacteria, yeasts and moulds are able to grow in pharmaceutical products when nutrients are available and when environmental conditions are suitable. The diversity of the catabolic activities of micro-organisms was reviewed by Gottschalk (1986a), and the regulation of microbial growth in response to physical and chemical agents was presented by Moat and Foster (1988). An understanding of the factors controlling microbial growth is necessary in order to determine the most suitable preservative system needed in any product (refer to Chapter 1, where these factors are considered in detail).

Growth of bacteria, yeasts or moulds on, or in, products may make those products unsafe and unacceptable for use. The hazards of using contaminated products are due to the effect of micro-organisms or harmful microbial by-products on human health. Several surveys conducted between 1969 and 1977 revealed contamination of cosmetic, toiletry and pharmaceutical products (Dunnigan and Evans 1970; Bruch 1971; Baird 1977). McCarthy (1980) reported that similar patterns of contamination for non-sterile products were observed in both the pharmaceutical and cosmetic industries. He noted that this was not surprising, owing to the similarities of topical product development in these two industries.

There have been numerous reports of infections due to use of contaminated products (see Chapter 2). Hand lotions and creams were identified as sources of nosocomial infections that resulted in septicaemia due to Gram-negative organisms, particularly *Escherichia coli, Klebsiella pneumoniae, Enterobacter* and *Serratia* (Morse *et al.* 1967; Morse and Schonbeck 1968). Noble and Savin (1966) reported *Pseudomonas aeruginosa* contamination of a steroid cream preserved with chlorocresol, following modification of that cream by the addition of cetomacrogol emulsifying wax, paraffins, chlorocresol, and water. Although the final concentration of chlorocresol was 0.1% w/v, which should have been sufficient to inactivate contaminating *Ps. aeruginosa,* this micro-organism persisted in the product. (Note: Noble and Savin reported that 0.02% w/v chlorocresol was sufficient to inhibit several strains of *Ps. aeruginosa* on nutrient agar.) The cause of contamination was traced to a decrease in perservative level in the aqueous phase of the product, due to partitioning of the preservative into the oil phase. Contamination of the product (possibly with adapted organisms) was facilitated by the practice of refilling used containers. This demonstrates why a preservative system must be tailored to a specific product (Cowen and Steiger 1977).

Several studies have implicated inadequately preserved mascaras as the cause of eye injuries (Ahearn *et al.* 1974; Wilson *et al.* 1975; Wilson and Ahearn 1977). Curiously, new mascaras were rarely contaminated, whereas used mascaras often were contaminated with a variety of organisms (Ahearn *et al.* 1974). Bhadauria and Ahearn reported that the preservative systems in unused mascaras deteriorated with time (Bhadauria and Ahearn 1980). Similarly, Orth *et al.* (1987) followed the decrease in preservative efficacy in a protein-containing shampoo during stability testing at different temperatures.

The relative hazard created by microbiological contamination of cosmetic or pharmaceutical products may be related to the severity of infection or disease it causes. Dunnigan classified *Pseudomonas, Proteus, Staphylococcus, Serratia, Streptococcus, Penicillium, Aspergillus* and *Candida* genera as health hazards (Dunnigan 1968). Bruch (1972) refined the classification of objectionable micro-organisms according to product type. Madden (1979) listed several additional potentially pathogenic bacteria that were isolated from cosmetic products. Bruch's classification was reviewed with Madden (Madden 1990) and was modified to provide the listing of micro-organisms shown in Table 1. The direct effects of micro-organisms in infec-

Table 1 — Classification of objectionable micro-organisms by product type (Adapted from Bruch, with modifications recommended by Madden; Bruch 1972; Madden 1990)

Sterile drugs: any organism or pyrogen in a sterile product is **objectionable**.

Eye products: *Ps. aeruginosa* is **always objectionable**. Other *Pseudomonas* spp., *Staph. aureus, Serratia marcescens* and *Ser. liquifaciens* are **usually objectionable**

Non-sterile oral products: any enteric pathogen (i.e. *Salmonella* spp.) and *E. coli* is **always objectionable**. Other enteric organisms, such as *Enterobacter* spp., *Citrobacter* spp., *Pseudomonas* spp., proteolytic *Clostridium* spp., enterotoxigenic *Staph. aureus*, pathogenic yeasts (*Candida albicans*), and mycotoxin-producing fungi are **usually objectionable**

Non-sterile topical products: *Ps. aeruginosa, Klebsiella* spp., *Staph. aureus, Ser. marcescens* and *Ser. liquifaciens*, are **always objectionable**; whereas, *Ps. putida, Ps. multivorans, Clostridium perfringens, Cl. tetani*, and *Cl. novyi* are **usually objectionable**

Genitourinary tract products: *E. coli, Proteus* spp., *Ser. marcescens, Ps. aeruginosa* and *Ps. multivorans* are **always objectionable**; whereas, *Klebsiella* spp., *Acinetobacter anitratus* and *Acin. calcoaceticus* are **usually objectionable**

tions and disease have been appreciated for some time; however, the insidious role of micro-organisms in inflammation and in modifying the host immune response is only beginning to be appreciated.

Products intended for use on, or in, the body must be safe. Even though the aerobic plate and total viable counts of the finished product may reveal the presence of <10 colony-forming units (c.f.u.) ml^{-1}, residual microbial by-products may produce undesirable reactions. The problems created by microbial contamination can be minimized by use of raw materials that do not have a history of unacceptable microbial load, by adherence to validated manufacturing practices to reduce the risk of microbial contamination during processing, and by sterilizing products or using effective preservative systems in aqueous formulations.

2.2 Preservation of the product during use

In 1970, Halleck published the recommendations of the Preservation Subcommittee of the Toiletry Goods Association (TGA) Microbiology Committee (Halleck 1970).

These recommendations stated that preservation studies should consider product formulation, manufacturing conditions, packaging, product stability and continued effectiveness of the preservative system during the intended use by the consumer.

In 1984, Eiermann noted that data obtained from surveys and during US Food and Drug Administration (FDA) inspections of cosmetic manufacturers suggested that microbiological contamination of cosmetics during manufacturing was no longer a major regulatory issue (Eiermann 1984). He indicated that the question of whether these products remain uncontaminated when used by consumers had not been resolved. This is addressed in the tentative final order regulating 'over-the-counter' (OTC) antimicrobial drug products, in which the FDA used the term 'effectively preserved' to include preservation during use by the consumer (Eiermann 1984). It is believed that normal use of some products by consumers repeatedly subjects these products to contamination. For example, hair care products (shampoos, conditioners, anti-dandruff products) are used while showering, which exposes these products to dilution with water and contamination with micro-organisms. Repeated use of creams, which requires dipping a finger into a jar to obtain the product, may expose the cream to contamination and dilution with soil, micro-organisms and moisture on fingers. Also, adaptation may occur in product residues present on the threads of the cap or neck of the container if the residues become diluted with water or contaminated with body fluids (blood, urine, tissue fluids). These micro-organisms may become adapted to the product and may be introduced into that product when the cap is next removed, resulting in microbial contamination of the residual product.

2.3 Microbial adaptation

Micro-organisms have diverse metabolic capabilities and are able to utilize virtually any organic and some inorganic compounds as substrates for growth. The regulation of bacterial metabolism in response to substrates in the environment and the problem of microbial adaptation have been recognized by several workers (Orth and Lutes 1985; Gottschalk 1986b; Levy 1987). Close and Nielsen (1976) reported the isolation of a strain of *Ps. cepacia* from oil-in-water (o/w) emulsions preserved with methyl- and propyl-*p*-hydroxybenzoic acid esters (methylparaben and propylparaben, respectively). This isolate could hydrolyse both paraben esters and it could use propylparaben as the sole source of carbon and energy in minimal media. Orth (1981) reported the growth of adapted *Ps. cepacia* in an adequately preserved hand and body lotion. Yablonski (1978) noted the importance of equipment cleaning and sanitization in preventing microbial contamination in manufacturing plants. Improperly cleaned and sanitized equipment provides dilute product residues that enable micro-organisms to adapt to the product (Orth 1981).

Levy (1987) stated that preservative efficacy testing should be performed using test organisms that exhibit the highest level of resistance towards a preserved product. Strains selected for such tests should be at least as difficult to inactivate as micro-organisms which may contaminate the product, either during manufacturing or use by the consumer. The use of specially adapted micro-organisms is not, however, recommended for routine testing because it is believed that many organisms of importance to the cosmetic and pharmaceutical industries may be adapted to survive and grow in adequately preserved products (Orth 1981, 1984). Thus, use of adapted organisms in preservative efficacy testing may make the tests impossible to perform because these organisms may not die when introduced into products to which they are adapted.

The proper solution to the problem of microbial adaptation does not rest with increasing the potency of preservative systems in all products, because this may lead to the use of preservative levels well in excess of those normally required. Instead, alternative types of packaging or product reformulation may be indicated to eliminate conditions which assist the adaptation process. Also, it may be possible to select a preservative that has an adaptation index (AI) close to unity (Orth and Lutes 1985) or a preservative with low dilution coefficient (η; also known as the concentration exponent) (Russell *et al.* 1979; Hurwitz and McCarthy 1985; Hugo and Denyer 1987; see also Chapter 11). This may help to minimize the risk of adaptative contamination arising through product abuse because preservatives of this type are less affected by dilution than are preservatives with larger AI or η-values, and should, therefore, exercise more effective control against contaminating micro-organisms.

3   RECOGNITION OF THE PRESERVATIVE SYSTEM CONCEPT

The preservative action of a formulation often is considered to be due solely to the preservatives used. In practice, however, the preservative system of a product involves both specific preservative chemicals and the physicochemical constitution of the product (Orth *et al.* 1987). Preservative chemicals do not act independently of the product. Thus, factors such as pH, water activity (a_w), nutrient availability, surfactant concentration, sequestering agents, non-aqueous components, insoluble ingredients and interfering materials (i.e. antibiotics, antioxidants) will influence the preservative action of any given formulation (see Chapter 12).

There are many formula components that may contribute to the preservative system of a product (Table 2). The choice of preservative is dependent on the

Table 2 — Formula components that may contribute to the preservative system of a product (Adapted from Orth and Milstein 1989)

Preservatives, antibiotics
Acids, alkalis
Alcohols (e.g. ethyl, isopropyl, benzyl)
Cationic surfactants (e.g. cetyl pyridinium chloride)
Anionic surfactants (e.g. soap, sodium lauryl sulphate)
Esters (e.g. glyceryl monolaurate, sucrose hexadecanoate)
Humectants (e.g. glycerol, propylene glycol, sorbitol)
Aqueous solutes (e.g. sugars, dextrins, salts)
Phenolic antioxidants (e.g. *tert*-butyl hydroxyanisole (BHA) and *tert*-butyl hydroxytoluene (BHT))
Chelating agents (e.g. tetrasodium EDTA)
Glycols (e.g. propylene glycol, butylene glycol)
Colours
Fragrances and flavours

formulation (Cowen and Steiger 1977). Thus, preservatives may be unnecessary in an ointment base because of the absence of water. Also, the presence of antibiotics in a formula may make the use of specific preservatives unnecessary; however, the type and concentration of antibiotic will determine whether additional antimicrobial agents are required.

Micro-organisms may be metabolically injured or 'stressed' by exposure to various physical or chemical conditions, such as heating to sublethal temperatures, freezing, drying, hydrogen peroxide and acid pH (Busta 1978; Przybylski and Witter 1979; Gilbert 1984). Sublethal injury is characterized by a loss of selective permeability of the cell membrane, leakage of intracellular components into the surrounding medium, degradation of ribosomes and ribonucleic acid, and decreased enzyme activity. Stressed micro-organisms generally are more susceptible to secondary stresses created by adverse physicochemical conditions found in preservative systems than uninjured micro-organisms (Flowers *et al.* 1977; Przybylski and Witter 1979; Gilbert 1984).

4 THE IDEAL PRESERVATIVE

Understanding the characteristics of an ideal preservative helps to provide the basis for rational selection of the most suitable agent(s) for a given formulation. The desired characteristics of an ideal preservative were discussed by several workers (Croshaw 1977; Orth and Lutes 1985) and are summarized below.

(a) It should have a broad spectrum of activity. Ideally, a single preservative should be used as this will reduce costs and possibly may reduce the irritation or toxicity potential of the formula.

(b) It should be effective and stable over the range of pH values encountered in cosmetic and pharmaceutical products. Ideally, the preservative should be able to function effectively at any pH compatible with any product applied topically or taken internally. In addition, it should be chemically stable so that there is no loss of preservative efficacy during the expected shelf-life of the product.

(c) It should be compatible with other ingredients in the formulation and with packaging materials. This attribute would prevent loss of preservative potency as a result of interactions with formula components and/or packaging materials. It should not alter the therapeutic properties of a drug (i.e. loss of potency of active ingredients or alteration in the pharmacokinetic behaviour of the active ingredients), a phenomenon that may occur if the preservative reacted with formulation components.

(d) It should not affect the physical properties of the product (i.e. colour, clarity, odour, flavour, viscosity, texture, etc.). Ideally, it should not produce any interactions with formulation components that may alter the appearance, texture, aroma or performance of the formulation.

(e) It should have a suitable o/w partition coefficient to ensure an effective concentration of the preservative in the aqueous phase of the product. Biological reactions take place in aqueous systems or at the interface of o/w systems; consequently, it is necessary to have sufficient preservative in the water phase to ensure adequate preservation of the product.

(f) It should inactivate micro-organisms quickly enough to prevent microbial adaptation to the preservative system. Preservatives are used in aqueous products to make them bactericidal or fungicidal in a short enough time to meet acceptance criteria (Orth 1979) and to reduce the likelihood of microbial persistence in anhydrous products that may be contaminated and moistened during use. It is believed that contaminating micro-organisms may be able to develop resistance to a product if the preservative system does not inactivate them quickly enough to prevent genetic (Levy 1987) or biochemical modifications [i.e. enzyme induction (Gottschalk 1986b; Moat and Foster 1988; Rodwell 1988), modification of metabolic pathways (Gottschalk 1986b; Mayes 1988a), detoxification mediated by hydroperoxidases and oxygenases (Mayes 1988b)] that enable micro-organisms to adapt to the product.

(g) It should be safe to use. Safety of the preservatives includes handling of pure or concentrated materials in the manufacturing plant as well as the effect of preservatives in the finished formulation on the consumer. Ideally, the product should be non-toxic by oral ingestion, non-irritant and non-sensitizing.

(h) It should comply with governmental regulations. Manufacturers of preservative chemicals should be registered, as required by governmental regulations. The preservative should be used in accordance with permissible levels, where applicable.

(i) It should be cost-effective to use. From a commercial perspective, an effective concentration should add little to the cost of the formulated product.

A more detailed treatment of some of these points can be found in Chapters 11, 12, 14 and 15. The parabens have been used more often than any other preservative in cosmetic products (Decker and Wenninger 1987); however, no single preservative meets all the above characteristics of the ideal preservative for all formulations.

5 SELECTION OF TYPE AND CONCENTRATION OF PRESERVATIVE

Having established candidate preservatives based on their individual characteristics and the nature of the formulation, the final selection and concentrations required for satisfactory preservation of products are ascertained by preservative efficacy testing. Official methods of testing are covered in Chapter 13A. The determination of preservative efficacy by the linear regression method (Orth 1979) is described in Chapter 13B. The reader is directed to publications by Orth (1981, 1984) for comparisons of this method with official tests.

6 RATIONAL DEVELOPMENT OF A PRODUCT PRESERVATIVE SYSTEM

The steps required for the rational development of a product preservative system were discussed recently (Orth and Milstein 1989). The first step is to review the product formula and type to determine what are the most likely challenge organisms, then to decide which preservatives are indicated, and finally which preservative test method is most appropriate. Samples of the product may then be prepared, with at least one sample containing an inadequate preservative system, one or two samples with the preservative level close to the expected target concentration, and at least one sample with excess preservative. This provides samples with a range of concentrations of the preservative under investigation and which may now be tested for preservative efficacy.

As mentioned earlier, several preservative efficacy test methods may be used (Lorenzetti 1984; Orth 1984; Parker 1984); however, it is important to employ a test method that is reliable and is capable of indicating the concentration of preservative required in order for the preservative system of the product to meet acceptance criteria. The linear regression method (Chapter 13B) is recommended because it provides quantitative data on the kinetics of inactivation. Thus, the D-value for each concentration of the preservative used may be determined with each test organism. If the preservative concentrations were selected correctly, a family of survivor curves will be obtained.

In addition to the testing required for development of an adequate preservative system, abuse testing should also be considered. If appropriate, this testing should determine whether product abuse may cause contamination of the product and/or weakening of the preservative system. Maintenance of preservative efficacy and an aerobic plate count of <10 c.f.u. g^{-1} would indicate that the product preservative system passes the abuse test.

7 OVERVIEW
The goal of a preservative system is to satisfactorily preserve a product against microbial challenge while it is in trade channels and in the hands of consumers. To successfully achieve this, full consideration must be given to all the factors which may influence preservative activity and to select for testing those preservative systems which come closest to the ideal. A preservative efficacy test may then be used to determine the type and minimum effective concentration of preservative(s) required to preserve a product satisfactorily to meet the recommended acceptance level.

In order to meet the objective of pharmaceutical product preservation, which is to ensure that the product is microbiologically safe and stable, it may be appropriate to perform a risk assessment. In this, it will be necessary to determine whether increasing the potency of the preservative system (i.e. by use of higher concentrations of preservatives, by use of additional preservatives, or both) offers the best practical solution to the problem of product preservation, or whether reformulating the product and/or using alternative modes of packaging (i.e. unit-dose packages, contamination-resistant packages, etc.) should also be considered.

8 REFERENCES
Ahearn, D. G., Wilson, L. A., Julian, A. J., Reinhardt, D. J. and Ajello, G. (1974) Microbial growth in eye cosmetics: contamination during use. *Dev. Ind. Microbiol.* **15** 211–216.

Baird, R. M. (1977) Microbial contamination of cosmetic products. *J. Soc. Cosmet. Chem.* **28** 17–20.

Bhadauria, R. and Ahearn, D. G. (1980) Loss of effectiveness of preservative systems of mascaras with age. *Appl. Environ. Microbiol.* **39** 665–667.

Bruch, C. W. (1971) Cosmetics: sterility vs. microbial control. *Am. Perfum. Cosmet.* **86** (4) 45–50.

Bruch, C. W. (1972) Objectionable micro-organisms in non-sterile drugs and cosmetics. *Drug Cosmet. Ind.* **111** (4) 51–54, 151–156.

Busta, F. F. (1978) Introduction to injury and repair of microbial cells. *Adv. Appl. Microbiol.* **23** 195–201.

Close, J. and Nielsen, P. A. (1976) Resistance of a strain of *Pseudomonas cepacia* to esters of *p*-hydroxybenzoic acid. *Appl. Environ. Microbiol.* **31** 718–722.

Cowen, R. A. and Steiger, B. (1977) Why a preservative system must be tailored to a specific product. *Cosmet. Toilet.* **92** (3) 15–16, 18–20.

Croshaw, B. (1977) Preservatives for cosmetics and toiletries. *J. Soc. Cosmet. Chem.* **28** 3–16.

Decker, R. L. and Wenninger, J. A. (1987) Frequency of preservative use in cosmetic formulas as disclosed to FDA—1987. *Cosmet. Toilet.* **102** (12) 21–23.

Dunnigan, A. P. (1968) Microbiological control of cosmetic products. Proceedings of the Joint Conference. Cosmetic Science, Washington, DC, April 21–23, 1968. Cited in: McCarthy, T. J. (1984) Formulated factors affecting the activity of preservatives. In: Kabara, J. J. (ed.) *Cosmetic and drug preservation: principles and practice.* Marcel Dekker, New York, pp. 359–388.

Dunnigan, A. P. and Evans, J. R. (1970) Report of a special survey: microbiological contamination of topical drugs and cosmetics. *TGA Cosmet. J.* **2** 39–41.

Eiermann, H. J. (1984) Cosmetic product preservation: safety and regulatory issues. In: Kabara, J. J. (ed.), *Cosmetic and drug preservation: principles and practice.* Marcel Dekker, New York, pp. 559–569.

Federal Food, Drug, and Cosmetic Act of 1938, as amended (1976) Sections 601 and 602, 21 USC 361 and 362.

Flowers, R. S., Martin, S. E., Brewer, D. G. and Ordal, Z. J. (1977) Catalase and enumeration of stressed *Staphylococcus aureus* cells. *Appl. Environ. Microbiol.* **33** 1112–1117.

Gilbert, P. (1984) The revival of micro-organisms sublethally injured by chemical inhibitors. In: Andrew, M. H. E. and Russell, A. D. (eds), *The Revival of Injured Microbes.* Academic Press, London, pp. 175–197.

Gottschalk, G. (1986a) Catabolic activities of aerobic heterotrophs. *Bacterial Metabolism,* 2nd edn. Springer-Verlag, New York, pp. 141–177.

Gottschalk, G. (1986b) Regulation of bacterial metabolism. *Bacterial Metabolism,* 2nd edn. Springer-Verlag, New York, pp. 178–207.

Halleck, F. E. (1970) A guideline for the determination of adequacy of preservation of cosmetics and toiletry formulations. *TGA Cosmet. J.* **2** 20–23.

Hugo, W. B. and Denyer, S. P. (1987) The concentration exponent of disinfectants and preservatives (biocides). In: Board, R. G., Allwood, M. C. and Banks, J. G. (eds), *Preservatives in the food, pharmaceutical and environmental industries SAB Technical Series No. 22.* Blackwell Scientific Publications, Oxford, pp. 281–291.

Hurwitz, S. J. and McCarthy, T. J. (1985) Dynamics of disinfection of selected preservatives against *Escherichia coli. J. Pharm. Sci.* **74** 892–894.

Levy, E. (1987) Insights into microbial adaptation to cosmetic and pharmaceutical products. *Cosmet. Toilet.* **102** (12) 69–74.

Lorenzetti, O. J. (1984) A preservative evaluation program for dermatological and cosmetic preparations. In: Kabara, J. J. (ed.), *Cosmetic and drug preservation: principles and practice.* Marcel Dekker, New York, pp. 441–463.

Madden, J. M. (1979) Cosmetic microbiology: viewpoint of the Food and Drug Administration. In: *Advances in Industrial Microbiology,* Vol. 21. Society of Industrial Microbiology, Washington, DC, pp. 149–156.

Madden, J. M. (1990) Personal communication.

Mayes, P. A. (1988a) Regulation of carbohydrate metabolism. In: Murry, R. K., Granner, D. K., Mayes, P. A. and Rodwell, V. W. (eds), *Harper's biochemistry*, 21st edn. Appleton and Lange, Norwalk, CT, pp. 186–197.

Mayes, P. A. (1988b) Biologic oxidation. In: Murry, R. K., Granner, D. K., Mayes, P. A. and Rodwell, V. W. (eds) *Harper's biochemistry*, 21st edn, Appleton and Lange, Norwalk, CT, pp. 100–107.

McCarthy, T. J. (1980) Microbiological control of cosmetic products. *Cosmet. Toilet.* **95** (8) 23–27.

Moat, A. G. and Foster, J. W. (1988) *Microbial physiology,* 2nd edn. Wiley, New York, pp. 523–578.

Morse, L. J. and Schonbeck, L. E. (1968) Hand lotions — a potential nosocomial hazard. *New Engl. J. Med.* **278** 376–378.

Morse, L. J., Williams, H. L., Grenn, Jr, F. P., Eldridge, E. E. and Rotta, J. R. (1967) Septicemia due to *Klebsiella pneumoniae* originating from a hand-cream dispenser. *New Engl. J. Med.* **277** 472–473.

Noble, W. C. and Savin, J. A. (1966) Steroid cream contaminated with *Pseudomonas aeruginosa. Lancet* **i** 347–349.

Orth, D. S. (1979) Linear regression method for rapid determination of cosmetic preservative efficacy. *J. Soc. Cosmet. Chem.* **30** 321–332.

Orth, D. S. (1981) Principles of preservative efficacy testing. *Cosmet. Toilet.* **96** (3) 43–44, 48–52.

Orth, D. S. (1984) Evaluation of preservatives in cosmetic products. In: Kabara, J. J. (ed.), *Cosmetic and drug preservation: principles and practice.* Marcel Dekker, New York, pp. 403–421.

Orth, D. S. and Lutes, C. M. (1985) Adaptation of bacteria to cosmetic preservatives. *Cosmet. Toilet.* **100** (2) 57–59, 63, 64.

Orth, D. S. and Milstein, S. R. (1989) Rational development of preservative systems for cosmetic products. *Cosmet. Toilet.* **104** (11) 91, 92, 94–100, 102, 103.

Orth, D. S., Lutes, C. M., Milstein, S. R. and Allinger, J. J. (1987) Determination of shampoo preservative stability and apparent activation energies by the linear regression method of preservative efficacy testing. *J. Soc. Cosmet. Chem.* **38** 307–319.

Parker, M. S. (1984) Design and assessment of preservative systems for cosmetics. In: Kabara, J. J. (ed.), *Cosmetic and drug preservation: principles and practice.* Marcel Dekker, New York, pp. 389–402.

Przybylski, K. S. and Witter, L. D. (1979) Injury and recovery of *Escherichia coli* after sublethal acidification. *Appl. Environ. Microbiol.* **37** 261–265.

Rodwell, V. W. (1988) Enzymes: regulation of activities. In: Murry, R. K., Granner, D. K., Mayes, P. A. and Rodwell, V. W. (eds), *Harper's biochemistry*, 21st edn, Appleton and Lange, Norwalk, CT, pp. 82–92.

Russell, A. D., Ahonkhai, I. and Rogers, D. T. (1979) A review. Microbiological applications of the inactivation of antibiotics and other antimicrobial agents. *J. Appl. Bacteriol.* **46** 207–245.

Wilson, L. A. and Ahearn, D. G. (1977) *Pseudomonas*-induced corneal ulcers associated with contaminated eye mascaras. *Am. J. Ophthamol.* **84** 112–119.

Wilson, L. A., Julian, A. J. and Ahearn, D. G. (1975) The survival and growth of microorganisms in mascara during use. *Am. J. Ophthamol.* **79** 596–601.

Yablonski, J. I. (1978) Microbiological aspects of sanitary cosmetic manufacturing. *Cosmet. Toilet.* **93** (9) 37–50.

11

Antimicrobial preservatives and their properties

S. P. Denyer
Department of Pharmaceutical Sciences, University of Nottingham, University
Park, Nottingham, NG7 2RD, UK
and
K.-H. Wallhaeusser
6238 Hofheim a.Ts., Lessingstrasse 20, West Germany

1 INTRODUCTION

Choosing a suitable preservative agent for a pharmaceutical product requires careful consideration of the product type, its usage, formulation characteristics and likely microbial challenge (see Chapter 10). Selection is then made largely from a common pool of agents used in food, cosmetic, toiletry and pharmaceutical products, and experience has identified a limited range most generally suited to the pharmaceutical situation (Wallhaeusser 1974; Akers 1984; Chapman 1987; Bloomfield 1988; Table 1). In this chapter, attention is focused on this limited list of preservative agents in

Table 1 — Principal preservative agents used in pharmaceuticals and their major areas of application

Preservative agent	Pharmaceutical products			
	Injectable	Ophthalmic	Topical	Oral
Benzalkonium chloride	+	+	+	
Benzoic acid (+ salts)			+	+
Benzyl alcohol	+		+	
Bronopol			+	+
Cetrimide		+	+	
Chlorbutanol	+	+		
Chlorhexidine		+	+	
Chlorocresol	+		+	
Cresol	+		+	
Ethanol				+
Parabens (methyl, ethyl, butyl, propyl, benzyl +salts)	(+)	(+)	+	+
Phenol	+		+	
Phenoxyethanol			+	
Phenylethanol	+	+		
Phenylmercuric salts		+		
Sorbic acid			+	+
Sulphites, inorganic	+			
Thiomersal	+	+		

(+); Martindale (1982) cautions against use in these products.
N.B. Germany and some other countries will not permit Bronopol to be used in pharmaceutical products, only in cosmetics.

order to illustrate the varied properties and qualities of this diverse group of pharmaceutical excipients. On occasions, however, none of the agents described may be suited to a particular application, in which case the wider range of monographs compiled by Wallhaeusser (1984, 1988) are recommended for consultation. In the final analysis, the ultimate selection of a preservative agent may be a compromise between registration acceptability (Chapter 14), antimicrobial efficacy (Chapters 13A and 13B) and product compatibility (Chapter 12).

2   FACTORS AFFECTING PRESERVATIVE ACTIVITY

Preservative efficacy is influenced by factors both intrinsic and extrinsic to the target organisms. Intrinsic factors include the nature, structure and composition, and condition of the micro-organism together with its capacity to resist, degrade or inactivate the preservative agent. Detailed treatment of these factors is given in Russell (1982), Gilbert and Wright (1987), Gilbert (1988), Hugo (1988) and Chopra (1990).

   To the formulator, the extrinsic factors which reflect the external environment in which the preservative acts are probably of the most immediate relevance and are undoubtedly of a more controllable nature. Changes in preservative concentration, product pH, storage temperature and product composition can all significantly influence antimicrobial activity. To some extent these influences are predictable provided the properties of preservative agents are fully recognized. The following sections consider the potential influence of such parameters on the performance of preservative agents.

2.1   Concentration

Investigations at the turn of this century (reviewed in Hugo and Denyer 1987) clearly demonstrated the exponential relationship between rate of microbial death and concentration of antimicrobial agent. This can be described by the equation

$$C_1^\eta \, t_1 = C_2^\eta \, t_2 \tag{1}$$

where C_1 and C_2 represent two concentrations of the antimicrobial agent and t_1 and t_2 their respective times to achieve the same level of reduction in viable count. The exponent η is a measure of the effect of changes in concentration (or dilution level) on microbial death rate and is termed the concentration exponent or dilution coefficient.

   Information derived from such kinetic studies can be used to calculate the concentration exponent of a microbiocidal preservative agent from a mathematical rearrangement of equation (1) (see equation (2) below) or by a graphical method (Fig. 1).

$$\eta = \frac{\log t_2 - \log t_1}{\log C_1 - \log C_2} \tag{2}$$

In practical terms, the activity of a compound with a high concentration exponent will be markedly decreased by dilution while that of an agent with low η value will be less severely affected (Table 2). Conversely, an increase in concentration will be of much greater benefit to a compound of high η value than to a compound with a low concentration exponent. Example concentration exponents are given for a range of preservatives in Table 3.

   It is likely that the concentration exponent in some way reflects the nature of the interaction between preservative agent and microbial target (Hugo and Denyer

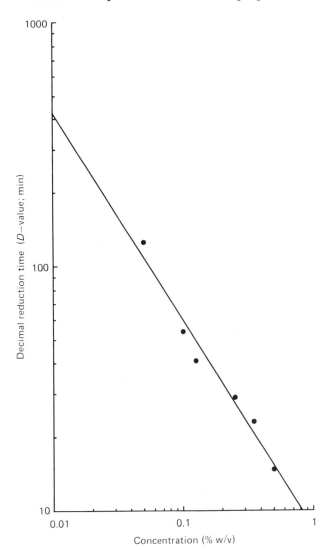

Fig. 1 — Determination of the concentration exponent for Bronopol by linear regression analysis, where the slope of the line (0.85) gives the concentration exponent (courtesy Dr S. Jassim).

1987). Indeed, variations in concentration exponent are reported and these appear to reflect differences in both experimental design (i.e. antimicrobial end-point) and target organism. Some indication of this variation between organism type is seen in the average values of Table 3, and more detailed examples of this variation are given in the papers of Beveridge *et al.* (1980), Karabit *et al.* (1985, 1986, 1988) and Mackie *et al.* (1986). Clearly, experimentation is necessary if a precise value for the concentration exponent is required for a particular situation.

In summary, the activity of a preservative system can be substantially influenced

Table 2 — Loss of activity of a preservative on dilution according to its concentration exponent

Concentration exponent	Fraction of activity remaining on dilution to	
	1/2	1/3
1	1/2	1/3
2	1/4	1/9
3	1/8	1/27
4	1/16	1/81
5	1/32	1/243
6	1/64	1/729
7	1/128	1/2187
8	1/256	1/6560

Table 3 — Preservative characteristics

Preservative agent	Concentration exponent[a]	Optimal pH range
Benzalkonium chloride	3.5, 1.8 (y), 9 (m)	Broad; 4–10
Benzoic acid (+ salts)	3.5 (y)	Acidic; 2–5
Benzyl alcohol	6.6, 4 (y), 2 (m)	Acidic; ≤5
Bronopol	0.9	5–7
Cetrimide	1	Broad; 4–10
Chlorbutanol	2	Acidic; ≤4
Chlorhexidine	1.9	Neutral; 5–8
Chlorocresol	8.3	Acidic; ≤8.5
Cresol	8	Acidic; ≤9
Ethanol	4.5, 5.7 (y), 3 (m)	Acidic
Parabens (methyl, ethyl, butyl, propyl, benzyl + salts)	2.5	Broad; 3–9.5
Phenol	5.8, 4 (y), 4.3 (m)	Acidic; ≤9
Phenoxyethanol	9	Broad
Phenylethanol	5.6	Acidic; ≤7
Phenylmercuric salts	1	Neutral; 6–8
Sorbic acid	3.1	Acidic; ≤6.5
Sulphites, inorganic	1.3, 1.6 (y), 1.8 (m)	Acidic; ≤4
Thiomersal	1	Neutral; 7–8

[a]Determined against bacteria unless indicated (m) for mould or (y) for yeast.

by changes in concentration and this may lead to its failure. While this change may arise by simple dilution (i.e. in the mixing of two differently preserved creams; Hugo *et al.* 1984) it will also occur by any mechanism which leads to a reduction in active agent. This could include complexation of preservative with product ingredients (see Chapter 12), partitioning of antimicrobial agent into a non-aqueous phase or container material, or through pH influences on ionization and activity.

2.2   Effect of pH
The antimicrobial activity of many preservative agents is strongly influenced by environmental pH, variously through changes in ionic status, altered interaction with target groups on the microbial cell, and variable partitioning between product and micro-organism. In general, a negatively-charged microbial cell will interact most strongly with a cationic agent at high pH whilst effectively repelling anionic agents. Furthermore, a compound which exerts its activity by partitioning into the target cell is likely to do so most efficiently in its unionized rather than its ionized form. For instance, the activity of weak acid preservatives such as benzoic and sorbic acids resides principally in the unionized (undissociated) form and greatest activity is therefore evident at pH's at or below their pK_a (4.2 and 4.76, respectively) where the fraction undissociated will be 50% or greater. With a knowledge of preservative pK_a it is possible to determine the extent of ionization (dissociation) from equation (3), and thereby predict the likely influence of pH on activity:

$$\text{Undissociated fraction of weak acid preservative} = \frac{1}{1 + \text{antilog (pH} - pK_a)} \tag{3}$$

The influence of pH may extend beyond the confines of activity alone, influencing preservative stability (Moore and Stretton 1981; Chapman 1987), interactions with pharmaceutical excipients (see Chapter 12), and partitioning behaviour in multiple-phase systems (section 2.4). Optimal pH ranges are given for selected preservative agents in Table 3.

2.3   Effect of temperature
As with many chemical reactions the activity of preservative agents usually increases with an increase in temperature although the effects are often complicated by the temperature dependency of the target organism (Kostenbauder 1983). Over a narrow temperature range, which may extend from refrigeration temperatures to body heat, and in a limited concentration range it is possible to describe the effect of temperature on preservative activity using equation (4):

$$Q_{10} \text{ (change in activity per 10°C change in temperature)} = \frac{t_{(T)}}{t_{(T+10)}} \tag{4}$$

where $t_{(T)}$ repesents the death time at temperature T°C and $t_{(T+10)}$ the death time at $(T+10)$°C. It is usual to report temperature sensitivity over a 10°C temperature difference (Q_{10} value) but a temperature coefficient (θ) for a 1°C temperature change can be similarly calculated; θ values are generally in the order of 1–1.5 as a consequence of the apparent geometric nature of the temperature/activity relationship (Berry and Michaels 1950).

Some temperature coefficients (Q_{10} values) for selected agents are given in Table 4. From these values, it can be seen that preservative agents respond differently to

Table 4 — Influence of temperature on preservative activity

Preservative agent	Temperature coefficient (Q_{10})
Benzalkonium chloride	2.9–5.8
Benzyl alcohol	2.3–7.2
Bronopol	2.9
Chlorhexidine	3–16
Chlorocresol	3–5
Cresol	3–5
Ethanol	45
Phenol	5
Sorbic acid	2.3

temperature variations and this may be important in extrapolating preservative efficacy test data from the usual room temperature to the recommended range of product storage temperatures (see also Chapter 12). In particular, this may have important implications in products which are recommended for refrigerated storage between periods of usage (Allwood 1982).

2.4 Effect of partitioning in multiple-phase systems
It has long been recognized (Bean *et al.* 1962, 1965; Bean 1972) that antimicrobial activity primarily resides in the aqueous phase of a preserved two-phase system and is therefore dependent upon the equilibrium concentration of the preservative in this phase. Preservatives will partition between oil and water phases in accordance with their partition coefficients (Table 5) and the relative ratio of oil and water present in the system. This partitioning behaviour and its influence on the aqueous concentration of preservative agent (C_w) can be described by equation (5):

$$C_w = \frac{C(\theta + 1)}{K_w^o \theta + 1} \tag{5}$$

where C represents the overall concentration of preservative, K_w^o the oil:water partition coefficient, and θ the oil:water ratio. It follows that if K_w^o is high, then it becomes extremely difficult to maintain adequate preservative levels in the aqueous phase without an excessive total preservative concentration. This formula can be applied to follow the behaviour of a preservative in a simple two-phase system and a worked example for chlorocresol is given by McCarthy (1984).

The oily phase can generally be considerd to represent any water-immiscible material, but it must be remembered that the K_w^o of a preservative may vary considerably depending upon the type of oil present. Indeed, it is generally

Table 5 — Examples of solubility and partition characteristics for preservative agents

Preservative agent	Water solubility (20–25°C)	Vegetable oil:water partition (K_w^o)	Emulgent:water partition (R)
Benzalkonium chloride	High	<1.0	High
Benzoic acid	Slight[a]	3–6	Medium
Benzyl alcohol	Moderate	1.3	Low
Bronopol	High	0.11	Low
Cetrimide	Moderate	<1.0	High
Chlorbutanol	Slight		Medium
Chlorhexidine	Slight–high[b]	0.04 (diacetate)	High
Chlorocresol	Slight	117–190	High
Cresol	Moderate		Medium/low
Ethanol	Miscible		
Parabens (methyl, ethyl, butyl, propyl, benzyl)	Slight–poor[a] (decrease with increasing chain length)	7.5 (methyl) 80 (propyl) 280 (butyl)	High
Phenol	Moderate		Low
Phenoxyethanol	Moderate		Low
Phenylethanol	Moderate		Low
Phenylmercuric salts	Slight	<1.0	Low
Sorbic acid	Slight[c]	3.5	
Sulphites, inorganic	High		
Thiomersal	High		Low

Solubility limits: high, >25%; moderate, >1%; slight, >0.05%; poor, <0.05%.
[a]Sodium salts moderate–high solubility.
[b]Digluconate (high), diacetate (moderate), dihydrochloride (slight).
[c]Potassium salt (high), calcium salt (moderate).

recognized that partition from water into vegetable oils is more efficient than into mineral oils (Bean 1972; McCarthy 1984); furthermore, water solubility is not necessarily a predictor of partitioning behaviour (Table 5). Additionally, the pH of the system may substantially affect partition, as may also the droplet size, and hence surface interfacial area, of the oil phase during mixing.

The above mathematical method describes a simple system which would rarely be found in emulsion and cream formulations. In these situations, a stable formulation would usually be maintained by the addition of an emulgent, usually a non-ionic surface-active agent. To account for this third component, Bean *et al.* (1969) extended their equation to accommodate the possible partitioning of preservative into the micellized emulgent or their complexation:

$$C_w = \frac{C(\theta + 1)}{K_w^o \, \theta + R} \tag{6}$$

In this equation, C, θ and K_w^o have the same meanings as before, C_w is now the free concentration in the water, and a new term R, the ratio of total preservative in the aqueous phase to the free (unbound) preservative in that phase, is introduced. The relative order of magnitude of R for a range of preservative agents is given in Table 5. In relatively simple systems, with a single non-ionic emulgent and preservative, a clear linear relationship exists between R and surfactant concentration (Bean 1972; Kostenbauder 1983); relationships also dependent upon preservative concentration have been described (Dempsey 1988). More complex models have been developed along the above lines (Garrett 1966) to include multiple preservative agents or mixed emulgent systems (Kazmi and Mitchell, 1976, 1978a, 1978b).

Within the literature there are examples of potentiation of antimicrobial activity associated with the presence of low concentrations of non-ionic surfactants (Allwood 1973; Lehmann 1988; see also Chapter 12). This can be attributed to a surfactant-based permeabilization of the bacterial cell to the antimicrobial agent, but this phenomenon occurs only over a narrow concentration range of emulgent and above the critical micelle concentration preservative is displaced into the micellar system.

The effective preservation of multiple-phase systems is thus a complex task, and due consideration must be given to the partitioning properties of the preservative agent(s), the nature and amount of the oil phase, and the properties of the emulgent system. At the very best, partitioning of preservative into the oil phase can be said to provide a reservoir of active agent to replenish declining aqueous levels; more likely, unrecognized and unaccounted for partitioning will lead to loss of preservative capability.

2.5   Prediction of preservative behaviour
The mathematical treatments described in earlier sections (2.1–2.4) can be employed to predict the consequences of formulation changes or other external influences on the antimicrobial activity of a preservative system. Indeed, Bean (1972) has shown, from a theoretical perspective, how changes in more than one factor can be accommodated in a combined mathematical approach. It is likely, however, that a more complex range of influences will arise in practice and the predictive capability of these formulae may then be only qualitative at best. Under these circumstances, experimentation will be required to discover the precise significance of every relevant variable. To this end, the recently reported application of factorial design to the evaluation of preservative efficacy in pharmaceutical systems is highly relevant (Karabit et al. 1989).

3   SPECTRUM OF ACTIVITY
In general, a preservative agent should offer a microbiocidal capability although clearly the ability to hold contaminating organisms in stasis will be satisfactory in most instances. In this respect, the sporicidal activity of many preservatives is often extremely limited, but good activity against the vegetative form of the organism should be sufficient. The capacity of a preservative system should also be sufficient to withstand the anticipated microbial challenge levels, especially in situations where multiple contamination episodes may arise.

An ideal preservative should possess broad-spectrum activity against both Gram-positive and Gram-negative bacteria, moulds and yeasts. In practice, few preservatives have this capability (Table 6) and this, combined with the constraints imposed by formulation design and product type, place further limitations on the spectrum which can be achieved by use of a single agent in a formulation. Great care must therefore be taken to ensure that a perceived gap in activity does not lead to the selection of insensitive organisms or the creation of conditions favourable for a less adaptable spoilage organism by the growth of the primary insensitive contaminant. In these respects, considerable concern has been raised regarding the recognized

Table 6 — Range of antimicrobial activities

Preservative agent	Bacteria		Yeasts	Moulds
	Gram-positive	Gram-negative		
Benzalkonium chloride	+ +	(+ +)*	(+ +)	+
Benzoic acid (+ salts)	+ +	(+ +)	+	+
Benzyl alcohol	+ +	+	+	+
Bronopol	(+ +)	+ +	+	+
Cetrimide	+ +	(+ +)*	(+ +)	+
Chlorbutanol	+ +	+ +	(+ +)	+
Chlorhexidine	+ +	+ + *	(+ +)	+
Chlorocresol	+ +	(+ +)	+	+
Cresol	(+ +)	+	+	+
Ethanol	+ +	+ +	(+ +)	(+ +)
Parabens (methyl, ethyl, butyl, propyl, benzyl + salts)	(+ +)	+ *	(+ +)	(+ +)
Phenol	(+ +)	+	+	+
Phenoxyethanol	(+ +)	+ +	+	+
Phenylethanol	(+ +)	+ +	+	+
Phenylmercuric salts	+ +	+ +	(+ +)	(+ +)
Sorbic acid	(+ +)	(+ +)	+ +	(+ +)
Sulphites, inorganic	+	+	(+ +)	(+ +)
Thiomersal	+ +	(+ +)	(+ +)	+

+ + , active; (+ +), moderately active; + , weakly active; * poorly active against *Pseudomonas* spp.

Pseudomonas gap of certain preservative agents (Croshaw 1977), since this genus represents a major, and potentially pathogenic, contaminant of many pharmaceutical preparations (see Chapter 2). This has led to the widespread use of preservative combinations, not necessarily to achieve potentiation or synergy (section 4), but simply to combat the likely range of contaminants. Such combinations include mixtures of parabens in place of single esters (this has the principal benefit of increasing the total paraben level that can be held in solution), parabens with phenoxyethanol, Bronopol and parabens (particularly useful in alkaline preparations where the rapid 'knock-down' effect of the alkali-labile Bronopol can be supplemented by the long-term activity of the parabens), and benzalkonium chloride with chlorhexidine gluconate (Croshaw 1977).

4   POTENTIATION AND SYNERGY

An occasional benefit from the use of preservative agents in combination is an enhancement in activity, which if to a sufficiently marked degree can be considered to represent true synergy. This phenomenon, although elusive, has been widely reported (see, for example, Denyer and King 1988 and Lehmann 1988), and several examples are given in Fig. 2. Synergy is rarely a property deliberately sought for in preservative combinations, and it should not be confused with the broadening of antimicrobial spectrum described in section 3. If achieved it is often by serendipity although the basis for its prediction has been described (Denyer *et al.* 1985; Denyer and King 1988; Denyer 1990).

The extent of synergy between preservative agents is dependent upon their

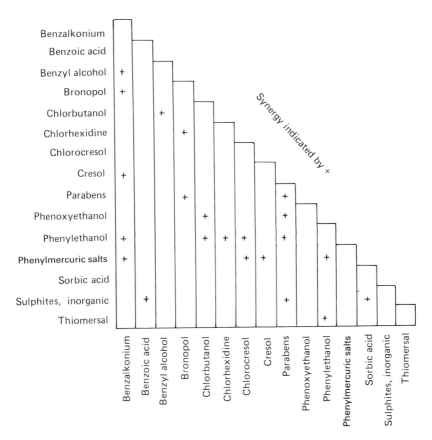

Fig. 2 — Examples of reported synergistic combinations of preservative agents.

relative ratios; this will be controlled not only by their initial concentrations within the formulation, but also by those factors which influence their availability in active form (section 2). Thus, if attempts are made to select synergistic combinations of preservatives, due attention must be given to their individual physicochemical properties in order to predict their likely behaviour in a formulated system. The extent of synergy can be tested in simple solution or in more complex formulations and some of the methodological approaches to this have been described (Denyer *et al.* 1985; Denyer and King 1988; Hodges and Hanlon 1990; McCarthy and Ferreira 1990). The laboratory examination of preservative combinations will also eliminate those with the potential for antagonism.

An additional phenomenon to synergy, also known to arise in the presence of preservatives, is one of potentiation. Here the activity of an antimicrobial agent is enhanced by the inclusion of a microbiologically inactive or only weakly active component which presumably sensitizes the microbial target to preservative action. The classic example of potentiation is that involving ethylenediaminetetracetic acid (EDTA), which has been clearly shown to enhance the activity of a range of preservative agents (Table 7), especially against *Ps. aeruginosa* (Hart 1984). A further example has already been considered in section 2.4 where low concentrations of non-ionic surfactants assist the antimicrobial action of preservative agents.

With the limitations existing in our current list of preservative agents, it is likely that the use of preservatives in combination will continue to increase. To maximize their potential, and to avoid unfortunate mismatches, their properties must be fully understood and exploited. In this respect, the potential benefits of synergy and the potentiating effects of formulation ingredients (see Chapter 12) should be exploited to advantage.

Table 7 — A selection of preservatives whose action is potentiated by EDTA

Benzalkonium chloride
Bronopol
Cetrimide
Chlorhexidine
Parabens
Phenol
Phenylethanol
Sorbic acid

5 TOXICITY

Whilst seeking to achieve maximum antimicrobial activity from preservative agents we need also to minimize adverse reaction in the user. Thus preservative agents are required to be selectively toxic and acceptable in all aspects of toxicity including acute, subacute and chronic exposure, local reactions, reproductive toxicity, mutagenicity and carcinogenicity (Schneider 1984; Hayden 1988). These demands have resulted in a reduction in the range of preservatives considered acceptable for pharmaceutical use, limited the application of others, and imposed considerable restrictions upon novel biocidal agents (Allwood 1978; Bloomfield 1986). Table 8 summarizes our current knowledge concerning the toxigenic potential of those preservatives most frequently used in pharmaceutical preparations. The classification scheme used is that employed in the Blaue Liste (a collection of toxicological data for cosmetic ingredients; Fiedler *et al.* 1989), from which much of the information is drawn. A further treatment of preservative toxicities can be found in Bronaugh and Maibach (1984), Lautier (1984) and Wallhaeusser (1984, 1988).

Current opinion would suggest that a satisfactory balance between antimicrobial effect and toxicity may be achieved by careful selection of preservative concentration. In some instances, it may be acceptable to achieve only a growth inhibitory or weak killing effect in order to avoid the toxicological consequences which may arise from higher levels of preservative agent. The need to exercise proper control over recalcitrant organisms is still, of course, a prerequisite to effective preservation.

Table 8 — Toxicological background for selected preservative agents

Preservative agent	T^a	RT^a	SI^a	MI^a	A^a	AT	TG
Benzalkonium chloride	T4		⊕	⊕	A2	−	−
Benzoic acid	T3			⊕	A2^d		
Benzyl alcohol	T3	b			A2		
Bronopol	T4		⊕	⊕	A2	−	−
Cetrimide	T4		⊕	⊕	A2	−	−
Chlorbutanol	T3			⊕	A2		
Chlorhexidine					A2	+	
Chlorocresol	T3		⊕	⊕	A2	−	
Cresol	(T3)	(+)	(⊕)	(⊕)	(A2)		
Ethanol	(T2)				(A1)	(−)	(−)
Parabens	T3		⊕	⊕	A3		
Phenol	(T4)	(+)	(⊕)	(⊕)	(A2)		
Phenoxyethanol	T3				A1		
Phenylethanol	(T3)				(A1)		−
Phenylmercuric salts	T5		⊕	⊕	A3		
Sorbic acid	T2		⊕	⊕	A2^c		
Sulphites, inorganic	T3		⊕	⊕	A3^e	+	
Thiomersal	T4		⊕	⊕	A3		

^{a}Toxicity data are drawn from the Blaue Liste except where indicated with parentheses.
^{b}Conflicting reports: E. Menczel and H. J. Maibach (*Acta Derm. Venerol.* (1972) **52**, 38) and H. Wollman *et al.* (*Pharmazie* (1967) **22**, 455).
^{c}Allergic reactions only at topical concentrations in excess of 1% (E. Lück. *Parfum. u. Kosmet.* (1964) **45**, 123).
^{d}Occasional reactions from oral ingestion by very sensitive persons.
^{e}Pseudoallergic and anaphylactic reactions following inhalation or oral ingestion.
NB: The absence of an indication of toxicity does not necessarily imply no toxicological hazard

T:	Acute oral toxicity (rat)	
	T1; relatively harmless	$(>15 \text{ g kg}^{-1})$
	T2; hardly toxic	$(5–15 \text{ g kg}^{-1})$
	T3; slightly toxic	$(0.5–5 \text{ g kg}^{-1})$
	T4; moderately toxic	$(50–500 \text{ mg kg}^{-1})$
	T5; highly toxic	$(1–50 \text{ mg kg}^{-1})$
	T6; extremely toxic	$(<1 \text{ mg kg}^{-1})$
RT:	Systemic toxicity; resorptive toxicity (from large areas of topical application; especially possible in children)	
	− ; none	
	+ ; recognized to occur	
SI:	Skin irritation	
	− ; none	
	+ ; in low concentrations	
	⊕; in high concentrations	
MI:	Mucous membrane irritation	
	− ; none	
	+ ; in low concentrations	
	⊕; in high concentrations	
A:	Allergy quota, allergic reactions	
	A0; unknown	
	A1; in single cases	
	A2; seldom	
	A3; notable occurrence	
AT:	Mutagenicity, Ames test	
	+ or −	
TG:	Teratogenicity	
	+ or −	

One further approach taken in an attempt to minimize the toxicological potential of preservative systems is to use combinations where submaximal levels of the component agents can be employed; in this regard the potential benefit of combining agents which demonstrate antimicrobial synergy is obvious. It must be remembered, however, that the toxicological behaviour of individual agents may also be modified in combination, as may also be the case when specific formulation ingredients are present.

6 PRESERVATIVE MONOGRAPHS

In this section, brief monographs are presented for the preservative agents summarized in Table 1 (see section 1). The information given is designed to be read in conjunction with data given elsewhere in this chapter. The tolerance of challenge organisms to the inactivators suggested for use in the preservative efficacy test (PET) must be confirmed by preliminary experimentation and, if found unsuitable, membrane filtration should be considered as an alternative approach. Dilution will always be a useful adjunct to the use of specific inactivators, especially with those preservatives known to possess a high concentration exponent. Typical in-use preservative concentrations are given for guidance only, as the actual concentration employed will depend upon the product type; maximum authorized concentrations for use in cosmetic products are given in Chapter 14. A further appreciation of preservative behaviour in formulated products can be gained by consulting Chapters 10 and 12. Additional reference information is available in Martindale (1989) and Wallhaeusser (1984, 1988).

6.1 Benzalkonium chloride
Synonym(s): mixture of alkyldimethylbenzylammonium chlorides.
CAS number: 139-07-1.
Class of compound: cationic quaternary ammonium.
Structural formula: general formula $[C_6H_5.CH_2.N(CH_3)_2.R]Cl$, where R represents a mixture of the alkyls from C_8H_{17} to $C_{18}H_{37}$, with the principal components represented by $C_{12}H_{25}$ and $C_{14}H_{29}$.
Stability: good, stable to autoclaving conditions.
Compatibility: incompatible with anionic surfactants, soaps, citrates, nitrates, iodides, heavy metals (including silver salts), alkalis, some oxidants, some commercial rubber mixes, proteins, blood; sorbed by some plastic materials.
PET inactivator: lecithin and a non-ionic surfactant such as Lubrol W or Tween 80 (Letheen broth).
Typical in-use concentration: 0.01–0.25%.

6.2 Benzoic acid (and salts)
Synonym(s): benzene carboxylic acid; sodium benzoate salt.
CAS number: 65-85-0.
Class of compound: organic weak acid (or salt).
Structural formula: $C_6H_5.CO_2H$; molecular weight 122.1, sodium benzoate 162.
Stability: stable at low pH.

Compatibility: incompatible with ferric salts and salts of heavy metals, non-ionic
     surfactants, quaternary compounds and gelatin; loss of activity in presence of
     proteins and glycerol.
PET inactivator: dilution and non-ionic surfactant such as Tween 80.
Typical in-use concentration: 0.1–0.5%.

6.3   Benzyl alcohol
Synonym(s): benzenemethanol, phenylcarbinol, phenylmethanol.
CAS number: 100-51-6.
Class of compound: alcohol.
Structural formula: $C_6H_5.CH_2OH$, molecular weight 108.1.
Stability: stable to autoclaving conditions; slowly oxidizes to benzaldehyde and
     benzoic acid in air, reduced by saturating solutions with nitrogen; dehydrates at
     low pH.
Compatibility: incompatible with oxidizing agents; inactivated by non-ionic
     surfactants.
PET inactivator: dilution and non-ionic surfactant such as Tween 80.
Typical in-use concentration: 1%.

6.4   Bronopol
Synonym(s): 2-bromo-2-nitropropane-1,3-diol.
CAS number: 52-51-7.
Class of compound: alcohol.
Structural formula: $C_3H_6BrNO_4$, molecular weight 200.
Stability: stable in aqueous solution at low pH (<5) and can be stored at room
     temperatures for up to 2 years with no decomposition or for at least 1 month at
     50°C; decomposition increases in the light, at elevated temperatures and in
     alkaline pH. Decomposition accelerated in presence of iron and aluminium.
     Unstable in anhydrous solutions of glycerol.
Compatibility: little or no inactivation by anionic, cationic or non-ionic surfactants,
     proteins or serum; some inactivation in blood; sulphydryl compounds (cysteine,
     thioglycollate), thiosulphate and metabisulphite are markedly antagonistic.
PET inactivator: sulphydryl compounds such as cysteine or thioglycollate.
Typical in-use concentraion: 0.01–0.1%.

6.5   Cetrimide
Synonym(s): alkyltrimethylammonium bromide, tetradecyltrimethylammonium
     bromide; cetyltrimethylammonium bromide, cetrimonium bromide and CTAB
     were formerly applied to cetrimide as the hexadecyltrimethylammonium bro-
     mide preparation.
CAS number: 57-09-0.
Class of compound: cationic quaternary ammonium.
Structural formula: chiefly tetradecyltrimethylammonium bromide with small
     amounts of dodecyl- and hexadecyltrimethylammonium bromides. Contains not
     less than 96% of alkyltrimethylammonium bromides calculated as $C_{17}H_{38}BrN$,
     molecular weight 336.4. The main component was formerly $C_{19}H_{42}BrN$ (hexa-
     decyltrimethylammonium bromide; British Pharmacopoeia 1953).

Stability: stable in solution and to autoclaving conditions.

Compatibility: incompatible with soaps and other anionic surfactants, nitrates (including phenylmercuric nitrate), heavy metals, some oxidants, some alkalis, some rubbers, proteins and blood.

PET inactivator: lecithin and a non-ionic surfactant such as Lubrol W or Tween 80 (Letheen broth).

Typical in-use concentration: 0.01–0.1%.

6.6 Chlorbutanol

Synonym(s): 1,1,1-trichloro-2-methylpropan-2-ol, chlorbutol, chlorobutanol, acetonechloroform.

CAS number: 57-15-8.

Class of compound: alcohol.

Structural formula: $C_4H_7Cl_3O$, molecular weight 177.5.

Stability: decomposes in aqueous solutions when heated, especially under alkaline conditions.

Compatibility: incompatible with some non-ionic surfactants and alkalis; sorbed by polyethylene and polypropylene containers.

PET inactivator: dilution and non-ionic surfactant such as Tween 80.

Typical in-use concentration: 0.3–0.5%.

6.7 Chlorhexidine

Synonym(s): 1,6-bis(5-*p*-chlorophenylbiguanido)hexane, as (di)acetate, (di)gluconate and (di)hydrochloride salts.

CAS number: 55-56-1 (chlorhexidine base).

Class of compound: cationic bisbiguanide.

Structural formula: base formula $C_{22}H_{30}Cl_2N_{10}$; diacetate ($2C_2H_4O_2$), molecular weight 625.6; digluconate ($2C_6H_{12}O_7$), molecular weight 897.8; dihydrochloride (2HCl), molecular weight 578.4.

Stability: generally unstable at high temperatures decomposing to give trace amounts of 4-chloroaniline, but diacetate and digluconate salts can be sterilized by autoclaving at 115°C for 30 minutes; alkaline pH promotes decomposition.

Compatibility: incompatible with soaps and other anionic agents, various gums and sodium alginate; forms insoluble salts with borates, bicarbonates, carbonates, chlorides, citrates, phosphates, and sulphates at concentrations of 0.05%.

PET inactivator: lecithin and a non-ionic surfactant such as Lubrol W or Tween 80 (Letheen broth).

Typical in-use concentration: 0.01–0.1%.

6.8 Chlorocresol

Synonym(s): 4-chloro-3-methylphenol, *p*-chloro-*m*-cresol, PCMC.

CAS number: 59-50-7.

Class of compound: halogenated phenolic.

Structural formula: C_7H_7ClO, molecular weight 142.6.

Stability: aqueous solutions turn yellow in light and air; solutions in water are stable to autoclaving and those in oil or glycerol to 160°C exposure for 1 hour.

Compatibility: reduction in activity in the presence of non-ionic surfactants; discoloration with iron salts.

PET inactivator: dilution and non-ionic surfactant such as Tween 80.

Typical in-use concentration: 0.1%.

6.9   Cresol

Synonym(s): 3-cresol, *m*-cresol, cresylic acid.

CAS number: 1319-77-3.

Class of compound: phenolic.

Structural formula: $CH_3.C_6H_4.OH$, a mixture of *ortho*, *meta* and *para* isomers but predominantly the *meta* isomer, molecular weight 108.1.

Stability: aqueous solutions turn yellow in light and air.

Compatibility: reduced activity in the presence of non-ionic surfactants.

PET inactivator: dilution and non-ionic surfactant such as Tween 80.

Typical in-use concentration: 0.3%.

6.10   Ethanol

Synonym(s): ethyl alcohol, dehydrated alcohol, absolute alcohol, alcohol (95% ethanol).

CAS number: 64-17-5.

Class of compound: alcohol.

Structural formula: C_2H_5OH, molecular weight 46.1.

Stability: aqueous solutions stable to autoclaving in closed containers, but special conditions are required (see: Christensen, H. H. and von Marcussen, O. (1943) *Acta Path. Microbiol. Scand.* **20** 735).

Compatibility: used as a solvent or co-solvent in pharmaceutical preparations and as a basis for the production of tinctures.

PET inactivator: dilution.

Typical in-use concentration: rarely used solely for its preservative capability, which is only satisfactory at concentrations above 15–20% and is optimal at 60–70%.

6.11   Parabens

Synonym(s): esters of *p*-hydroxybenzoic acid (methyl, ethyl, propyl, butyl and benzyl), and their sodium salts, PHB esters, NIPA esters.

CAS number: methyl (99-76-3), ethyl (120-47-8), propyl (94-13-3), butyl (94-26-8), benzyl (94-18-8).

Class of compound: benzoic acid ester.

Structural formula: $HO.C_6H_5CO_2.R$, where R represents CH_3 (methyl ester, molecular weight 152.1), C_2H_5 (ethyl ester, molecular weight 166.2), C_3H_7 (propyl ester, molecular weight 180.2), C_4H_9 (butyl ester, molecular weight 194.2), or $CH_2.C_6H_5$ (benzyl ester, molecular weight 228.2); the general formula for the sodium salt is $Na.O.C_6H_5CO_2.R$ with a molecular weight increase of 22 over each respective ester.

Stability: stable; chemical stability decreases as pH increases, with significant hydrolysis taking place at strongly alkaline pH's and elevated temperatures; acidic solutions can generally withstand autoclaving conditions; sensitive to excessive light exposure.

Compatibility: some reduction in activity seen with anionic agents, non-ionic surfactants, methylcellulose, gelatin, povidone and proteins; incompatible with alkalis and iron salts.

PET inactivator: dilution and non-ionic surfactant such as Tween 80.

Typical in-use concentration: up to 0.4% single ester or 0.8% for a mixture of esters; generally 0.2% methyl paraben, 0.15% ethylparaben, 0.02% propyl- and butylparaben, and 0.006% benzylparaben.

6.12   Phenol

Synonym(s): carbolic acid, hydroxybenzene.

CAS number: 108-95-2.

Class of compound: phenolic.

Structural formula: $C_6H_5.OH$, molecular weight 94.1.

Stability: excessive light exposure in air will catalyse oxidation and lead to discoloration of solution; aqueous solutions are autoclavable and oily solutions can be sterilized by 150°C treatment for 1 hour.

Compatibility: incompatible with alkali salts, iron salts, and certain drugs; activity reduced by non-ionic surfactants.

PET inactivator: dilution and non-ionic surfactant such as Tween 80.

Typical in-use concentration: 0.25–0.5%.

6.13   Phenoxyethanol

Synonym(s): 2-phenoxyethanol, phenoxetol, ethylene glycol monophenyl ether, β-phenoxyethyl alcohol.

CAS number: 122-99-6.

Class of compound: phenolic derivative.

Structural formula: $C_8H_{10}O_2$, molecular weight 138.2.

Stability: stable; aqueous solutions sterilized by autoclaving.

Compatibility: compatible with anionic and cationic surfactants; reduced activity in presence of some non-ionic agents.

PET inactivator: dilution and non-ionic surfactant such as Tween 80.

Typical in-use concentration: 1.0%.

6.14   Phenylethanol

Synonym(s): 2-phenylethanol, β-phenylethyl alcohol, phenethyl alcohol, benzyl carbinol.

CAS number: 60-12-8.

Class of compound: alcohol.

Structural formula: $C_6H_5.CH_2.CH_2OH$, molecular weight 122.2.

Stability: poor stability with oxidants.

Compatibility: partially inactivated by non-ionic surfactants.

PET inactivator: dilution and non-ionic surfactant such as Tween 80.

Typical in-use concentration: 0.3–0.5%.

6.15   Phenylmercuric salts

Synonym(s): as phenylmercuric acetate (PMA, acetoxyphenylmercury), phenylmercuric borate, and phenylmercuric nitrate (PMN) salts.

CAS number: acetate (62-38-4), borate (8017-88-7), nitrate (55-68-5).

Class of compound: cationic organic mercurial.

Structural formula: $C_6H_5HgO.CO.CH_3$ (acetate salt, molecular weight 336.7), $C_6H_5.Hg.O.B(OH)_2$ and $C_6H_5.Hg.OH$ (basic borate salt, molecular weight 633.2), $C_6H_5.Hg.NO_3$ and $C_6H_5.Hg.OH$ (basic nitrate salt, molecular weight 634.4).

Stability: sensitive to excessive light and air exposure.

Compatibility: incompatible with halides, aluminium and other metals, ammonia and ammonium salts, sulphides and thioglycollates; activity may be reduced in presence of anionic emulsifying and suspending agents; can adsorb to polyethylene and certain rubber components; compatible with some non-ionic surfactants.

PET inactivator: sulphydryl compounds such as cysteine or thioglycollate.

Typical in-use concentration: 0.001–0.002%.

6.16 Sorbic acid

Synonym(s): 2,4-hexadienoic acid, 2-propenyl acrylic acid, calcium or potassium sorbate salts.

CAS number: 110-44-1.

Structural formula: $C_6H_8O_2$, molecular weight 112.1; potassium sorbate $C_6H_7KO_2$, molecular weight 150.2.

Stability: sensitive to light and air exposure; unstable in a variety of containers except when stored at refrigeration temperatures or in the presence of an antioxidant.

Compatibility: appears compatible with acacia and tragacanth mucilages; only slightly incompatible with non-ionic surfactants.

PET inactivator: dilution and non-ionic surfactant such as Tween 80.

Typical in-use concentration: 0.2%.

6.17 Sulphites, inorganic

Synonym(s): inorganic sulphites, including sodium/potassium sulphite, and sodium/potassium metabisulphite (pyrosulphite).

CAS number: sodium sulphite (10102-15-5), sodium metabisulphite (7681-57-4).

Class of compound: inorganic acid.

Structural formula: $Na_2SO_3.7H_2O$ and K_2SO_3 (sodium and potassium sulphites, molecular weights 252.1 and 158.3, respectively), $Na_2S_2O_5$ and $K_2S_2O_5$ (sodium and potassium metabisulphites, molecular weights 190.1 and 222.3, respectively).

Stability: unstable in solution, decomposing in air especially on heating.

Compatibility: sodium metabisulphite usually employed in acid conditions where antimicrobial activity is encouraged by liberation of sulphur dioxide and sulphurous acid; sodium sulphite is incompatible with strong acids and is usually preferred for use in alkali preparations; inorganic sulphites are incompatible with oxidizing agents.

PET inactivator: sulphydryl compounds such as cysteine and thioglycollate.

Typical in-use concentration: 0.1%.

6.18   Thiomersal
Synonym(s): sodium (2-carboxyphenylthio)ethylmercury, sodium *o*-(ethylmercur-ithio)benzoate, sodium ethyl mercurithiosalicylate, thiomersalate, thimerosal, mercurothiolate.

CAS number: 54-64-8.

Class of compound: anionic organic mercurial.

Structural formula: $C_9H_9HgNaO_2S$, molecular weight 404.8.

Stability: aqueous solutions are fairly stable to heat and can be sterilized by autoclaving, but are labile to light and less stable in alkaline conditions; traces of copper, iron and zinc ions increase heat lability.

Compatibility: incompatible with acids, iodine, heavy metal salts, non-ionics, lecithin, thioglycollate, and proteins; can adsorb to various types of rubber.

PET inactivator: sulphydryl compounds such as cysteine and thioglycollate or lecithin–Tween 80–thioglycollate medium.

Typical in-use concentration: 0.002–0.01%.

7   REFERENCES

Akers, M. J. (1984) Considerations in selecting antimicrobial preservative agents for parenteral product development. *Pharm. Technol.* May 36–46.

Allwood, M. C. (1973) Inhibition of *Staphylococcus aureus* by combinations of non-ionic surface-active agents and antibacterial substances. *Microbios* **7** 209–214.

Allwood, M. C. (1978) Antimicrobial agents in single- and multi-dose injections. *J. Appl. Bacteriol.* **44** Svii–Sxvii.

Allwood, M. C. (1982) The effectiveness of preservatives in insulin injections. *Pharm. J.* **229** 340.

Bean, H. S. (1972) Preservatives for pharmaceuticals. *J. Soc. Cosmet. Chem.* **23** 703–720.

Bean, H. S., Richards, J. P. and Thomas, J. (1962) The bactericidal activity against *Escherichia coli* of phenol in oil-in-water dispersions. *Boll. Chim. Farm.* **101** 339–346.

Bean, H. S., Heman-Ackah, S. M. and Thomas, J. (1965) The activity of antibacter-ials in two-phase systems. *J. Soc. Cosmet. Chem.* **16** 15–30.

Bean, H. S., Konning, G. H. and Malcolm, S. A. (1969) A model for the influence of emulsion formulation on the activity of phenolic preservatives. *J. Pharm. Pharmacol.* **21** 173S–180S.

Berry, H. and Michaels, I. (1950) The evaluation of the bactericidal activity of ethylene glycol and some of its monoalkyl ethers against *Bacterium coli*. *J. Pharm. Pharmacol.* **2** 243–249.

Beveridge, E. G., Boyd, I. and Jessen, G. W. (1980) The action of 2-phenoxyethanol upon *Pseudomonas aeruginosa* NCTC 6749. *J. Pharm. Pharmacol.* **32** 17P.

Bloomfield, S. F. (1986) Control of microbial contamination. Part 2: current problems in preservation. *Br. J. Pharmacol.* March 72–79.

Bloomfield, S. F. (1988) Control of microbial contamination in non-sterile pharma-ceuticals, cosmetics and toiletries. In: Bloomfield, S. F., Baird, R., Leak, R. E. and Leech, R. (eds), *Microbial quality assurance in pharmaceuticals, cosmetics and toiletries*. Ellis Horwood, Chichester, pp. 9–14.

British Pharmacopoeia (1953) HMSO, London.

Bronaugh, R. L. and Maibach, H. I. (1984) Safety evaluation of cosmetic preservatives. In: Kabara, J. J. (ed.), *Cosmetic and drug preservation: principles and practice (Cosmetic Science and Technology Series, Vol. 1)*. Marcel Dekker, New York, pp. 503–531.

Chapman, D. G. (1987) Preservatives available for use. In: Board, R. G., Allwood, M. C. and Banks, J. G. (eds), *Preservatives in the food, pharmaceutical and environmental industries, SAB Technical Series 22*. Blackwell Scientific Publications, Oxford, pp. 177–195.

Chopra, I. (1990) Bacterial resistance to disinfectants, antiseptics and toxic metal ions. In: Denyer, S. P. and Hugo, W. B. (eds), *Mechanisms of action of chemical biocides: their study and exploitation, SAB Technical Series 27*. Blackwell Scientific Publications, Oxford (in press).

Croshaw, B. (1977) Preservatives for cosmetics and toiletries. *J. Soc. Cosmet. Chem.* **28** 3–16.

Dempsey, G. (1988) The effect of container materials and multiple-phase formulation components on the activity of antimicrobial agents. In: Bloomfield, S. F., Baird, R., Leak, R. E. and Leech, R. (eds), *Microbial quality assurance in pharmaceuticals, cosmetics and toiletries*. Ellis Horwood, Chichester, pp. 94–103.

Denyer, S. P. (1990) Mechanisms of action of biocides. *Int. Biodet.* **26** 89–100.

Denyer, S. P. and King, R. O. (1988) Development of preservative systems. In: Bloomfield, S. F., Baird, R., Leak, R. E. and Leech, R. (eds), *Microbial quality assurance in pharmaceuticals, cosmetics and toiletries*. Ellis Horwood, Chichester, pp. 156–170.

Denyer, S. P., Hugo, W. B. and Harding, V. D. (1985) Synergy in preservative combinations. *Int. J. Pharm.* **25** 245–253.

Fiedler, H. P., Ippen, H., Kemper, F. H., Lupke, N.-P., Schulz, K. H. and Umbach, W. (1989) *Blaue Liste: Inhaltsstoffe kosmetischer Mittel*. Editio Cantor, Aulendorf, FRG.

Garrett, E. R. (1966) A basic model for the evaluation and prediction of preservative action. *J. Pharm. Pharmacol.* **18** 589–601.

Gilbert, P. (1988) Microbial resistance to preservative systems. In: Bloomfield, S. F., Baird, R., Leak, R. E. and Leech, R. (eds), *Microbial quality assurance in pharmaceuticals, cosmetics and toiletries*. Ellis Horwood, Chichester, pp. 171–194.

Gilbert, P. and Wright, N. (1987) Non-plasmidic resistance towards preservatives of pharmaceutical products. In: Board, R. G., Allwood, M. C. and Banks, J. G. (eds), *Preservatives in the food, pharmaceutical and environmental industries, SAB Technical Series 22*. Blackwell Scientific Publications, Oxford, pp. 255–279.

Hart, J. R. (1984) Chelating agents as preservative potentiators. In: Kabara, J. J. (ed.), *Cosmetic and drug preservation: principles and practice (Cosmetic Science and Technology Series Vol. 1)*. Marcel Dekker, New York, pp. 323–337.

Hayden, J. (1988) Safety evaluation of preservatives. In: Bloomfield, S. F., Baird,

R., Leak, R. E. and Leech, R. (eds), *Microbial quality assurance in pharmaceuticals, cosmetics and toiletries*. Ellis Horwood, Chichester, pp. 147–155.

Hodges, N. A. and Hanlon, W. (1990) Detection and measurement of combined biocide action. In: Denyer, S. P. and Hugo, W. B. (eds), *Mechanisms of action of chemical biocides: their study and exploitation, SAB Technical Series 27*. Blackwell Scientific Publications, Oxford (in press).

Hugo, W. B. (1988) The degradation of preservatives by microorganisms. In: Houghton, D. R., Smith, R. N. and Eggins, H. O. W. (eds), *Biodeterioration 7*. Elsevier Applied Sciences, London, pp. 163–170.

Hugo, W. B. and Denyer, S. P. (1987) The concentration exponent of disinfectants and preservatives (biocides). In: Board, R. G., Allwood, M. C. and Banks, J. G. (eds), *Preservatives in the food, pharmaceutical and environmental industries, SAB Technical Series 22*. Blackwell Scientific Publications, Oxford, pp. 281–291.

Hugo, W. B., Denyer, S. P., York, H. L. and Tucker, J. D. (1984) Preservative activity in diluted corticosteroid creams. *J. Hosp. Infect.* **5** 329–333.

Karabit, M.S., Juneskans, O. T. and Lundgren, P. (1985) Studies on the evaluation of preservative efficacy. I. The determination of antimicrobial characteristics of phenol. *Acta Pharm. Suec.* **22** 281–290.

Karabit, M. S., Juneskans, O. T. and Lundgren, P. (1986) Studies on the evaluation of preservative efficacy. II. The determination of antimicrobial characteristics of benzyl alcohol. *J. Clin. Hosp. Pharm.* **11** 281–289.

Karabit, M. S., Juneskans, O. T. and Lundgren, P. (1988) Studies on the evaluation of preservative efficacy. III. The determination of antimicrobial characteristics of benzalkonium chloride. *Int. J. Pharm.* **46** 141–147.

Karabit, M. S., Juneskans, O. T. and Lundgren, P. (1989) Factorial designs in the evaluation of preservative efficacy. *Int. J. Pharm.* **56** 169–174.

Kazmi, S. J. A. and Mitchell, A. G. (1976) The interaction of preservative and nonionic surfactant mixtures. *Can. J. Pharm. Sci.* **11** 10–17.

Kazmi, S. J. A. and Mitchell, A. G. (1978a) Preservation of solubilized and emulsified systems. I. Correlation of mathematically predicted preservative availability with antimicrobial activity. *J. Pharm. Sci.* **7** 1260–1265.

Kazmi, S. J. A. and Mitchell, A. G. (1978b) Preservation of solubilized and emulsified systems. II. Theoretical development of capacity and its role in antimicrobial activity of chlorocresol in cetamacrogol-stabilized systems. *J. Pharm. Sci.* **67** 1266–1271.

Kostenbauder, H. B. (1983) Physical factors influencing the activity of antimicrobial agents. In: Block, S. S. (ed.), *Disinfection, sterilization and preservation*, 3rd edn. Lea and Febiger, Philadelphia, pp. 811–828.

Lautier, F. (1984) Dermal and ocular toxicity of antiseptics: methods for the appraisal of the safety of antiseptics. In: Kabara, J. J. (ed.), *Cosmetic and drug preservation: principles and practice (Cosmetic Science and Technology Series, Vol. 1)*. Marcel Dekker, New York, pp. 483–501.

Lehmann, R. H. (1988) Synergisms in disinfectant formulations. In: Payne, K. R. (ed.), *Industrial biocides, Critical Reports on Applied Chemistry, Vol. 23*. Wiley, Chichester, pp. 68–90.

Mackie, M. A. L., Lyall, J., McBride, R. J., Murray, J. B. and Smith, G. (1986)

Antimicrobial properties of some aromatic alcohols. *Pharm. Acta Helv.* **61** 333–336.

Martindale (1982) *The Extra Pharmacopoeia*, 28th edn. Pharmaceutical Press, London.

Martindale (1989) *The Extra Pharmacopoeia* 29th edn. Pharmaceutical Press, London.

McCarthy, T. J. (1984) Formulated factors affecting the activity of preservatives. In: Kabara, J. J. (ed.), *Cosmetic and drug preservation: principles and practice (Cosmetic Science and Technology, Vol. 1)*. Marcel Dekker, New York, pp. 359–388.

McCarthy, T. J. and Ferreira, J.-H. (1990) Attempted measurement of the activity of selected preservative combinations. *J. Clin. Pharm. Therapeut.* **15** 123–129.

Moore, K. E. and Stretton, R. J. (1981) The effect of pH, temperature and certain media constituents on the stability and activity of the preservative, Bronopol. *J. Appl. Bacteriol.* **51** 483–494.

Russell, A. D. (1982) Factors influencing the efficacy of antimicrobial agents. In: Russell, A. D., Hugo, W. B. and Ayliffe, G. A. J. (eds), *Principles and practice of disinfection, preservation and sterilisation*. Blackwell Scientific Publications, Oxford, pp. 107–133.

Schneider, F. H. (1984) Evaluation of chemical toxicology of chemicals. In: Kabara, J. J. (eds), *Cosmetic and drug preservation: principles and practice (Cosmetic Science and Technology, Vol. 1)*. Marcel Dekker, New York, pp. 533–558.

Wallhaeusser, K.-H. (1974) Antimicrobial preservatives in Europe: experience with preservatives used in pharmaceuticals and cosmetics. International symposium on preservatives in biological products. *Dev. Biol. Stand.* **24** 9–28.

Wallhaeusser, K.-H. (1984) Appendix B. Antimicrobial preservatives used by the cosmetic industry. In: Kabara, J. J. (ed.), *Cosmetic and drug preservation: principles and practice (Cosmetic Science and Technology Series, Vol. 1)*. Marcel Dekker, New York, pp. 605–745.

Wallhaeusser, K.-H. (1988) *Praxis der Sterilisation–Desinfektion–Konservierung*, 4th edn. Thieme, Stuttgart/New York.

12

Interactions between preservatives and pharmaceutical components

H. Van Doorne
Vakgroep Farmaceutische Technologie, Biofarmacie en Receptuur, Antonius
Deusinglaan 2, 9713 AW Groningen, The Netherlands

1   INTRODUCTION

Many commodities are susceptible to microbial deterioration and therefore require adequate protection. Thus, the preservation of products such as wood, paper, fabric, paints, alcoholic and non-alcoholic beverages, foods, cosmetics and pharmaceuticals has become an indispensable and economically important aspect of modern technology. The objective of preservation is (1) to prolong the shelf-life of the product by minimizing the growth potential of micro-organisms, and (2) to safeguard the consumer from the potential hazards associated with the use of products with unacceptably high levels of contamination.

The choice of a preservative for a given pharmaceutical preparation is based on a number of factors. The type of preparation and the route of administration are primary criteria on which such a choice is based. Importantly, however, the activity of an antimicrobial compound may also be adversely affected by the other components of the preparation. As there is generally no need to specify these interactions, they are usually referred to as incompatibilities. On the other hand some compounds are known to enhance the activity of antimicrobial agents. Knowledge and understanding of such interferences will help the formulator of pharmaceutical and cosmetic preparations to choose a suitable preservative.

It is the purpose of this contribution to review the most important interactions between preservatives and pharmaceutical components. Whenever possible the physicochemical nature of the interactions will be discussed.

2. PHYSICOCHEMICAL RELATED EFFECTS

2.1 The effect of pH

The choice of the pH of a preparation is mainly based on solubility and stability of the therapeutically active components and on the tolerance of body tissues which come into contact with the preparation. The pH may also be chosen to give the preparation its required rheological properties or its appearance. An example of the latter is the addition of triethanolamine to creams containing stearic acid, as in Phenergan Creme (formulary of the Dutch pharmacists). The stearic acid salts which are formed give the cream its relatively hard consistency and a mother-of-pearl-like appearance. Sorbic acid, which was originally used as the preservative, appeared to be completely ineffective (Van Doorne 1980). The pH of the formulation can influence the availability of the active form of an ionizable preservative (Bean 1972). Moreover, it may alter the ionization of components of the formulation. Some of the preservative –component interactions observed may be pH dependent.

A discussion of the effect of pH on preservative activity is beyond the scope of this chapter. The reader is referred to Chapter 11.

2.2 Adsorption by solids

It is extremely difficult to protect solid/liquid dispersions against microbial attack. A recent survey (Vanhaecke *et al.* 1987) showed that eight out of 12 marketed antacid suspensions failed to meet the United States Pharmacopeia (USP) XXI (1985) requirements for preservative activity. Although the main cause of the failures was the incompatibility of pH with the chosen preservative, interaction with the solid components could not be excluded.

Liquid or semi-solid pharmaceutical preparations may contain varying amounts of solids, ranging from 0 to 50%. In addition to the solid material, suspensions contain thickening agents such as natural clays (veegum, bentonite) or semi-synthetic compounds such as modified celluloses, or polyvinylpyrrolidone (PVP). Solids in suspensions are used as therapeutically active components (e.g. suspensions of antibiotics or corticosteroids, suspending agents (e.g. bentonite and veegum), or as colouring agents (e.g. calamine).

The binding of preservatives by solid particles has been studied by many workers in this field (Bean and Dempsey 1971; Yousef *et al.* 1973a, 1973b; McCarthy 1969; Myburgh and McCarthy 1980a, 1980b). For a review of the older literature the reader is referred to McCarthy and Myburgh (1977). Interactions with suspending agents are discussed in section 2.3.

Both therapeutically active compounds and other raw materials may adsorb considerable amounts of preservative. Pioneer investigations in this field were conducted by Batuyios and Brecht (1957), who studied the adsorption of some quaternary ammonium compounds (QAC) by talc and kaolin. A striking example of interaction with therapeutically active compounds was given by Beveridge and Hope (1967). These authors studied the reason for the observed spoilage of sulphadimidine mixture BPC and found that the preservative (benzoic acid) was adsorbed by the undissolved sulphonamide. Another example of adsorption of preservatives by suspended drug particles was given by Raab and Windisch (1970), who studied the influence of suspensions of corticosteroids on the antimicrobial activity of some QACs by using a manometric technique. Bean and Dempsey (1971) studied the effect of suspended procaine penicillin particles on the bactericidal activity of benzalkonium chloride. Benzalkonium chloride was found to be adsorbed by procaine penicillin. Adsorbed benzalkonium chloride still had some antimicrobial activity, as the suspension possessed a greater antimicrobial activity than the corresponding supernatant, from which the solid material had been removed by centrifugation.

The available information clearly shows that binding almost invariably results in a decrease in activity of the preservative. Whilst the ionic preservatives (QACs, chlorhexidine) are as a rule strongly bound, the weakly anionic compounds such as methylparaben are not.

2.3 Interaction with suspending agents

The interaction between preservatives and natural suspending agents has been examined on a number of occasions. Particular attention has been paid to natural clays and hydrocolloids. In a study of eight preservatives, only chlorhexidine was found to be adsorbed to a great (33%) extent by tragacanth (McCarthy and Myburgh 1974).

In a study on the adsorption of preservatives, including sorbic acid and benzalkonium chloride by starch, McCarthy (1969) observed that sorbic acid was adsorbed to only a limited extent, whereas chlorhexidine was almost completely (97%) adsorbed. The interaction between benzalkonium chloride and some suspending agents, including bentonite, veegum, tragacanth and sodium alginate, was studied by Yousef *et al.* (1973b). In general the interaction resulted in a decrease in antimicrobial activity. According to the extent of the antagonism, the materials were classified into four categories: (i) highly antagonistic (attapulgite, bentonite, veegum, magnesium trisilicate and Tween); (ii) moderately antagonistic (kaolin, tragacanth and sodium alginate); (iii) slightly antagonistic (talc, gum arabic, agar, carboxymethyl cellulose sodium, methyl cellulose, starch, aerosil and calamine); (iv) non-antagonistic (polyethylene glycols). An exception to the general rule, that adsorption leads to loss of activity, was observed by El-Nakeeb *et al.* (1975) who, in a study of the effect of pectin on the antimicrobial activity of some preservatives, observed that benzalkonium chloride was inactivated, whereas the activities of methylparaben and phenylmercuric nitrate were increased.

Mansour and Guth (1968) studied the complexation of benzoic and sorbic acid by various starches in aqueous solutions. The amylose part, rather than the amylopectin part of the starches, was found to complex with the preservatives.

Semi-synthetic thickeners may also decrease the free aqueous concentration of preservatives. However, the chemical nature of these interactions has not been studied in detail and conflicting results have been reported. Thus DeLuca and Kostenbauder (1960) reported that benzalkonium chloride was not antagonized by methylcellulose, whereas Yousef *et al.* (1973a) observed a marked antagonism.

Tromp *et al.* (1976) reported a 7% loss of benzalkonium chloride in the presence of hypromellose and Myburgh and McCarthy (1980b) observed a decreased activity of cetylpyridinium chloride in the presence of hypromellose. Richards (1976) pointed out that the reaction between hypromellose and benzalkonium chloride occurred during sterilization.

Most of the published work deals with simple aqueous dispersions. Myburgh and McCarthy (1980b) studied systems in which preservative, suspending agent and solid material were present simultaneously. They concluded that the activity of a preservative in a suspended system could not be predicted, especially since suspending agents and suspended solid particles may act synergistically or antagonistically with preservatives.

2.4   Interaction with emulsifiers
Many chemical preservatives are lipophilic compounds (e.g. parabens), or compounds containing a substantial lipophilic part in the molecule (e.g. QACs). Exceptions are Bronopol and phenylmercuric compounds. The lipophilic nature of the molecules makes them liable to micellar solubilization by emulsifiers. Interaction between antimicrobials and non-ionic emulsifiers was first reported by Bolle and Mirimanoff (1950). In their studies of iodine solubilized by surface-active compounds Allawala and Riegelman (1953a, 1953b) demonstrated that it was the thermodynamic activity rather than the overall concentration of the iodine that was related to the antimicrobial activity. Pisano and Kostenbauder (1959) obtained similar results for combinations of parabens with Tween 80. In the following three decades numerous papers on this issue were published.

A mathematical model for the physicochemical interaction of preservatives with emulsifiers was developed by Kazmi and Mitchell (1978a). The theory was extended to solubilized disperse systems (emulsions) by taking into account the partition of the preservative between oil and water phase (Kazmi and Mitchell 1978b). Using chlorocresol these authors confirmed the observations of Pisano and Kostenbauder (1959) that short-term antimicrobial activity can be related to the free (unbound) preservative concentration in the aqueous phase and that preservative solubilized within the surfactants does not contribute to preservation. Nevertheless there is some scope for argument.

(a) The activity of benzalkonium chloride and to a lesser extent of chlorhexidine was increased by a low (0.02%) concentration of Tween 80, but a higher concentration (0.5%) completely eliminated the inhibitory effect of both antimicrobials (Brown and Richards 1964). These results can be understood, if it is assumed that: (i) Tween 80 causes a change in the sensitivity of the cell, e.g. by altering the cellular envelope, as suggested by Brown and Richards (1964); and (ii) benzalkonium chloride is solubilized by the higher concentration of Tween 80 to such an extent that the free aqueous concentration is below a minimal effective level. In the case of the lower concentration, solubilization of the preservative will occur because the Tween 80 concentration is still above the critical micelle concentration, but the amount of preservative that is bound will be negligible.
(b) Yamaguchi *et al.* (1982) studied the effect of various non-ionic surfactants on the antimicrobial activity of butylparaben. Their results indicated that the concentration of free butylparaben is primarily responsible for its antimicrobial activity against *Candida albicans*, but that the total concentration of butylparaben in the system determines its activity against *Pseudomonas aeruginosa*. An explanation for these findings was not given. The preservative effect of butylparaben-containing liposome preparations was found to be roughly proportional to the free concentration of the preservative (Komatsu *et al.* 1986).
(c) Kazmi and Mitchell (1978b) concluded that the preservation of emulsified systems depended on free preservative concentration. However, they pointed out that the bound part of the preservative serves as a reservoir, from which new preservative will be liberated when it is lost due to absorption onto the container surface, or due to chemical decomposition, etc.
(d) Methylparaben can be solubilized by sodium lauryl sulphate in concentrations above the critical micelle concentration of sodium lauryl sulphate (0.2%) (Van Doorne 1977). In keeping with this observation sodium lauryl sulphate (1.5%) was found to antagonize the activity of methylparaben against *Ps. aeruginosa*. The inhibitory action of sodium lauryl sulphate has been known for many years (Birkeland and Steinhaus 1939), and a selective medium for the detection of coli–aerogenes bacteria in water and dairy products is based on its use (Dyett 1957). This selective activity may explain the observation of Jund and Carrère (1971) who found a potentiation by sodium lauryl sulphate of the activity of some preservatives (including methylparaben), particularly against *Staphylococcus aureus*.

It is concluded that the interaction between lipophilic preservatives and surface-active compounds usually results in a reduction of preservative activity. However, occasionally deviations from this general rule have been observed, depending on the type and concentration of emulsifier and even on the type of test organism used.

2.5   Miscellaneous antagonizing interactions

In the previous sections a number of relatively well-understood phenomena were reviewed. Little systematic work has been carried out on the interaction between formulation components such as pharmacologically active compounds and preservatives. Richards and McBride (1972) observed that benzalkonium chloride was less effective in the presence of atropine than in the presence of either pilocarpine or physostigmine. Chlorhexidine, on the other hand, was less effective in physostigmine eye-drops than in pilocarpine preparations. The latter observation was ascribed to sodium metabisulphite, which was present only in the physostigmine eye-drops. Chlorhexidine was known to be incompatible with sulphates and therefore probably so with sulphites. Tromp *et al.* (1977) compared the antimicrobial activities of 22 eye-drop formulations with the activities of the corresponding basic solutions. None of the therapeutically active compounds were found to exert a significant and consistent antagonizing effect upon the preservative. Phenylmercuric nitrate, which is a poor, slow-acting preservative (Tromp *et al.* 1977), is antagonized in its action by ethylenediaminetetraacetic acid (EDTA) (Brown 1968; Richards and Reary 1972), and by sodium thiosulphate. The effect of EDTA is ascribed to complexation of the mercury atom. The interaction with sodium thiosulphate could not be explained. The activity of thiomersal, a different mercury-containing preservative, was also antagonized by EDTA (Richards and Reary 1972).

Richards and Richards (1979) observed antagonism of antibacterial activity between EDTA–benzalkonium chloride, and EDTA–chlorhexidine combinations with *Ps. cepacia* and *Staph. aureus*. These observations are remarkable, as EDTA has been shown to increase the activity of both preservatives against *Ps. aeruginosa* (cf. section 2.6).

Despite the fact that the parabens are considered to be relatively inert chemical compounds, their inactivation by other formulation ingredients has been observed on at least two occasions. Meyer (1958) observed that the activity of parabens was decreased in the presence of 7-oxyethyl-theophyllin, and Toama *et al.* (1981) observed an antagonism between three parabens and saccharin.

Another example of a group of compounds showing antagonism when combined with preservatives are the cyclodextrins. Cyclodextrins have been studied extensively as additives for foods, cosmetics and pharmaceuticals. Owing to their ability to form inclusion complexes, the aqueous solubility, chemical stability or bioavailability of a complexed drug molecule may be improved. Particularly β-cyclodextrin (a cyclic oligosaccharide, consisting of seven glucose units) and its derivatives are capable of forming inclusion complexes with many pharmaceutically relevant compounds, including preservatives, such as sorbic acid and the parabens (Lach and Cohen 1963), and antibiotics (Van Doorne *et al.* 1988). The antimicrobial activity of the guest molecules is lost due to this complexation (Van Doorne *et al.* 1988; Uekama *et al.* 1980).

2.6   Potentiation of preservative activity

Occasionally satisfactory preservation of complex pharmaceutical or cosmetic products cannot be achieved by means of a single compound. A combination of two or more antimicrobially active compounds can solve such problems. If the effect produced by the combined agents is greater than the sum of the effects of the individual compounds, the combination is synergistic. Obviously, such a combination is advantageous as an enhanced antimicrobial activity is obtained at reduced individual concentrations. In this way the risk of undesired side effects, such as allergy, may be reduced. In a recent review (Denyer *et al.* 1985) 45 synergistic combinations are mentioned. Some of the synergistic combinations which are used in marketed preparations are summarized in Table 1. A further discussion of synergy is given in Chapter 11.

Table 1 — Examples of synergistic antibacterial combinations used in marketed preparations

Compound A	Compound B	Type of preparation	Reference
Chlorhexidine	EDTA	Ophthalmic solutions	Richards and McBride (1972)
Chlorhexidine	phenylethanol	Ophthalmic preparations	Richards and McBride (1972)
Parabens	Germall	Cosmetic creams	Berke and Rosen (1970); Jacobs *et al.* (1975)
Parabens	Glycols	Dermatological preparations	Prickett *et al.* (1961); Van Doorne and Dubois (1980)
Parabens	2-phenoxy-ethanol	Cosmetics	Parker *et al.* (1968)
QAC	EDTA	Eye-drops, contact lens solutions	Richards (1971); Clausen (1973)
Sorbic acid	glycerylmonolaurate	Cosmetics	Kabara (1980)

Few reports have been published on the mechanism of synergy. An exception is the potentiating effect of EDTA on the activity of quaternary ammonium compounds and other preservatives against Gram-negative bacteria. The outer-membrane–peptidoglycan complex is stabilized by divalent cation bridges. Owing to the chelating action of EDTA the divalent ions are removed from the complex, which causes destabilization of the outer membrane and loss of lipopolysaccharide. In this way compounds that are otherwise excluded from the cell may gain easier access to the inner part of the cells, such as the cytoplasmic membrane (Gray and Wilkinson 1965; Leive 1965; Gilbert 1988). In this respect *Ps. cepacia* seems to be an unusual organism as its resistance to both benzalkonium chloride (Richards and Richards 1979) and chloramphenicol (Nielsen and Close 1982) is increased by EDTA.

Propylene glycol is particularly useful in dispersed systems such as creams. In addition to its synergistic activity propylene glycol increases the aqueous solubility of lipophilic preservatives such as the parabens; as a consequence the oil/water partition coefficient is reduced, leading to an increased concentration of the preservative in the water phase of the preparation (Van Doorne and Dubois 1980).

3. THE EFFECT OF TEMPERATURE ON PRESERVATIVE EFFICACY AND AVAILABILITY

The microbial stability of pharmaceutical preparations is influenced by temperature through at least three different and unrelated mechanisms:

(a) Temperature affects the metabolic state of micro-organisms.
(b) Increase in temperature enhances the activity of preservatives.
(c) Temperature affects interaction of preservatives with other formulation ingredients.

3.1 Metabolic state
Growth of micro-organisms in any medium, including unpreserved or marginally preserved pharmaceutical preparations, is dependent on temperature. The growth rate increases as the temperature approaches the optimum temperature of the contaminating flora. The optimum temperature of many pathogenic species is about 37°C. Van Doorne and Neuteboom (1984) showed that many natural contaminants in samples of purified water from local pharmacies were unable to grow at 37°C. Optimum recovery of micro-organisms was obtained at temperatures between 22 and 30°C.

3.2 Preservative activity
The temperature dependence of the rate of a simple chemical reaction is expressed by the well-known Arrhenius equation, which in its logarithmic form is written as:

$$\log k = \frac{E_a}{2.303R} \cdot \frac{1}{T} + \text{constant} \tag{1}$$

where k is the reaction rate constant, E_a is the activation energy, R is the gas constant and T is the absolute temperature. In the pharmaceutical literature the temperature coefficient Q_{10} is frequently used to express the effect of change of temperature on the antimicrobial activity of a preservative or disinfectant (see Chapter 11).

The Q_{10} value gives an indication of the extent to which the activity of a preservative is changed by a 10°C change in temperature. Even if death were the result of a simple chemical reaction (which is not necessarily the case), the value of Q_{10} is still dependent on temperature. Recorded values range from 4.0 (phenol, *Staph. aureus*) to 45 (ethanol, *Escherichia coli*). However, the Q_{10} for the activity of ethanol against *Staph. aureus* was only 9. Thus as Q_{10} seems to be not only dependent on the temperature but also on the type of organisms, its usefulness is very limited (Sykes 1965). The survival times of four different bacteria inoculated into some BPC mixtures at four temperatures between 15°C and 37°C were measured by Westwood and Pin-Lim (1972). An increase in temperature caused a reduction in survival time of vegetative cells of *Ps. aeruginosa*, *Staph. aureus* and *E. coli*. Spores of *Bacillus subtilis* were unaffected.

3.3 Preservative interactions

In the previous sections of this chapter a number of interactions of preservatives with formulation ingredients have been discussed. All these interactions are quantitatively dependent on temperature, thus:

(a) Adsorption of preservatives by solid ingredients decreases with increasing temperature.

(b) Micellar solubilization is dependent on temperature. As compared to a true molecular dispersion, the solubilized system is thermodynamically less favourable. Therefore, an increase in temperature will result in a decrease in the extent of solubilization (entropy $(\Delta S) > 0$).

(c) Oil/water partition coefficient is dependent on temperature. Between 20°C and 70°C an increase in the partition coefficient K_w^o of methylparaben between Cetiol V (a fatty oil) and water was observed. At still higher temperatures a decrease of the K_w^o was seen (Van Doorne and Dubois 1980).

(d) Interaction with packaging material is dependent on temperature.

Owing to the complexity of these effects it is impossible to predict how the activity of a preservative in a specific preparation will change with changing temperature. The USP XXII (1990) test for the effectiveness of antimicrobial preservatives is carried out at ambient (20–25°C) temperature. For products that are to be stored under other conditions (refrigerator, tropics) it seems advisable, however, to run an additional test under the intended storage conditions. In such tests micro-organisms capable of growth and multiplication at the specified temperature should be used in addition to the usual test-panel.

4 THE EFFECT OF WATER ON PRESERVATIVE EFFICACY AND AVAILABILITY

4.1 Water as an intrinsic factor

Lowering the water content has always been a convenient method of protecting foods from microbial spoilage. In the late 1930s it was recognized that the water content was not the governing factor in this context. The concept of water activity allowed a more quantitative approach to the influence of water on microbial proliferation. The water activity (a_w-value) is defined as the ratio between water vapour pressure of a preparation and the water vapour pressure of pure water at the same temperature. Protection of pharmaceutical preparations against microbial spoilage can be achieved by adding sugar or polyalcohols as in syrups, some suspensions and solutions. Since micro-organisms cannot develop resistance against reduced a_w-values (Curry 1985), it is a very safe method; its application is, however, limited in practice. Tönnesen and Jensen (1970) studied the survival of bacteria in concentrated haemodialysis solution. Gram-positive bacteria showed higher resistance than Gram-negative species and the spore-forming bacteria were unaffected. Increasing the storage temperature greatly reduced the ability of the organisms to survive in these hypertonic solutions.

Anagnostopoulos and Kroll (1978), and Kroll and Anagnostopoulos (1981) studied the effect of water activity on the activity of phenol against *Serratia marcescens*. Although some differences were observed between the non-penetrating solute (sucrose) and the penetrating solute (glycerol) the decimal reduction time of *Serratia marcescens* in water ($a_w = 1.00$) was generally lower than in the solutions ($1.00 > a_w \geqslant 0.92$). Results obtained through viable counting (Anagnostopoulos and Kroll, 1978) were paralleled by those obtained when potassium leakage was used as a lethality index (Kroll and Anagnostopoulos 1981).

4.2 Water as an extrinsic factor

Although dry oral preparations do not rank high as microbial hazards, an outbreak of infection in the 1960s (Kallings *et al.* 1966) illustrated that tablets may contain dangerously high levels of bacteria. The presence of these organisms was ascribed to the use of contaminated raw materials, rather than to growth during storage. As long as tablets are stored under dry conditions, spoilage due to growth is unlikely to occur (Blair *et al.* 1988).

However, in tropical regions with a hot and humid climate (31°C and 75–100% RH), growth of micro-organisms cannot be excluded, particularly when the products are stored and dispensed in a non-protective packaging, or even without any packaging. Parker (1984) suggested that the addition of preservatives to tablets could be effective. Few studies have been published on the microbiological stability of tablets (Waterman *et al.* 1973; Fassihi and Parker 1977; Blair *et al.* 1987). None of these studies included the effect of tropical conditions; moreover, storage conditions with respect to humidity were uncontrolled (Fassihi *et al.* 1978). The effect of addition of preservatives on the microbiological stability of tablet formulations under various conditions has recently been investigated (Bos *et al.* 1989). No microbial growth was observed on tablets stored at 75% RH. The addition of preservatives (methylparaben or sorbic acid) yielded no measurable effect on the viability of the test organisms. However, when tablets were stored at 95% RH, visible growth of fungi was observed after four weeks of storage. Sorbic acid (1% w/w) and methylparaben (1% w/w) added to the tablet formulations were found to be fungicidal under these storage conditions.

Whenever considering the addition of a preservative to a solid dosage form, a study on the interaction between the preservative and the components must be carried out.

5 INTRINSIC EFFECTS

A number of components of pharmaceutical preparations exert measurable antimicrobial effects, although they are used for reasons other than their antimicrobial activity. Some well-known examples are discussed briefly here.

5.1 Reducing agents

Lowering the redox potential reduces the growth rate of aerobic and facultatively anaerobic micro-organisms. Vacuum packing is a convenient method to prolong shelf-life, especially of foodstuffs. Reducing compounds are used in pharmaceuticals to minimize the risk of oxidative degradation of other components. Sodium metabisulphite, which is used in some ophthalmic preparations, was shown to have a bactericidal effect on *Ps. aeruginosa* and *Staph. aureus*. The effect was found to be dependent on pH. At pH values of 5 and above no bactericidal activity could be observed (Richards and Reary 1972). Butyl hydroxy anisole is an example of another reducing agent with antimicrobial activity (Lamikanra 1982). Butyl hydroxy anisole is added to fats in order to prevent rancidity. Owing to its high o/w partition coefficient it is unsuitable as a preservative, but its presence will nevertheless have a positive effect on the microbial stability of creams and ointments.

Ascorbic acid, either alone or in combination with citric acid, has frequently been used to protect food such as fruit or fish from deterioration. The prolonged shelf-life was the result of the inhibition of oxidative reaction, rather than inhibition of microbial growth. Ascorbic acid has only very weak antimicrobial activity (Broderson 1946) and its limited chemical stability in solution prohibits its use as a preservative in water-containing pharmaceutical products.

5.2 Essential oils

The antimicrobial activity of essential oils and their possible use as preservatives have been reviewed by Kabara (1984). The essential oils probably play an important role in the plant's mechanism of defence against microbial attack. The essential oils of many plants which are used as herbs and spices, such as lemon grass, thyme, marjoram, nutmeg, bergamot and many others, have significant antimicrobial activity against bacteria, yeasts and moulds. It is theroretically possible to use these compounds for surface disinfection, in personal care products and for the preservation of products such as shampoos. The concentrations necessary, however, are generally over 1% and the characteristic odour of the compounds tend to give the products a somewhat medicinal character (Blakeway 1986). Peppermint oil has considerable antimicrobial activity and it was long thought that preparations such as peppermint water BP were adequately preserved. However, in a survey of the microbial contamination of medicines administered to hospital patients, 15 out of 33 samples were found to have been contaminated with *Ps. aeruginosa* (Anon. 1971), and shortly after that McKenny (1972) reported on the poor microbiological quality of BPC peppermint mixtures. It was subsequently demonstrated (Wilson 1972) that *Ps. aeruginosa* was capable of growth in peppermint-containing preparations. Nowadays, these preparations contain a preservative, such as methylparaben.

5.3   Chelating agents
As mentioned in section 2.6, EDTA is frequently employed in antimicrobial combinations to enhance the activity of preservatives such as the QACs. In addition to this potentiating effect, EDTA has a weak antimicrobial activity itself.

5.4   Antibiotics
The presence of antibiotics and related compounds in pharmaceutical preparations will certainly affect the contaminant's ability to survive and grow. Antibiotics should not be used as preservatives, because of the danger of (cross-)resistance. An exception to this rule is pimaricin, which is used to prevent mould growth on the crust of cheese. Nisin and tylosin, two other antibiotics, have been studied for their effect on spore-forming organisms in thermally processed foods. Although these antibiotics may significantly reduce the thermal processing requirements of a number of foods, their use as food additives has not been universally accepted. They are not used as preservatives in cosmetics or pharmaceuticals (Pflug and Holcombe 1983).

Owing to the selective action of many antibiotics, their preparations usually also need to contain an adequate preservative. During formulation studies it must be realized that suspended antibiotics may adsorb the preservative (section 2.2) and that occasionally antagonism between an antibiotic and a preservative may be observed.

5.5   Alcohols
Pharmaceutical and cosmetic preparations may contain alcohols (particularly ethanol) as a solvent or co-solvent. Homeopathic and phytotherapeutic preparations, in addition to many cosmetics, frequently contain high levels of ethanol. Any product containing more than 20% ethanol can be considered to be adquately preserved.

Propylene glycol is an alcohol which is frequently used in creams and ointments. Propylene glycol is known to enhance the activity of the parabens (Prickett *et al.* 1961). In a concentration of 15% it has a significant antimicrobial activity (Van Doorne and Dubois 1980).

The *in vitro* antibacterial activity of the oligomeric alcohol polyethylene glycol 400, as studied by Chirife *et al.* (1983), was ascribed to two effects: (i) lowering of the a_w-value, and (ii) a specific action of the molecule on the cell.

5.6   Miscellaneous compounds
Systematic studies into the antimicrobial activity of pharmaceutical compounds have not been performed, and only some incidently observed effects have been reported.

The antimicrobial activity of sodium lauryl sulphate has already been discussed in section 2.4.

Local anaesthetics such as tetracaine, benoxinate and cocaine were found to be lethal for *C. albicans*, *Ps. aeruginosa* and *Staph. epidermidis* (Kleinfeld and Ellis 1967). Unpreserved commercial preparations of methohexital sodium and sodium thiopental were found to be toxic for 13 different strains of micro-organisms (Highsmith *et al.* 1982). It is, however, uncertain whether the observed effects could be ascribed to a toxic action of the compounds *per se*, or whether the high (10.5) pH of the preparations was responsible.

Survival of *Staph. epidermidis* in solutions containing various levels of ^{99m}Tc was studied by Stathis *et al.* (1983). They concluded that the inoculum (100 c.f.u. ml^{-1}) was killed after having received an estimated dose of radiation of about 1000 rad (10 Gy). A decayed ('cold') solution of pertechnetate had no effect on the micro-organisms. Thus the bactericidal effect could be ascribed to radiation damage and not to a toxic effect of the pertechnetate itself. Non-radioactive components of nine commonly used technetium-labelled radiopharmaceuticals were found to support growth of five different types of organisms (Abra *et al.* 1980).

Intravenous infusions and parenteral nutrition solutions generally support growth of micro-organisms (Holmes and Allwood 1979a, 1979b; Baggerman 1980). Based on available evidence Baggerman (1980) concluded that glucose 5% and fat emulsions showed particular growth-promoting properties. There appears to be a remarkable difference between amino acid solutions prepared from crystalline amino acids and those prepared from casein hydrolysate. Whilst the former ones only supported growth of some yeasts and were toxic to other types of micro-organisms, the latter ones were good growth media for all types of organisms studied. According to Failla *et al.* (1975) this is due to the presence of relatively high concentrations of glycine in the crystalline amino acid mixture. Glycine in a concentration of 1.54% was found to be toxic for all types of bacteria studied, whereas the growth rate of *C. albicans* was only reduced by a factor of two. Microbiologists are familiar with the inhibitory nature of glycine as it is an indispensable component of Baird-Parker's selective medium for *Staph. aureus*.

6 OVERVIEW

In this chapter some interactions between components of pharmaceutical preparations and preservatives have been discussed. Some of the interactions are based on well-known physical phenomena such as adsorption, partition and micellar solubilization. However, occasionally this behaviour is not predictable because of a unique characteristic of a certain organism, leading to unexpected and unpredictable phenomena. The interactions are complex and manifold, which implies that the activity of a given preservative in any preparation consisting of several components cannot be predicted. It may, however, be possible to predict qualitatively the effect of a change of the formulation on the preservative activity.

Confirmation by means of a well-designed challenge test will always be necessary. Examination of used preparations, so-called microbiological post-marketing surveillance, will further increase our knowledge and understanding of preserving pharmaceutical preparations.

7 REFERENCES

Abra, R. M., Bell, N. D. S. and Horton, P. W. (1980) The growth of micro-organisms in some parenteral radiopharmaceuticals. *Int. J. Pharm.* 5 187–193.

Allawala, N. A. and Riegelman, S. (1953a) The release of antimicrobial agents from solutions of surface-active agents. *J. Am. Pharm. Assoc. Sci. Ed.* 42 267–275.

Allawala, N. A. and Riegelman, S. (1953b) The properties of iodine in solutions of surface active agents. *J. Am. Pharm. Assoc. Sci. Ed.* 42 396–401.

Anagnostopoulos, G. D. and Kroll, R. G. (1978) Water activity and solute effect on the bactericidal action of phenol. *Microbios Lett.* **7** 69–74.

Anon. (1971) Microbial contamination of medicines administered to hospital patients. *Pharm. J.* **207** 96–99.

Baggerman, C. (1980) Groei van micro-organismen in infusie-vloeistoffen. *Pharm. Weekbl.* **115** 1329–1337.

Batuyios, N. H. and Brecht, E. A. (1957) An investigation of the incompatibilities of quaternary ammonium germicides in compressed troches. I. The adsorption of cetylpyridinium chloride and benzalkonium chloride by talc and kaolin. *J. Am. Pharm. Assoc. Sci. Ed.* **46** 490–492.

Bean, H. S. (1972) Preservatives for pharmaceuticals, *J. Soc. Cosm. Chem.* **23** 703–720.

Bean, H. S. and Dempsey, G. (1971) The effect of suspensions on the bactericidal activity of *m*-cresol and benzalkonium chloride. *J. Pharm. Pharmacol.* **23** 699–704.

Berke, P. A. and Rosen, W. A. (1970) Germall, a new family of antimicrobial preservatives for cosmetics. *Am. Perfum. Cosmet.* **85** 55–60.

Beveridge, E. G. and Hope, I. A. (1967) Inactivation of benzoic acid in sulphadimidine mixture for infants BPC. *Pharm. J.* **198** 457–458.

Birkeland, J. and Steinhaus, E. (1939) Selective bacteriostatic action of sodium lauryl sulfate and of 'Dreft'. *Proc. Soc. Exp. Biol. Med.* **40** 86–92.

Blair, T. C., Buckton, G. and Bloomfield, S. F. (1987) Water available to *Enterobacter cloacae* contaminating tablets stored at high relative humidities. *J. Pharm. Pharmacol.* **39** 125P.

Blair, T. C., Buckton, G. and Bloomfield, S. F. (1988) Preservation of solid oral dosage forms. In: Bloomfield, S. F., Baird, R., Leak, R. E. and Leech, R. (eds), *Microbial quality assurance in pharmaceuticals, cosmetics and toiletries*. Ellis Horwood, Chichester, pp. 104–118.

Blakeway, J. (1986) The anti-microbial properties of essential oils. *Soap Perf. Cosmet.* **59** 201, 203, 207.

Bolle, A. and Mirimanoff, A. (1950) Antagonism between non-ionic detergents and antiseptics. *J. Pharm. Pharmacol.* **2** 685–692.

Bos, C. E., Van Doorne, H. and Lerk, C. F. (1989). Microbiological stability of tablets stored under tropical conditions. *Int. J. Pharm.* **55** 175–182.

Broderson, R. (1946) Antimicrobial action of ascorbic acid. *Acta Pharmacol. Toxicol.* **2** 109–117.

Brown, M. R. W. (1968) Survival of *Pseudomonas aeruginosa* in fluorescein solution: preservative action of PMN and EDTA. *J. Pharm. Sci.* **57** 389–392.

Brown, M. R. W. and Richards, R. M. E. (1964) Effect of polysorbate (Tween) 80 on the resistance of *Pseudomonas aeruginosa* to chemical inactivation. *J. Pharm. Pharmacol.* **16** 51T–55T.

Chirife, J., Herszage, L., Joseph, A., Bozzini, J. P., Leardini, N. and Kohn, E. S. (1983) In vitro antibacterial activity of concentrated polyethylene glycol 400 solutions. *Antimicrob. Agents Chemother.* **24** 409–412.

Clausen, O. G. (1973) An examination of the bactericidal and fungicidal effects of cetylpyridinium chloride, separately and in combinations embodying EDTA and benzyl alcohol. *Pharmaz. Ind.* **35** 869–874.

Curry, J. (1985) Water activity and preservation. *Cosmet. Toilet.* **100** 53–55.

DeLuca, P. P. and Kostenbauder, H. B. (1960) Interaction of preservatives with macromolecules. IV. Binding of quaternary ammonium compounds by non-ionic agents. *J. Am. Pharm. Assoc. Sci. Ed.* **49** 430–437.

Denyer, S. P., Hugo, W. B. and Harding, V. D. (1985) Synergy in preservative combinations. *Int. J. Pharm.* **25** 245–253.

Dyett, E. J. (1957) Lauryl sulfate broth for the testing of ice-cream for *E. coli. Lab. Pract.* **6** 327–328.

El-Nakeeb, M. A., Yousef, R. T. and Fawzi, M. A. (1975) Effect of pectin on the bacteriostatic and bactericidal activities of some preservatives. *Pharmaz. Ind.* **37** 1063–1065.

Failla, M. L., Benedict, C. D. and Weinberg, E. D. (1975) Microbial growth in parenteral nutrition solutions. *Antonie van Leeuwenhoek* **41** 319–328.

Fassihi, A. R. and Parker, M. S. (1977) The influence of water activity and oxygen tension upon the survival of *Aspergillus* and *Penicillium* species on tablets. *Int. Biodeterior. Bull.* **13** 75–80.

Fassihi, A. R., Parker, M. S. and Dingwall, D. (1978) The preservation of tablets against microbial spoilage. *Drug. Dev. Ind. Pharm.* **4** 515–527.

Gilbert, P. (1988) Microbial resistance to preservative systems. In: Bloomfield, S. F., Baird, R., Leak, R. E. and Leech, R. (eds), *Microbial assurance in pharmaceuticals, cosmetics and toiletries*. Ellis Horwood, Chichester, pp. 171–194.

Gray, G. W. and Wilkinson, S. G. (1965) The action of ethylene diaminetetra-acetic acid on *Pseudomonas aeruginosa. J. Appl. Bacteriol.* **28** 153–164.

Highsmith, A. K., Greenhood, G. P. and Allen, J. R. (1982) Growth of nosocomial pathogens in multiple-dose parenteral medication vials. *J. Clin. Microbiol.* **15** 1024–1028.

Holmes, C. J. and Allwood, M. C. (1979a) The microbial contamination of intravenous infusions during clinical use. *J. Appl. Bacteriol.* **46** 247–267.

Holmes, C. J. and Allwood, M. C. (1979b) The growth of micro-organisms in parenteral nutrition solutions containing amino acids and sugars. *Int. J. Pharm.* **2** 325–335.

Jacobs, G., Henry, S. M. and Cotty, V. F. (1975) The influence of pH, emulsifier and accelerated ageing upon preservative requirements of oil/water emulsions. *J. Soc. Cosmet. Chem.* **26** 105–117.

Jund, Y. and Carrère, C. (1971) Détermination de l'activité bactériostatique et fongistatique de quelques conservateurs, en présence de différents types d'excipients modernes pour pommades. *Ann. Pharm. Franç.* **29** 161–172.

Kabara, J. J. (1980) GRAS antimicrobial agents for cosmetic products. *J. Soc. Cosmet. Chem.* **31** 1–10.

Kabara, J. J. (1984) Aroma preservatives. In: Kabara, J. J. (ed.), *Cosmetic and drug preservation*. Marcel Dekker, New York, pp. 237–273.

Kallings, L. O., Ringertz, O., Silverstolpe, L. and Ernerfeldt, F. (1966) Microbiological contamination of medicinal preparations. *Acta Pharm. Suec.* **3** 219–228.

Kazmi, S. J. A. and Mitchell, A. G. (1978a) Preservation of solubilized and emulsified systems. I: Correlation of mathematically predicted preservative availability with antimicrobial activity. *J. Pharm. Sci.* **67** 1260–1265.

Kazmi, S. J. A. and Mitchell, A. G. (1978b) Preservation of solubilized emulsified systems. II: Theoretical development of capacity and its role in antimicrobial activity of chlorocresol in cetomacrogol-stabilized systems. *J. Pharm. Sci.* **67** 1266–1271.

Kleinfeld, J. and Ellis, P. P. (1967) Inhibition of micro-organisms by topical anesthetics. *Appl. Microbiol.* **15** 1296–1298.

Komatsu, H., Higaki, K., Okamoto, H., Miyagawa, K., Hashida, M. and Sezaki, H. (1986) Preservative activity and in vivo percutaneous penetration of butylparaben entrapped in liposomes. *Chem. Pharm. Bull.* **34** 3414–3422.

Kroll, R. G. and Anagnostopoulos, G. D. (1981) Potassium leakage as a lethality index of phenol and the effect of solute and water activity. *J. Appl. Bacteriol.* **50** 139–147.

Lach, J. L. and Cohen, J. (1963) Interaction of pharmaceuticals with Schardinger dextrins. II. Interaction with selected compounds. *J. Pharm. Sci.* **52** 137–142.

Lamikanra, A. (1982) Effects of butyl hydroxyanisole (BHA) on the leakage of cytoplasmic materials from *Staphylococcus aureus* and *Escherichia coli*. *J. Appl. Bacteriol.* **53** xvi.

Leive, L. (1965) Release of lipopolysaccharide by EDTA treatment of *E. coli*. *Biochem. Biophys. Res. Commun.* **21** 290–296.

Mansour, Z. and Guth, P. (1968) Complexing behavior of starches with certain pharmaceuticals. *J. Pharm. Sci.* **57** 404–411.

McCarthy, T. J. (1969) The influence of insoluble powders on preservatives in solution. *J. Mond. Pharm.* **4** 321–329.

McCarthy, T. J. and Myburgh, J. A. (1974) The effect of tragacanth gel on preservative activity. *Pharm. Weekbl.* **109** 265–268.

McCarthy, T. J. and Myburgh, J. A. (1977) Further studies on the influence of formulation on preservative activity. *Cosmet. Toilet.* **92** 33–36.

McKenny, J. (1972) Microbial contamination of BPC peppermint mixtures. *J. Hosp. Pharm.* **30** 188–192.

Meyer, G. (1958) Wirkungsabnahme von *p*-Oxybenzoesaure estern durch 7-oxyaethyltheophylin. *Arzneimittelforschung* **8** 196–197.

Myburgh, J. A. and McCarthy, T. J. (1980a) Inactivation of preservatives in the presence of particulate solids. *Pharm. Weekbl. Sci. Ed.* **2** 137–142.

Myburgh, J. A. and McCarthy, T. J. (1980b) The influence of suspending agents on preservative activity in aqueous solid/liquid dispersions. *Pharm. Weekbl. Sci. Ed.* **2** 1411–1416.

Nielsen, P. A. and Close, J. A. (1982) Edetate disodium mediated chloramphenicol resistance in *Pseudomonas cepacia*. *J. Pharm. Sci.* **71** 833–834.

Parker, M. S. (1984) The preservation of oral dosage forms. *Int. J. Pharm. Tech. Prod. Manuf.* **5** 20–24.

Parker, M. S., McCafferty, M. and MacBride, S. (1968) Phenonip: a broad spectrum preservative. *Soap Perfum. Cosmet.* **41** 647–649.

Pflug, I. J. and Holcomb, R. G. (1983) Principles of thermal destruction of microorganisms. In: Block, S. S. (ed), *Disinfection, sterilization and preservation*. Lea and Febiger, Philadelphia, pp. 751–810.

Pisano, F. D. and Kostenbauder, H. B. (1959) Interaction of preservatives with macromolecules. II. Correlation of binding data with required preservative concentrations of p-hydroxybenzoates in the presence of Tween 80. *J. Am. Pharm. Assoc. Sci. Ed.* **48** 310–314.

Prickett, P. S., Murray, H. L. and Mercer, N. H. (1961) Potentiation of preservatives (parabens) in pharmaceutical formulations by low concentrations of propylene glycol. *J. Pharm. Sci.* **50** 316–320.

Raab, W. and Windisch, J. (1970) The influence of corticosteroids on antibacterial activity of surface active compounds. *Chemotherapy* **15** 26–34.

Richards, R. M. E. (1971) Inactivation of resistant *Pseudomonas aeruginosa* by antibacterial combinations. *J. Pharm. Pharmacol.* **23** 141S–146S.

Richards, R. M. E. (1976) Effect of hypromellose on the antibacterial activity of benzalkonium chloride. *J. Pharm. Pharmacol.* **28** 264.

Richards, R. M. E. and McBride, R. J. (1972) The preservation of ophthalmic solutions with antibacterial combinations. *J. Pharm. Pharmacol.* **24** 145–148.

Richards, R. M. E. and Reary, J. M. E. (1972) Changes in antibacterial activity of thiomersal and PMN on autoclaving with certain adjuvants. *J. Pharm. Pharmacol.* **24** 84P–89P.

Richards, R. M. E. and Richards, J. M. (1979) *Pseudomonas cepacia* resistance to antibacterials. *J. Pharm. Pharmacol.* **68** 1436–1437.

Stathis, V. J., Miller, C. M., Doerr, G. F., Coffey, J. L. and Hladik, W. B. III (1983) Effect of Technetium Tc 99m pertechnetate on bacterial survival in solution. *Am. J. Hosp. Pharm.* **40** 634–637.

Sykes, G. (1965) In: *Disinfection and sterilization: theory and practice*, 2nd edn. Chapman and Hall, London, pp. 21–23.

Toama, M. A., Mahrous, H., El-Fatatry, H. M. and Swealem, A. A. (1981) Microbiological studies of saccharin- sodium methyl, propyl, and butyl parabens interactions. *Pharmaz. Ind.* **43** 874–877.

Tönnesen, H. and Jensen, V. G. (1970) Survival of bacteria in concentrated haemodialysis solution. *Dansk Tidsskr. Farm.* **44** 32–36.

Tromp, Th. F. J., Dankert, J., De Rooy, S. and Huizinga, T. (1976) De conservering van oogdruppels. III. Een onderzoek naar de interactie van hydroxypropyl-methylcellulose en benzalkonium chloride. *Pharm. Weekbl.* **111** 561–569.

Tromp, Th. F. J., Nusman-Schoterman, Z., Snippe, H. and Huizinga, T. (1977) De conservering van oogdruppels. V. Onderzoek naar de invloed van geneesmiddelen op de conserverende eigenschappen van basis-oplossingen. *Pharm. Weekbl.* **112** 461–466.

Uekama, K., Ikeda, Y., Hirayama, F., Otagiri, M., and Shibata, M. (1980) Inclusion complexation of p-hydroxybenzoic acid esters with α- and β-cyclodextrins: dissolution behaviors and antimicrobial activities. *Yakugaku Zasshi* **100** 994–1003.

United States Pharmacopeia XXI (1985) United States Pharmacopeial Convention, Rockville, MD, p. 1151.

United States Pharmacopeia XXII (1990) United States Pharmacopeial Convention, Rockville, MD.

Van Doorne, H. (1977) Interactions between micro-organisms and some components of pharmaceutical preparations. Thesis, Leiden.

Van Doorne, H. (1980) De conservering van farmaceutische preparaten in het licht van de Nederlandse Farmacopee. *Pharm. Weekbl.* **115** 207–212.

Van Doorne, H. and Dubois, F. L. (1980) The preservation of lanette wax cream (FNA). *Pharm. Weekbl. Sci. Ed.* **2** 19–24.

Van Doorne, H. and Neuteboom, A. (1984) Comparison of media and temperature of incubation for microbiological examination of purified water. *Pharm. Weekbl. Sci. Ed.* **6** 105–110.

Van Doorne, H. V., Bosch, E. H. and Lerk, C. F. (1988) Formation and antimicrobial activity of complexes of β-cyclodextrin with some antimycotic imidazole derivatives. *Pharm. Weekbl. Sci. Ed.* **10** 80–85.

Vanhaecke, E., Remon, J. P., Pijck, J., Aerts, R. and Herman, J. (1987) A comparative study of the effectiveness of preservatives in twelve antacid suspensions. *Drug Dev. Ind. Pharm.* **13** 1429–1446.

Waterman, R. F., Sumner, E. D., Baldwin, J. N. and Warren, F. W. (1973) Survival of *Staphylococcus aureus* on pharmaceutical oral solid dosage forms. *J. Pharm. Sci.* **62** 1317–1320.

Westwood, N. and Pin-Lim, B. (1972) Survival of *E. coli, Staph. aureus, Ps. aeruginosa* and spores of *B. subtilis* in BPC mixtures. *Pharm. J.* **208** 153–154.

Wilson, J. V. (1972) Growth of *Ps. aeruginosa* in peppermint water BP. *J. Hosp. Pharm.* **30** 179–181.

Yamaguchi, M., Asaka, Y., Tanaka, M., Mitsui, T. and Ohta, S. (1982) Antimicrobial activity of butylparaben in relation to its solubilization behaviour by nonionic surfactants. *J. Soc. Cosm. Chem.* **33** 297–307.

Yousef, R. T., El-Nakeeb, M. A. and Salama, S. (1973a) Effect of some pharmaceutical materials on the bactericidal activities of preservatives. *Can. J. Pharm. Sci.* **8** 54–58.

Yousef, R. T., El-Nakeeb, M. A. and Salama, S. (1973b) Effect of some pharmaceutical materials on the bacteriostatic and bactericidal activity of benzalkonium chloride. *Pharmaz. Ind.* **35** 154–156.

13A

Official methods of preservative evaluation and testing

Michael J. Akers
Lilly Research Laboratories, Lilly Corporate Center, Indianapolis, Indiana 42685, USA

C. Julia Taylor
Lilly Research Centre, Windlesham, Surrey, GU20 6PH, UK

1 INTRODUCTION

Antimicrobial preservative agents are formulated in pharmaceutical products to assist in protecting the product from adventitious microbial contamination during manufacture, storage and use. Such agents are chemicals which themselves are subject to the same environmental stress factors leading to degradation and/or inactivation as those experienced by the active ingredients they are attempting to protect. In order to assure the producer, regulatory assessor and user of preserved products that antimicrobial preservative agents are active, valid scientific appraisal of antimicrobial activity in the finished product under a range of conditions must be carried out. This chapter focuses on testing procedures used to evaluate antimicrobial preservative effectiveness in pharmaceutical dosage forms. Such tests can be applied both to preserved sterile and non-sterile products and can be used to test formulations at the beginning and end of their shelf-life.

From a compendial standpoint, preservative efficacy testing was not a requirement of finished dosage forms until 1970 (United States Pharmacopeia (USP) XVIII). The USP method was derived from the work of several industrial scientists, including Eisman *et al.* (1963) and Kenney *et al.* (1964). The USP preservative efficacy test procedures have evolved little over the past twenty years, as seen in Table 1 comparing the procedures of the USP XVIII (1970) with those of USP XXII (1990). The preservative efficacy test requires that inocula of given species of test micro-organisms should be individually introduced into samples of the preserved product. This challenge should include representatives of the Gram-positive and Gram-negative bacterial species, moulds and yeasts and should be presented in sufficient size to enable kinetic information to be obtained. Compendial tests have been designed to ensure reproducible results across all laboratories. While the preservative efficacy test has survived scrutiny and criticism from many scientists over the years, it still has several limitations which will be addressed in this chapter.

2 MATHEMATICAL APPROACH TO PRESERVATIVE EVALUATION

There are several references available explaining the growth and death kinetics of micro-organisms (Han *et al.* 1976; Akers 1979; Davis *et al.* 1980; Avis and Akers 1986). In the conductance of the preservative efficacy test, growth of organisms is not as relevant as their death due to the antimicrobial activity of the formulation. Death kinetics generally are logarithmic and so the initial concentration of challenge micro-organism should be sufficient to evaluate microbial loss over several log-cycles. In this respect, therefore, it is far easier to measure a 10^3 or greater reduction in a microbial population if the initial population is high (10^5–10^6) than if it is low (10^3–10^4).

If microbial death were both logarithmic and linear, then simple decimal reduction time (*D*-value) calculations probably would be acceptable for measuring preservative efficacy. However, in many cases, the death of micro-organisms is non-linear; such death curves are a result either of multiple bacterial cell sites which must be inactivated or the selection of more resistant survivors which may, in fact, cause 'regrowth' ('grow-back') of the micro-organism in the product. In the preservative efficacy test *Pseudomonas aeruginosa* particularly demonstrates a propensity to regrow in pharmaceutical solutions.

Table 1 — Basic comparison of preservative efficacy test from USP XVIII and from USP XXII

Criteria	USP XVIII (1970)	USP XXII (1990)
Test organisms	*C. albicans* (ATCC 10231) *Asp. niger* (ATCC 16404) *E. coli* (ATCC 4352) *Ps. aeruginosa* (ATCC 9027) *Staph. aureus* (ATCC 6538)	*C. albicans* (ATCC 10231) *Asp. niger* (ATCC 16404) *E. coli* (ATCC 8739) *Ps. aeruginosa* (ATCC 9027) *Staph. aureus* (ATCC 6538)
Medium	Suggest soybean casein digest agar	Suggest soybean casein digest agar
Inoculum growth, preparation and final cell density	Bacteria: 37°C, 18–24 h *C. albicans*: 25°C, 48 h *Asp. niger*: 25°C, 1 week 5×10^7 ml^{-1}	Bacteria; 30–35°C, 18–24 h *C. albicans*: 20–25°C, 48 h *Asp. niger*: 20–25°C, 1 week 1×10^8 ml^{-1}
Test procedures	Add 20 ml of test product to each of 5 sterile tubes	Conduct test, if possible, in 5 original product containers. Otherwise, transfer 20 ml to each of 5 sterile tubes
	Each tube inoculated with 1.25–5×10^5 org. ml^{-1}. Incubate tubes at 30–32°C	Each container or tube inoculated with 10^5–10^6 org. ml^{-1}. Incubate at 20–25°C
Required pass result	No increase in *C. albicans* or *Asp. niger* 0.1% of initial bacteria left and remains below that level for a 7-day period within 28-day test period	No increase in *C. albicans* or *Asp. niger* $\leq$0.1% of initial bacteria concentration remaining by 14th day and remains at or below these levels during the remainder of the test period

Some manufacturers and researchers have advocated the use of *D*-value calculations as rapid procedures for determining effectiveness of antimicrobial preservatives in pharmaceutical and cosmetic products (see Chapter 13B). Such rapid methods are acceptable to screen and estimate antimicrobial activity of preservative agents alone and in combination (Moore 1978; Akers *et al.* 1984). However, as pointed out by Cooper (1989), these methods are limited in their ability to predict activity primarily due to the loss of exponential (logarithmic) activity for some preservatives in their lethal effect over a 28-day period.

3   GENERAL PRINCIPLES OF TEST METHODS AND RECOVERY PROCEDURES

A preservative efficacy test must be designed to provide conditions which will permit microbial survival, and possibly growth, in the product under test should that product be poorly preserved. Further, the test method must ensure satisfactory and efficient recovery of survivors. Assurance that such conditions are met validates the scientific credibility of the test results with respect to the presence or absence of acceptable antimicrobial activity on the part of the pharmaceutical formulation. This section will briefly consider the type of challenge organism used in compendial preservative efficacy tests, and how the test conditions maximize survival and recovery potential for these organisms.

3.1   Choice of challenge organisms

Test micro-organisms are chosen to represent potential contaminants in the environ-

Table 2 — Specified test organisms

	Organism	ATCC ref.	Other ref.
Bacteria	*Staphylococcus aureus*	6538	NCIB 9518 NCTC 10788
	Pseudomonas aeruginosa	9027	NCIB 8626
	Escherichia coli	8739	NCIB 8545
Moulds	*Aspergillus niger*	16404	IMI 149007
Yeasts	*Candida albicans*	10231	NCPF3179
	Zygosaccharomyces rouxii	—	NCYC 381

ment in which preparations are manufactured, stored and used. A common set of challenge organisms is generally employed (Table 2) representing Gram-positive and Gram-negative bacteria (with *Ps. aeruginosa* especially selected because of its recognized resistance to many antimicrobial agents), moulds and yeasts. This choice is inevitably a compromise between the need to include representative challenges whilst seeking to avoid excessively lengthy testing programmes. Additional organisms may be included for particular formulations. For example, in preparations with high sucrose content, growth of osmophilic yeasts is encouraged and these products should be tested against those organisms. Oral liquid preparations should be challenged with a suitable strain of *E. coli* as specified by the particular pharmacopoeia. Brief details of the specific requirements and properties of these organisms are given in Chapter 1.

It is always recommended that any organism likely to be a particular contaminant during manufacture and use of the product also be tested in a preservative efficacy test. In addition, mixed challenge testing is an acceptable option in developmental phases of product formulation.

3.2   Basic preservative efficacy test protocol

Preservative efficacy tests call for products to be inoculated with most or all of the above challenge micro-organisms at approximately 10^6 viable cells per millilitre or gram. These organisms are generally cultured on soybean casein digest agar medium (soya tryptone agar; bacteria) or Sabouraud dextrose agar medium (Sabouraud agar; fungi), and the inoculated product stored at temperatures between 20°C and 25°C (British and United States pharmacopoeiae) or at 25°C±1°C (German and Italian pharmacopoeiae). The inoculated product is incubated over 28 days, and examined visually and by plate count procedures to determine the number of viable micro-organisms remaining at each time interval specified in the particular compendium.

3.3   Preparation of the test inoculum

The test inocula are grown in 'stock cultures' on specified nutrient media. *Staph. aureus, E. coli, Ps. aeruginosa* and *Asp. niger* are grown on tryptone soya agar slopes, and *C. albicans* and *Z. rouxii* (an osmotolerant yeast; Chapter 1) are grown on Sabouraud agar slopes. The organisms are subcultured regularly, usually every four weeks. When required for the test, the bacteria are subcultured one day before use whereas the fungus, *Asp. niger,* may require between three and seven days for the spores to become established for sampling. The cells are harvested using a sterile diluent such as sterile peptone water, with the addition of adjuvants as required. In the case of *Asp. niger,* a low concentration of Tween 80 is used. Sterile glass beads can be used to mechanically remove the cells from the agar if necessary. Experience will usually indicate the volume of harvesting diluent to use to obtain a working inoculum of *circa* 10^8 c.f.u. ml^{-1}, but reference can be made to calibration graphs of optical density or total count against viable count (see Chapter 1 for methods) to determine the inoculum size. Ultimately, confirmation that the correct inoculum was employed is given in the preservative efficacy test controls. Inoculation of the test preparations is made with a known volume of the freshly prepared micro-organisms to achieve a final concentration of approximately 10^6 organisms per millilitre or gram. All procedures are conducted under aseptic conditions.

3.4   Temperature recommendations in the preservative efficacy test

Most micro-organisms can grow over a wide (30°C) temperature range, but optimal growth occurs within a more narrow range (usually 30–40°C for bacteria and yeasts, 20–25°C for moulds). In practice, the 20–25°C range is a suitable compromise between a temperature which will permit growth of all challenge organisms used in the preservative efficacy test (should the preservative fail drastically) and yet represents also a likely product storage temperature.

3.5   Other basic principles of preservative efficacy testing

3.5.1   Maintenance of aseptic environment and aseptic manipulations during the test

This is of obvious importance in order to avoid or minimize false positives due to adventitious contamination. Appropriate and adequate training in aseptic techniques and continued environmental monitoring of the laminar airflow work area must take place for preservative efficacy test procedures to be valid. These aspects are discussed in Chapters 4, 5 and 17.

3.5.2 Testing in the actual product container

Where the product container can be entered aseptically, the preservative efficacy test should be conducted in that original container. Potential problems, such as loss of antimicrobial preservative or adventitious contamination, can occur if the product is transferred from its original container. In addition, removal of the formulation to another container may result in preservative/container interactions (see Chapter 15) which are unrepresentative of the final product and which may lead to changes in preservative efficacy. However, in some instances, for example glass-sealed ampoules, where the product cannot be entered and maintained aseptically, samples from original containers are removed, pooled, and 10–20 ml of product are placed in each of five sterile rubber-stoppered vials. Such vials should be validated to ensure that they do not allow the antimicrobial preservative to permeate through or be absorbed by the rubber closure.

On occasions, the preservative efficacy test may need to be performed on deliberately broached containers to demonstrate the maintenance of preservative efficacy during the in-use lifetime of a multidose product. Here the broaching procedure should be designed to mimic the circumstances of actual use.

3.5.3 Regrowth

Occasionally, an organism will be observed to 'grow back' in the inoculated product. Microbial levels initially will decrease through, for example, the 14th day, then that level will increase at the 21st or 28th day. This, of course, is extremely disconcerting as it raises more questions than usually can be answered. Grow-back can occur for a variety of reasons, including loss of preservative stability/activity during the test, assay error, or mutational changes in the microbial cell(s).

3.5.4 Methods of sampling from products

The sampling method from products is continually revalidated by the use of controls. Sterile diluent is inoculated under identical conditions to the test product and is sampled at the same time. The sampling intervals are determined by the guidelines laid down under each preservative efficacy test. The sample of inoculated product is then serially diluted before incubating with the appropriate nutrients and under optimum temperature conditions.

3.5.5 Inactivation of antimicrobial agents

When a product contains an active or excipient which is itself an antimicrobial agent, its effect must be neutralized before proceeding with the test. There are three main methods of inactivation (Russell et al. 1979):

(a) *Inactivation by chemical means, e.g. by an enzyme.* In the case of antibiotics, such as cephalosporin, inactivation is achieved by an enzyme such as β-lactamase. The amount of the enzyme, inactivation time and temperature conditions should be predetermined. The enzyme is added after the first serial dilution of the product. The test procedure is then continued with the inactivated sample.

(b) *Dilution to sub-inhibitory level.* Often the dilution of the product as part of the test is sufficient to inactivate the antimicrobial effect of excipients, e.g. alcohols, organic acids and esters, and dyes (acridine). The inactivation of the preservative agent(s) may require the use of a specific neutralizer/inactivator solution as diluent (see Chapter 6A and Chapter 11, section 6).

(c) *Membrane filtration.* If the product possesses antimicrobial activity which is not inactivated by either of the above approaches, membrane filtration is necessary. The sample is filtered through a 0.45-μm filter after the first serial dilution has been completed. The membrane is rinsed with an appropriate diluent (e.g. 0.9% sodium chloride) and then aseptically transferred to a sterile solution of diluent. The micro-organisms are dislodged from the membrane into the diluent mechanically.

4   COMPARISON OF PRESERVATIVE EFFICACY TESTING METHODS CURRENTLY IN USE

Currently, four countries have included a preservative efficacy test in their national pharmacopoeia: Germany, Italy, the UK and the USA. The European Pharmacopoeia has produced many drafts for review, but has yet to agree on a final protocol. Hence, there is no preservative efficacy test in the current European Pharmacopoeia. This section will compare the four pharmacopoeial preservative efficacy test methods.

4.1   Choice of micro-organisms
Some consensus exists between the pharmacopoeiae on the minimum range of challenge organisms to be employed and these are summarized in Table 2. The background to this selection has been given in section 3.1.

4.2   Inoculation conditions
Tests involve a single inoculum of each organism. It has been suggested that repeated inocula of the same organism into the same product would be more realistic for multi-use preparations such as creams and ointments, but this has not been verified scientifically (Cowen and Steiger 1976; Orth 1979). The formulator should decide on the appropriate challenge tests for a product to show satisfactory resistance to contamination based on the intended application.

The preparation of the inoculum uses fresh cultures of each micro-organism, and the growth media, incubation conditions and recovery procedures are detailed in the various pharmacopoeiae. The formulation is challenged with 10^5–10^6 micro-organisms per millilitre or gram of product. Table 3 summarizes the precise test procedures stipulated by the pharmacopoeiae. The total volume of the inoculum is expressed as a percentage of the total volume of the formulation. The recommended storage conditions range between 20°C and 25°C.

Table 3 — Current test conditions for preservative efficacy methods

Test conditions	Pharmacopoeial method			
	British	German	US	Italian
Inoculum size (c.f.u. ml^{-1} or g^{-1})	10^6	10^5–10^6	10^5–10^6	10^5
Inoculum volume	≤1%	≤1%	≤1%	≤1%
Product storage	20–25°C	25°C (±1°C)	20–25°C	25°C (±1°C)

4.3 Interpretation of results

The interpretation of the results is based on the requirements of the regulatory bodies of each country. Table 4 summarizes the specifications of each country by product group. The British Pharmacopoeia preservative efficacy test is more stringent than those of the other European and US pharmacopeiae. The pharmacopoeial tests are issued as guidelines for the pharmaceutical industry and are open to individual interpretation of criteria. The test is applicable throughout a product's shelf-life, and formulations are generally tested at the beginning and end of this period. Depending on the product and regulatory situation, once the product's preservation efficacy has been established initially, chemical assays of the antimicrobial preservative showing sufficient potency (e.g. greater than 90% of label) throughout its shelf-life may suffice, i.e. repeat preservative efficacy testing is not always required.

5   COSMETIC, FOOD AND TOILETRY ASSOCIATION GUIDELINES FOR PRESERVATIVE EFFICACY TESTING

The Preservation Subcommittee of the Toilet Goods Association Microbiological Committee has issued guidelines for testing the adequacy of preservation in cosmetics and toiletry formulations (Halleck 1970). The recommended test organisms are primarily the same as for the pharmacopoeial tests (Table 2). There are two additional organisms in the test: *Penicillium luteum* (ATCC 9644), a second filamentous fungi, and *Bacillus cereus* or *B. subtilis* var. *globigii*. Both are regarded as common contaminants by the committee. The inclusion of other micro-organisms is left to the discretion of the investigator. The test conditions are summarized in Table 5.

It is recommended that the initial microbial load of the product is assessed prior to the start of the test. A high initial level of microbial contamination in the product may affect the interpretation of the test results. As a control, an unpreserved sample of the test product is challenged at the same time. A pure culture challenge on the product is preferred over a mixed challenge but a more severe test can be carried out by rechallenging the product after 28 days.

The preparation of the inoculum, sample preparation, sample dilution and recovery procedures are similar to the pharmacopoeial methods. The full diluent and media details are to be found in the report (Halleck 1970). The results are interpreted

Table 4 — Criteria for the interpretation of preservative efficacy test results

Type of product	German Pharmacopoeia (1986)			British Pharmacopoeia (1988)		
	Organism	Time	Viable count reduced by	Organism	Time	Viable count reduced by
Parenterals (multidose) and ophthalmics	*Ps. aeruginosa* *Staph. aureus*	24 h 7 d 28 d	10^2 10^3 10^3	*Ps. aeruginosa* *Staph. aureus*	6 h 24 h 7 d 14 d 28 d	10^3 ND ND ND ND
	C. albicans *Asp. niger*	14 d 28 d	10^1 10^1	*C. albicans* *Asp. niger*	7 d 14 d 28 d	10^2 NI NI
Topical formulations	*Ps. aeruginosa* *Staph. aureus*	14 d 28 d	10^3 10^3	*Ps. aeruginosa* *Staph. aureus*	48 h 7 d 14 d 28 d	10^3 ND ND ND
	C. albicans *Asp. niger*	14 d 28 d	10^1 10^1	*C. albicans* *Asp. niger*	14 d 28 d	10^2 NI
Oral (liquid products only)	*Ps. aeruginosa* *Staph. aureus* *E. coli*	14 d 28 d	10^3 10^3	*Ps. aeruginosa* *Staph. aureus* *E. coli*	7 d 14 d 28 d	10^2 NI NI
	C. albicans *Asp. niger*	14 d 28 d	10^1 10^1	*C. albicans* *Asp. niger*	14 d 28 d	NI NI

Type of product	US Pharmacopeia (1990)			Italian Pharmacopoeia (1985)		
	Organism	Time	Viable count reduced by	Organism	Time	Viable count reduced by
Parenterals (multidose) and ophthalmics	*Ps. aeruginosa* *Staph. aureus*	14 d 28 d	10^3 NI	*Ps. aeruginosa* *Staph. aureus*	6 h 24 h 7 d	10^2 10^3 10^5
	C. albicans *Asp. niger*	14 d 28 d	NI NI	*C. albicans* *Asp. niger*	24 h 7 d 14 d	NI 10^2 NI
Topical formulations	No recommendations			*Ps. aeruginosa* *Staph. aureus*	48 h 7 d 14 d 28 d	NI 10^2 10^3 NI
				C. albicans *Asp. niger*	7 d 28 d	10^2 NI
Oral (liquid products only)	No recommendations			*Ps. aeruginosa* *Staph. aureus* *E. coli*	48 h 7 d 21 d 42 d	10^2 10^3 NI NI
				C. albicans *Asp. niger*	21 d 42 d	10^1 NI

ND, none detected. NI, no increase thereafter.
If an additional organism is tested in a particular type of product, the interpretation of the result will fall into the appropriate category. For example, *Zygosaccharomyces rouxii* is an osmophilic yeast and the product should comply with the limits set for moulds and yeasts.

Table 5 — Test conditions for preservative efficacy test of cosmetics and toiletries

Variable	Test condition
Inoculum size (c.f.u. per ml or g)	Not less than 10^6
Sample size (product)	Not less than 20 ml or g
Product storage	Room temperature or temperature for maximum growth of organism
Test intervals	0, between 1 and 2, 7, 14 and 28 days

after the minimum 28–day time period. The committee has issued no definitive levels of contamination that are acceptable. The investigator is responsible for the final product decision.

6 NON-PHARMACOPOEIAL TESTING OF NON-STERILE PRODUCTS FOR PRESERVATIVE EFFICACY

In the last 15–20 years concern has increased over microbial contamination of non-sterile pharmaceutical formulations. A product being supplied to a country that does not have its own pharmacopoeial test has to comply with guidelines set down by the Committee of Official Laboratories and Drug Control Services and Section of Industrial Pharmacists (FIP) in their second report (Anon. 1976).

7 PRACTICAL CONSIDERATIONS OF PRESERVATIVE EFFICACY TESTING IN COMPLEX FORMULATIONS

The preservative efficacy test for aqueous solutions and water-soluble solids is relatively easy to carry out and interpret. However, for products such as oily solutions, ointments and other anhydrous items, the preservative efficacy test becomes more complex. This is because the microbial inocula are aqueous suspensions and thus depend on the water/oil partitioning properties of both the microbial cells and the antimicrobial preservative for interaction of preservative and organism to occur. It cannot be assured that efficient water/oil partitioning occurs, and therefore the preservative efficacy test for anhydrous-type products has its limitations. For example, a positive test result where bacterial levels do not decline is always questionable for anhydrous products because it cannot be assumed that the antimicrobial preservative in the oily product had adequate surface contact with the aqueous environment of the bacterial aqueous suspension. It could also be argued that by addition of an aqueous suspension of micro-organisms to a non-aqueous system the physicochemical characteristics of that system have so changed that a preservative efficacy test result would not reflect the true formulation behaviour.

A common technique for improving interfacial interaction of antimicrobial preservatives in anhydrous products with micro-organisms in aqueous suspensions is to use surface-active agents. Polysorbate 80 (Tween 80), Arlacel 80 and Tween 20 are commonly used surfactants in preservative efficacy testing of anhydrous products. A common procedure is to transfer 1 ml or 1 g of the anhydrous sample containing the microbial inoculum to 10 ml of a sterile mixture of equal volumes of Tween 20 and Arlacel 80, mix well, then add sterile phosphate buffer to make 100 ml, and mix well again to produce an emulsion. This emulsion (1 : 100 dilution) is then diluted further according to the usual compendial plate-counting procedure. Obviously, it is critical that thorough mixing of the dilutions takes place to maximize antimicrobial preservative interaction with the microbial inoculum. Once again, addition of such a surface-active mix will alter the physicochemical characteristics of the system and this may lead to interactions between the preservative and emulgent, or may alter the partitioning behaviour (see Chapter 11).

In view of these difficulties and since oil-based formulations are not usually considered suitable environments to support microbial growth, the question may be legitimately asked as to whether a preservative agent is really necessary. In such circumstances, the demonstration of low contamination at the time of manufacture may be sufficient to infer microbiological acceptability.

The pharmacopoeial testing of non-sterile formulations has been evaluated by several investigators. One particular area of interest has been in problems encountered when recovering micro-organisms from cream and emulsion-type formulations. The British Pharmacopoeia recommends the addition of up to 10% Polysorbate 80 to aid in the dispersion of the product. Wide variation in the recovery of the micro-organisms by this method has been reported (Allwood and Hambleton 1972, 1973; Brown *et al.* 1986).

Another factor in interpreting efficacy test results is the possible potentiation of preservative action during the test. In this respect, the choice of dispersants and co-solvents in dilution and recovery fluids must be made with care. Certainly, ethanol in concentrations as low as 5% can have a profound potentiating effect on the activity of antimicrobial agents (McCarthy *et al.* 1988). The use of alcohol as a diluting fluid in tests must be discouraged. Other potentiators include salts, antioxidants, sugars and polyols such as glycerol (Zeelie and McCarthy 1983; Griffith 1986).

8 REFERENCES

Akers, M. J. (1979) Dynamics of microbial growth and death in parenteral products. *J. Parenter. Drug. Assoc.* **33** 372–388.
Akers, M. J., Boand, A. V. and Binkley, D. A. (1984) Preformulation method for parenteral preservative efficacy evaluation. *J. Pharm. Sci.* **73** 903–905.
Allwood, M. C. and Hambleton, R. (1972) The recovery of *Bacillus megaterium* spores from WSP. *J. Pharm. Pharmacol.* **24** 671–672.
Allwood, M. C. and Hambleton, R. (1973) The recovery of bacteria from white soft paraffin. *J. Pharm. Pharmacol.* **25** 559–562.
Anon. (1976) Second joint report of the Committee of Official Laboratories and Drug Control Services and the Section of Industrial Pharmacists, FIP, July, 1975, *Pharm. Acta Helv.* **51** 33–40.
Avis, K. E. and Akers, M. J. (1986) Sterilization. In: Lachman, L., Lieberman, H.

A. and Kanig, J. L. (eds), *The theory and practice of industrial pharmacy*, 3rd edn. Lea and Febiger, Philadelphia, pp. 620–622.

British Pharmacopoeia (1988) Appendix XVIC, HMSO, London, pp. A200–A203.

Brown, M. W., Evans, C. P., Ford, J. L. and Pilling, M. (1986) A note on the recovery of microorganisms from an oil-in-water cream. *J. Clin. Hosp. Pharm.* **11** 117–123.

Cooper, M. S. (1989) *The Microbiological Update* **7** No. 1 (April issue).

Cowan, R. A. and Steiger, B. (1976) Antimicrobial activity: a critical review of test methods of preservative efficacy. *J. Soc. Cosmet. Chem.* **27** 467–481.

Davis, B. D., Dulbecco, R., Eisen, H. N. and Ginsberg, H. S. (1980) *Microbiology*, 3rd edn. Harper and Row, Hagerstown, MD.

Eisman, P. C., Jaconia, D. and Lazarus, J. (1963) A proposed microbiological method for studying the stability of preservatives in parenteral solutions. *Bull. Parenter. Drug Assoc.* **17** 10–17.

German Pharmacopoeia (1986) Part VIII, No. 1, pp 369–370 and Supplement (1989) pp. 71–72, Deutsche Apothekerverlag, Stuttgart, Govi-Verlag GmbH, Frankfurt.

Griffith, I. P. (1986) Preservation of non-sterile pharmaceuticals: Part 2. *Aust. J. Hosp. Pharm.* **16** 259–264.

Halleck, F. E. (1970) A guideline for the determination of adequacy of preservation of cosmetics and toiletry formulations. *TGA J.* Winter issue 20–23.

Han, Y. W., Zhang, H. I. and Krochta, J. M. (1976) Death rates of bacterial spores: mathematical models. *Can. J. Microbiol.* **22** 295–300.

Italian Pharmacopoeia (1985) 9th edn, Istituto Poligrafico e Zecca Dello Starto-Libreria Dello Starto, Roma, pp. 509–512.

Kenney, D. S., Grundy, W. E. and Otto, R. H. (1964) Spoilage and preservative tests as applied to pharmaceuticals. *Bull. Parenter. Drug Assoc.* **18** 10–19.

McCarthy, T. J., Van Eeden, A., Stephenson, N. and Newman, C. (1988) Interaction between ethanol and selected antimicrobial agents. *S. Afr. J. Sci.* **84** 128–131.

Moore, K. E. (1978) Evaluating preservative efficacy by challenge testing during the development stage of pharmaceutical products. *J. Appl. Bact.* **44** Sxliii–Slv.

Orth, D. S. (1979) Linear regression method for rapid determination of cosmetic preservative efficacy, *J. Soc. Cosmet. Chem.* **30** 321–332.

Russell, A. D., Ljeoma, A. and Rogers, D. T. (1979) A review: microbiological applications of the inactivation of antibiotics and other antimicrobial agents. *J. Appl. Bact.* **46** 207–245.

United States Pharmacopeia (1970) XVIII revision, Mack Publishing Company, Easton, PA.

United States Pharmacopeia (1990) XXII revision, United States Pharmacopeial Convention.

Zeelie, J. J. and McCarthy, T. J. (1983) Antioxidants: multifunctional preservatives for cosmetic and toiletry formulations. *Cosmet. Toilet.* **98** 51–52.

13B

Preservative evaluation and testing: the linear regression method

D. S. Orth
Neutrogena Corporation, 5755 West 96th Street, Los Angeles, CA 90045, USA

1   INTRODUCTION

Official methods of preservative efficacy testing generally require a test period of up to 28 days (see Chapter 13A). In development pharmaceutics, this is usually an unacceptable time-scale and a more rapid predictive method of preservative performance is often required (Leak and Leech 1988). A possible approach to this is offered by the linear regression method (Orth 1979), where the kinetics of cell death can be used to predict preservative behaviour in formulated products.

2   LINEAR REGRESSION METHOD

In the idealized microbiological growth curve, the four stages (phases) of growth are the lag phase, logarithmic phase, stationary phase and death phase (Chapter 1). Cellular death refers to the loss of viability of cells, as indicated by their ability to grow and form colonies on plating media. The death phase represents the dynamic response of the population of micro-organisms in a given system when the rate of cell death exceeds the rate of new cell formation.

In preservative efficacy testing, products containing various concentrations of preservatives are challenged with test organisms to determine whether the preservative system inactivates the test organisms quickly enough to meet acceptance criteria. The survivor curve is obtained by plotting the logarithm of the aerobic plate count as a function of the time after inoculation. The slope of the survivor curve gives the rate of death of the population of test organisms in the test samples. The negative reciprocal of the slope gives the decimal reduction time (D-value), which is the time required for a 1-log cycle (90%) reduction in the population when exposed to a constant lethal treatment (Orth 1979).

The linear regression method provides a means of determining the D-values for test organisms in samples of product and has been found to be a reliable method for determining the type and concentration of preservatives required in aqueous products (Orth 1979, 1984; Orth and Brueggen, 1982). Testing is performed by inoculating 0.1 ml of a saline suspension of each test organism into approximately 50 ml of test sample in screw-capped bottles. After inoculation, the bottles are shaken and the aerobic plate counts are determined immediately (for the zero-time determination) and at various times thereafter, typically at 2, 4, 24 and 48 hours for bacteria, and 4, 8, 24 and 48 hours for moulds. In addition, aerobic plate counts of the saline inocula of each test organism are determined. Additional samples are taken and aerobic plate counts are performed at 3, 5 or 7 days after inoculation, unless the previous aerobic plate count was <10 c.f.u. ml^{-1}, indicating that the preservative system had killed the test organisms introduced into the product.

Different organisms have different physiological and metabolic characteristics; consequently, they may exhibit differences in the rates of death when exposed to any given lethal treatment. The rationale for use of the linear regression method is that every organism has a characteristic rate of death when subjected to any lethal treatment (Orth 1979). Thus, the D-value provides a quantitative expression of the rate of death of the population of each test organism in the test sample. The survivor curve obtained when performing preservative efficacy tests by this method is functionally equivalent to the death phase of the idealized bacteriological growth curve (Orth and Milstein 1989).

2.1 Graphical determination of D-values

The D-value for each test organism in a test sample is determined from its survivor curve (Orth 1984). To illustrate this, let us assume that *Staph. aureus* was inoculated into a lotion and that aerobic plate counts of 10^6, 4×10^5, 10^4 and <10 c.f.u. ml^{-1} were obtained at 0, 2, 4 and 24 hours, respectively. These aerobic plate counts and the times at which they are determined are plotted using seven-cycle semilog graph paper. Alternatively, the log of the aerobic plate counts may be calculated and plotted as a function of the time on standard graph paper (values of <10 c.f.u. ml^{-1} are plotted as 0). The survivor curve is constructed by drawing a 'best-fit' straight line through the points, extrapolated to the X-axis, as shown in Fig. 1.

The X-intercept of the survivor curve represents the time for complete inactivation of the test population in the test sample. Here, the X-intercept is 24 hours, which is the time required for complete inactivation of *Staph. aureus*. The D-value is the

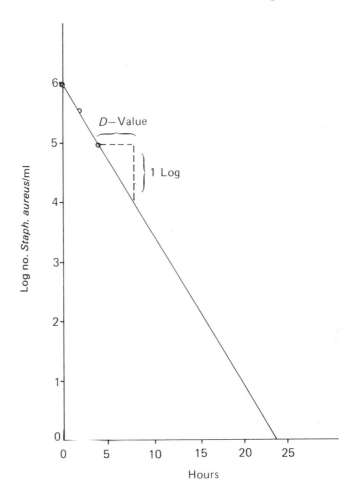

Fig. 1 — Survivor curve for *Staph. aureus* showing a decrease in the population from 10^6 organisms ml^{-1} to $<10\,ml^{-1}$ after 24 hours. The *D*-value in this example is 4 hours and is shown to be the time required for a 1 log cycle reduction in the aerobic plate count. Reprinted from Orth (1984), p. 407, by courtesy of Marcel Dekker, Inc.

time required for the preservative system to decrease the *Staph. aureus* population by 1-log cycle and is equal to the negative reciprocal of the slope of the survivor curve. The slope in this example is −0.25 log reduction per hour; consequently, the *D*-value is 4 hours.

2.2 Mathematical determination of *D*-values

D-values may be determined by use of least-squares linear regression analysis (Orth 1984) assuming a linear relationship of the form $y=mx+c$, where $y=$log number of *Staph. aureus* surviving per millilitre, $x=$time, $m=$slope and $c=Y$-intercept. This enables determination of the theoretical aerobic plate count at the time of inoculation (Y-intercept), the slope of the survivor curve from which the *D*-value can be calculated, and the correlation coefficient, r. These values may be obtained directly by use of a calculator capable of least-squares linear regression analysis. In this approach, the aerobic plate count values and the times at which they were determined are entered into the calculator, and the linear regression is produced. By using the data presented in Fig. 1 for the inactivation of *Staph. aureus*, the following results were obtained:

Y-intercept (c)	$=6.041$ (initial inoculum 1.1×10^6 ml^{-1})
Slope (m)	$=-0.25$ h^{-1}
D-value	$=4$ h (Note: the D-value is the negative reciprocal of the slope)
r	$=-0.99$
X-intercept	$=24.1$ h (Note: survivors are below the detection level (10 c.f.u. ml^{-1}) for aerobic plate count (i.e. $Y=0$) at X-intercept)

These calculations demonstrate that the predicted X-intercept was slightly greater than 24 hours. The reason for this is that the data do not fit the regression perfectly, because the r value$=-0.99$. (Note: an r-value of -1.00 indicates a perfect fit of the data to the regression, but, because of experimental variation, this is rarely achieved.) It is recommended that D-values over 10 hours should be reported to two significant figures to avoid creating a false impression of accuracy of the method. Similarly, D-values under 10 hours should be reported to the nearest decimal point.

The mathematical determination of D-values is preferred over the graphical determination, since it is much faster to enter data points in a calculator than it is to construct a graph (Orth 1984). Furthermore, the use of linear regression analysis enables accurate determination of the proper positioning of the curve, should a graph be necessary, and it provides a means of statistical quality control for each assessment (discussed below).

2.3   Reliability of the linear regression method

Although there are reports indicating that survivor curves may deviate from linearity in some cases (Akers *et al.* 1984; Orth 1984; Levy 1987), this has not been our normal experience when the preservative system inactivates test organisms quickly enough to meet acceptance criteria. Populations of spore-forming bacilli, however, appear to be inactivated in a biphasic manner with an initial, more rapid rate of inactivation of the vegetative cells being followed by a slower, sometimes negligible rate of inactivation of the spores (unpublished work). If the two portions of this biphasic curve are considered to be made up of two survivor curves, one for the population of vegetative cells and one for the population of spores, then D-values may be determined for both vegetative cells and for spores in test samples.

The reliability of the linear regression method was evaluated by repetitive analysis of the same sample on the same and different days (Orth and Brueggen 1982). It was found that the D-values obtained on each day were within 0.5 hours for four different bacteria, and the mean D-values for each set of three samples examined on different days were within 1.1 hours when D-values were $\leqslant 2.9$ hours. An analysis of variance revealed that the standard deviation values for the triplicate means ranged from 0.06 to 0.59. It is believed that the variation between replicate analyses of the same sample may increase somewhat as the observed D-values increase. In general, there has been an excellent agreement of the time predicted for the aerobic plate count to be <10 c.f.u. ml^{-1} and the actual time observed by performing aerobic plate count determinations.

2.4 Statistical quality control of the linear regression method
Use of the linear regression method of preservative efficacy testing offers a statistical approach to examining assay reliability. The r-value provides a measure of the precision of the assay and may be used to demonstrate preciseness of fit of the data to the regression (Orth and Brueggen 1982; Orth 1984). The data presented in Table 1 are the r-values for a number of assays taken from a page in a laboratory notebook. All of the r-values are negative for survivor curves in which the test organisms are dying. The closer the r-value is to -1.00, the better the aerobic plate count values fit the regression, as shown in the following example.

To set up the statistical quality control procedures, one may take the mean value ($\overline{X}$) for a number of analyses (a minimum of ten is recommended). When this is done using the r-values for assays 1–10 in Table 1, an $\overline{X}$ value of -0.98 is obtained. The

Table 1 — Correlation coefficients (r-values) determined during calculation of D-values by use of the linear regression method (see also Fig. 2)

Assay No.	r-value
1	-0.9599[a]
2	-0.9996
3	-0.9800
4	-0.9943
5	-0.9603
6	-0.9999
7	-0.9540
8	-0.9937
9	-0.9802
10	-0.9987
11	-0.9953
12	-0.8799
13	-0.9800

[a]r-values to four-decimal places used for calculations.

standard deviation (s) about this mean is also calculated. In this example, the s-value is 0.02, and the value for $2s$ is 0.04. One may set the 95% confidence limits about the mean by use of $\pm 2s$. Thus, any assay performed in which the r-value lies within the 95% confidence limits (-0.98 ± 0.04, or between -0.94 and -1.02) will be considered to be 'in control' (i.e. performing satisfactorily). This is illustrated in Fig. 2. It is evident that the r-values for the first 11 assays are within the 95% confidence limits. Assay 12 has an r-value of -0.88, which is outside the 95% confidence limits. The failure of the r-value to fall within the 95% confidence limits suggests that something went wrong during this assay or in performing the calculations. Failure of the data to fit the regression suggests that the survivor curve was not linear. This may be due to a mixed population of organisms, contamination in the test, lack of homogeneity in the sample or in the distribution of test organisms in the test samples, sampling errors, adaptation of the test organisms to the product, or other factors. It would be necessary therefore first to check the duplicate aerobic plate count values to see that the numbers and means were recorded correctly, and secondly to repeat the calculations for the linear regression to determine whether an error had been made there. If no error can be found, it should be concluded that the assay was outside the control limits, and it should be repeated. Note that assay 13 was in control because the r-value for this assay fell within the 95% confidence limits.

Other criteria for statistical quality control may be used, at the discretion of the laboratory. For example, one may use the running average of the mean D-value for a particular product, or $\pm 3s$ about $\overline{X}$ (for 99% confidence limits).

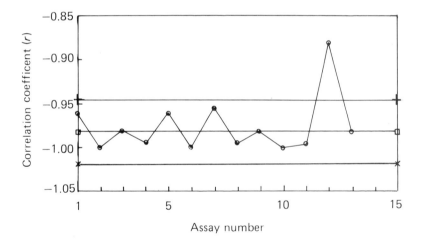

Fig. 2 — Statistical quality control of the linear regression method showing the $\overline{X}$ value (□——□) obtained in the first ten assays and the 95% confidence limits about this $\overline{X}$ value (×–× , upper limit +–+ lower limit).

3 APPLICATION OF THE LINEAR REGRESSION METHOD TO DEVELOPMENT OF A PRODUCT PRESERVATIVE SYSTEM

The reliable and reproducible nature of the linear regression method recommends it for the early stages in development of a product preservative system. In providing quantitative data on the kinetics of inactivation, it allows D-values to be determined for each test organism and preservative behaviour can be predicted and compared.

For example, let us assume that preservative testing with *Staph. aureus* in a lotion containing 0, 0.1, 0.2 and 0.3% w/v methylparaben gave *D*-values of >30, 10, 5 and 0.5 hours, respectively (Orth 1984). The family of curves for *Staph. aureus* in this lotion is shown in Fig. 3.

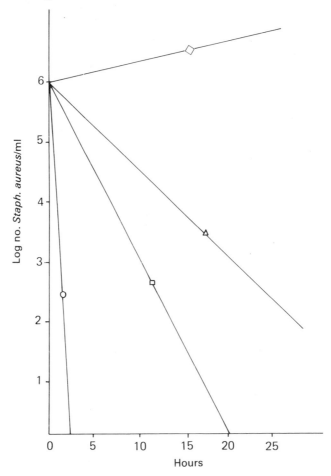

Fig. 3 — Series of survivor curves for *Staph. aureus* in lotion. *D*-Values of >30, 10, 5 and 0.5 hours were obtained in test samples containing 0% (◇), 0.1% (△), 0.2% (□) and 0.3% (○) methylparaben, respectively. Reprinted from Orth (1984), p. 409, by courtesy of Marcel Dekker, Inc.

From these data, the preservative death time curve may now be constructed by plotting *D*-values as a function of the concentration of preservative used to obtain these *D*-values. The preservative death time curve for *Staph. aureus* in this example is shown in Fig. 4. This curve is used to determine the concentration of preservative needed to meet acceptance criteria. Here, it is seen that a concentration of 0.2% w/v methylparaben is required to give a *D*-value of 4 hours for *Staph. aureus*. This approach is repeated for all test organisms, and the concentration of preservative needed for the product to meet the acceptance criteria with all the test organisms is

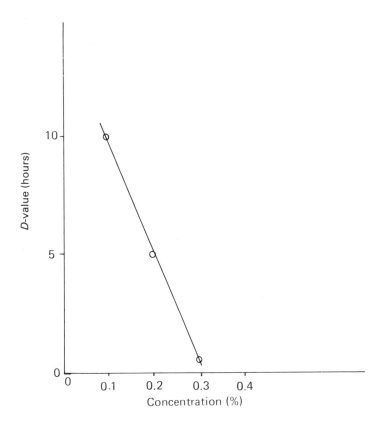

Fig. 4 — Preservative death time curve for *Staph. aureus* in lotion test samples used in Fig. 3. The *D*-value obtained in the absence of methylparaben (e.g. >30 hours) was not used in constructing this preservative death time curve because the bacteria were not being inactivated. Reprinted from Orth (1984), p. 410, by courtesy of Marcel Dekker, Inc.

then selected as the probable concentration required to preserve the formula satisfactorily. This is confirmed using this concentration in a new batch of product and retesting it to verify the predicted antimicrobial efficacy. Finally, samples are subjected to a stability test, in which samples of the product in finished product containers are stored at different temperatures (e.g. 3, 25, 37 and 50°C) for varying lengths of time before conducting preservative efficacy tests to demonstrate that the preservative system meets acceptance criteria and is stable (Orth *et al.* 1987). This testing should be performed with all appropriate test organisms in samples of the product prepared with each preservative being considered for use in the product.

The acceptance criteria used to judge the adequacy of a preservative system depend on the method of testing used and the regulatory requirements for that type of product. The quantitative rates of death provided by the linear regression method enable quantitative acceptance criteria to be based on *D*-values. For instance, pathogens should be killed within 24 hours in all multiple-use cosmetic products that are capable of supporting microbial growth (Orth 1979). Thus, products should have a preservative system that will give *D*-values of ≤4 hours for pathogens so that 10^6 pathogens per gram will be inactivated completely with 24 hours. The 24-hour period thus provides time for a contaminated product to self-sterilize before use one day later. Less stringent criteria are considered to be appropriate for non-pathogens. Thus, D-values of $\leqslant 28$ hours may be recommended for non-pathogenic vegetative bacteria, yeasts and moulds. Again, this period was selected to enable a product contaminated with 10^6 organisms per gram to self-sterilize within one week (Orth 1979). Non-sterile aqueous cosmetic and pharmaceutical products should be bacteriostatic or slowly bactericidal for *Bacillus* spores.

4   REFERENCES

Akers, M. J., Boand, A. V. and Binkley, D. A. (1984) Preformulation method for parenteral preservative efficacy evaluation. *J. Pharm. Sci.* **73** 903–905.

Leak, R. E. and Leech, R. (1988) Challenge tests and their predictive ability. In: Bloomfield, S. F., Baird, R., Leak, R. E. and Leech, R., (eds), *Microbial quality assurance in pharmaceuticals, cosmetics and toiletries*. Ellis Horwood, Chichester, pp. 129–146.

Levy, E. (1987) Insights into microbial adaptation to cosmetic and pharmaceutical products. *Cosmet Toilet.* **102** (12) 69–74.

Orth, D. S. (1979) Linear regression method for rapid determination of cosmetic preservative efficacy. *J. Soc. Cosmet. Chem.* **30** 321–332.

Orth, D. S. (1984) Evaluation of preservatives in cosmetic products. In: Kabara, J. J. (ed.), *Cosmetic and drug preservation: principles and practice*. Marcel Dekker, New York, pp. 403–421.

Orth, D. S. and Brueggen, L. R. (1982) Preservative efficacy testing of cosmetic products: rechallenge testing and reliability of the linear regression method. *Cosmet. Toilet.* **97** (5) 61–65.

Orth, D. S. and Milstein, S. R. (1989) Rational development of preservative systems for cosmetic products. *Cosmet. Toilet.* **104** (11) 91, 92, 94–100, 102, 103.

Orth, D. S.,, Lutes, C. M., Milstein, S. R. and Allinger, J. J. (1987) Determination of shampoo preservative stability and apparent activation energies by the linear regression method of preservative efficacy testing. *J. Soc. Cosmet. Chem.* **38** 307–319.

14

Preservatives: registration and regulatory affairs

R. K. Greenwood
Bios (Consultancy & Contract Research) Ltd, Pinewood, College Ride, Bagshot, Surrey GU19 5ER, UK

1 INTRODUCTION

Virtually every country in the world now subjects pharmaceuticals and other chemical products to official governmental, legal and scientific scrutiny before permitting their sale or supply to the public (Goldberg 1986; Christodoulou 1984). This process, referred to as registration, involves the formulation scientist in placing upon record all technical details about the product. These records usually form part of a Product Licence Application (PLA) or a Marketing Authorization (MA) and have to be presented in a prescribed way so that government authorities may review the data with ease (Anon. 1965, 1975a, 1975b, 1983a, 1985). Depending upon the quality of the data in the PLA and the efficiency of the bureaucratic process, the completion of this review may take anything from three months to five years (Anon. 1989).

On the basis of these records, possibly an inspection of the product and the conditions under which it is manufactured (Anon. 1975b), an authorization to market, sell and supply the product will either be granted or refused. Failure to convince the authorities at the first application carries a penalty of time-consuming and costly appeal procedures (Anon. 1984). A further, financial penalty may also be incurred through missed sales opportunities and erosion of the patent protection period (Lynd 1984). Moreover, patients will be denied the benefit of treatment with the product until such time that a licence is granted. Consequently, if the product is to reach the patient in reasonable time, the way that experiments are conducted, recorded and used in a registration application is of critical importance to the formulator.

Preservatives and preservation systems are a crucial part of any formulation containing them. However, since they are not the principal active ingredients in the product, they may be overlooked when it comes to testing or discussing results. This may lead to serious omissions in both the development programme and the database ultimately used in presentation to regulatory authorities. Such omissions may result in the product failing to gain that essential marketing authorization which is necessary for the product to reach the patient. Therefore, the formulator must be fully aware of the way preservatives and preservative systems in a product need to be researched and treated before attempting to present the regulatory case.

2 REGISTRATION

In preparing this chapter, it has been assumed the reader has some knowledge of the basic requirements for registration and the law relating to sale and supply of pharmaceutical goods to the public (Dale and Appelbe 1989). Formulators in the UK should at least be familiar with the Medicines Act 1968 (Anon. 1968) and well acquainted with the Guidance Notes on Applications for Product Licences (Anon. 1985) and its supplement (Anon. 1987a). These latter documents reflect European Community (EC)Directives 65/65/EEC, 75/318/EEC, 75/319/EEC, 83/570/EEC, 83/571/EEC, 87/19/EEC, 87/21/EEC and 87/22/EEC (Anon. 1965, 1975a, 1975b, 1983a, 1983b, 1986a, 1986b, 1986c) for the handling of pharmaceutical products throughout member states. They also provide the basis for many registration application requirements and procedures throughout Europe and serve as references for what is stated in this chapter. They are essential reading.

Since it can never be certain whether or not any part of an experimenter's work will ever be used to justify registration, it is better to conduct all studies to a standard acceptable to the authorities. Therefore, Medicines Act Leaflet MAL 2 (Anon. 1985) should be obligatory reading for all experimental scientists in the development field. Expertise in regulatory matters is not the objective, but a working familiarity with MAL 2 makes discussions with those who are expert so much easier to comprehend.

In order to reach any useful level of competence in the subject of registration and regulatory affairs, two to three years' full-time post-graduate on-the-job training is required. Virtually every country in the world now has some form of registration procedure and each one is idiosyncratic in its approach. Rather than attempting here to provide a potted version of the registration guidelines, this chapter is designed to offer practical registration information directed specifically towards preservatives in pharmaceuticals. The formulator should then have an insight into the kind of problems likely to occur in regulatory matters associated with preservatives during product development. However, if the formulator is to be assured that all regulatory matters will be properly researched, discussed and included in the development programme, then it has to be recommended that experienced professional regulatory advice be sought.

3 REGULATORY AUTHORITIES

The regulatory authorities who scrutinize licence applications are normally government agencies or departments staffed by civil servants. The predominant professionals are medical practitioners who consider clinical aspects and pharmacists who consider pharmaceutical aspects of the product. Some other scientists, as well as lawyers and administrators, are also included in the team. In the UK, the reviewing body is the Department of Health, Medicines Control Agency (MCA); in the USA, the Food and Drug Administration plays a similar role. Details of the competent authorities of all member states of the EC are provided in MAL 2 (Anon. 1985). It also provides details for a multistate application via the EC Committee on Proprietary Medicinal Products (CPMP), the body responsible for recommending the placement of medicinal products on the market in the EC.

Authorities mostly work in accordance with legislation laid down by government. Under the legislation, they issue Statutory Instruments and guidelines such as MAL 2 on all manner of topics. In the UK alone there are over 300 Statutory Instruments and 80 MAL documents which are relevant to the pharmaceutical and allied industries. During the process of assessment the authorities are mandated to consider the safety, the efficacy and the quality of each product and each ingredient of each product including, of course, preservatives. By the standards of the day, these three criteria must be satisfactory whether the product is new or long established, whether a new chemical entity (NCE) is involved or whether the product is a reformulation or a combination of established products (Anon. 1968). The standards of the day are subject to advances in scientific knowledge and the opinions held by the experts reviewing such products in each country. Unanimity between all parties is seldom seen; the success of an application is always a matter for speculation.

4 THE REGISTRATION PROCESS

Legislation controlling the registration process varies from country to country and, in some countries, even between states. Examples of the latter are found in the USA (Anon. 1982) and Australia (Marshall 1984). The way the product has to be registered, or even the need to register at all, should be checked at the earliest possible time. The particular characteristics or specifications of the product and the claims made for it will usually dictate the legal category into which the product will fall: for example, whether it is a human or veterinary medicine, a cosmetic, or a product which will have limited distribution or special labelling. There are many other factors which also need to be considered. Failure to address and understand these matters at the outset could result in the formulator preparing a product which is severely restricted to a particular market or even banned from some markets altogether.

At its simplest, registration is merely the filling in of an application form (Form MLA 201 in the UK) (Anon. 1985) obtained from and returned to the MCA for assessment. These forms usually adopt a stepwise procedure designed to draw from the applicant all relevant technical details about the product. Inevitably, such a generalized procedure sometimes fails to fit the particular needs of the product. Further, there are sections in the application such as that devoted to expert reports, where opinion rather than hard fact has to be expressed. A careful choice of words can be crucial to the success of the application and thoughtless or gratuitous comment can cause difficulties and delays. Contributions to the application are drawn from many different disciplines. Contradictions or inconsistencies between different sections also create problems for the assessors and subsequently the approval process.

4.1 Expert reports
The use of expert reports provides the assessor with an on-the-spot scientific audit for the application and, for the applicant, a means of commenting upon or explaining inconsistencies.

For members of the EC, registration applications follow a designated format. Apart from the scientific and technical supporting data, there is a requirement for three expert reports to provide a concise summary of that data in three sections:

(a) chemical and pharmaceutical;

(b) toxicological and pharmacological;
(c) clinical.

Each section of the summary must also include critical comments by experts and must be signed by them, together with identification of the place and date of issue (Anon. 1975b). These requirements are by no means universal but many countries are now prepared to accept data in this format.

The formulator should be aware that the expert report has to provide the authorities with a critical assessment of the formulator's work and reasoning behind experimentation. Consequently, most of the formulator's work will be summarized and become a major subject for the critique in the chemical and pharmaceutical section. When specific data are omitted or use is made of published literature as the basis for, say, an abridged application, the expert must show that this is justified and confirm the suitability of the product for its recommended use. Apart from being signed, the expert report should also be accompanied by a brief curriculum vitae indicating the educational background, training and occupation of the expert and the professional relationship with the applicant (Anon. 1975b).

The formulator can write his own expert report but quite clearly it is likely to be considered partisan and may be insufficiently critical of the experimental work and the interpretation placed upon results for the purposes of the authorities. This may well cause delays in the registration process and therefore it is recommended that a suitably qualified independent expert with registration experience be engaged to prepare the expert report.

4.2 Basic questions prior to formulation
Before a formulator begins the task of making a product, as a first step the following marketing and regulatory points should be determined:

(a) the country or countries in which the product will be sold;
(b) the label claims which are sought;
(c) the method of administration and type of packaging;
(d) the market outlets which are intended;
(e) the familiarity of the authorities with such a product, the active ingredients and, of course, the preservative systems likely to be required.

Having established these five parameters, a formulator may then determine the range of limitations likely to apply to this product in each market. An experienced scientist will probably give consideration to these matters under two main headings: registration requirements and regulatory affairs (Greenwood 1985). Briefly these can be defined as follows:

(a) *Registration requirements.* Refers to all matters associated with experimenting, collecting, collating and recording data on a product, and presenting it in the prescribed manner for scrutiny and approval by one or more government agencies. The experimental scientific data must be complete. It must also include arguments and reassurances which will demonstrate unequivocally to each agency that all current standards of safety, efficacy and quality have been satisfactorily applied to the product and that it has not been found wanting.

(b) *Regulatory affairs.* The process of gathering intelligence from each market where the product will be sold or supplied. It concerns not only the standards of safety, efficacy and quality but also all other legislative and political restraints which operate in those markets at the present time and in the foreseeable future.

Such information can come from the authorities, market experience or published data. The wider the range of sources, the more reliable will be the emerging formulation brief. As already stated, the registration processes, the standards set and the requirements for a particular product are not uniform thoughout the world. On the other hand, in order to recover fully the cost of research and development, a product has ideally to be registered and sold worldwide. Consequently, the formulator has to make an early choice about the preservatives to be used. Ideally, materials which are recognized by most authorities as safe and effective should be considered first. Alternatively, new or less established ingredients and systems of preservation may be developed about which the authorities may know little or nothing, but which would confer some advantage on the finished product. Work required in support of the former will usually be less onerous and cheaper than for the latter, which could easily make the same demand upon resources as that required for the registration of a new chemical entity. Therefore careful preliminary regulatory affairs research is required.

4.3   Regulatory affairs research
A good registration professional will not confine attention to the rules of registration alone, but will review any legislation which may influence the development process, obtaining a product licence or the marketing of the product. Typically, this includes regulations concerning patents (Lynd 1984), trade-marks (Keyes 1984), food and drug acts (Blanchfield 1984), cosmetics (Logan 1984), toiletries, borderline substances (Troup 1984), trade descriptions (Lawson 1984), notifications of new substances (Murray 1984) and environmental protection acts. Any or all of these could have a bearing upon the final product design and formulation chosen. Other areas for consideration might include adverse drug reactions (Penn 1982), product liability (Spink 1982; McIntosh 1987), clinical trial monitoring (Farrell 1982) and good clinical, laboratory and manufacturing practices (Broad 1981, Begg 1981). Not all aspects will need close attention at the outset of the formulation programme, but as development proceeds they should be considered at the appropriate time and the correct level of expertise engaged. Advice on registration and regulatory affairs is only effective if researches are conducted both in advance of and in *pari passu* with product development. Each decision concerning every part of the programme must include a total appreciation of any regulatory implication for the product. Only by recognizing such implications can informed decisions be made about the objectives and the conduct of project work.

Already it must be clear that registration is more complex than might at first appear to be the case. Amateurism in this field is definitely a thing of the past and the formulator is strongly advised to seek advice from a professional regulatory person before committing either time or money to any serious development programme. As both regulations and science constantly change, the prudent scientist will also make arrangements to receive a continuous update on regulatory affairs. Regular meetings between the formulator and a regulatory expert are now a crucial part of modern development management, if potential mismatches between the development programme and the final registration requirements in one or several markets are to be avoided. This will become even clearer when considering the scientific paramaters of the programme in more detail.

5   ATTITUDE TO PRESERVATIVES BY REGISTRATION AUTHORITIES

Before reviewing possible experimental support studies on preservatives, a moment of consideration should be given to the attitude authorities may have towards preservatives and how it might be possible to avoid expenditure on unnecessary experimentation.

If a product can be adequately preserved by using established and well-known preservatives, this simplifies laboratory work and the justification for the choice of preservatives. The registration authorities will still require experimental scientific proof of safety and efficacy but less than for an unfamiliar material or system.

5.1   Preservatives and antioxidants already recognized by certain authorities

A registration professional should be able to provide the formulator with an up-to-date list of preservatives which are accepted by the authorities for each country in which the product will be sold. Several means of identifying such preservatives may need to be reviewed. For example, national pharmacopoeias provide a useful indication of preservative acceptability for a particular authority. It is worth noting that for EC countries the European Pharmacopoeia (1988) takes precedence over national pharmacopoeias. Table 1 is compiled from Martindale (1989) and lists 30 authorities that specifically refer to certain preservatives and antioxidants in their national pharmacopoeias. Some national authorities provide lists of preservatives which are acceptable for specified purposes (United States Pharmacopeia 1990). No list has yet been provided in the EC for use in human and veterinary medicines, but some guidance can be gained from other sources. For example, in the UK, Statutory Instrument (SI) No. 533 (1989) lists permitted preservatives for use in foods which may be adapted for a particular formulation. An extract from this SI is given in Table 2. Similarly, the EC's Eighth Commission Directive (86/199/EC) (Anon. 1986d) provides a list of substances provisionally allowed and a list of preservatives allowed (see Table 3) for use in cosmetic products. Clearly these may be appropriate for use in topical products but it has to be noted they are still under review.

5.2   Authorities which do not list preservatives

Not all authorities provide lists of preservatives. This may imply that they accept any sensible, well-known system or that the matter has not been given any attention. The true situation needs to be discovered as early as possible. Some authorities are vague about their requirements; the regulatory sleuth has then to search for clues amongst various official forms and documents which the authorities provide.

Guidelines or registration application forms, for example, may not provide any specific reference to, or a section for, preservatives or such systems *per se*. That cannot be taken to mean the authority is disinterested in the way the product is preserved.

Table 1 — Some preservatives and antioxidants quoted in national and international pharmacopoeias, compiled from Martindale (1989)

Preservative antioxidant	Arg	Aus	Bel	BP	BP Vet	Braz	Chi	Cz	Eur	Egy	Fr	Ger	Hun	Ind	Int	It	Jap	Jug	Mex	Nord	Neth	Pol	Port	Rou	Rus	Spa	Sw	Turk	USNF	USP
Alcohol	*	*	*	* (1)	*	*	*	*		*	*	*	*				*	*	*	*	*	*	*	*	*	*	*	*	*	* (2)
Ascorbyl palmitate																												*		
Benzalkonium chloride (3)	*	*	*	* (4)		*	* (5)	*	*	* (6)	*	*	*	*		*		*	*	*	*	*	*	*	*	*	*	*	* (7)	*
Benzoic acid	*	*	*	*		*	*		*	*	*	*	*	*	*	*	*	*	*	*	*	*	*	*	*	*	*	*	*	
Benzyl hydroxybenzoate	*																													
Benzyl alcohol	*	*		*		*	*		*	*		*	*							*	*	*	*			*	*		*	*
Bronopol				*																										
Butyl hydroxybenzoate				*							*																			
Butylated hydroxyanisole (8)				*							*									*	*								*	*
Butylated hydroxytoluene	*	*		*		*	*				*				*					*					*		*		*	*
Chlorbutol	* (10)	* (11)	* (9)	* (11)		* (10)	* (9)	* (9)	* (11)	* (9)	* (11)	* (11)	* (9)	* (9)	* (10)	* (11)	* (12)	* (9)	* (10)	* (9)	* (11)	* (9)	* (10)		* (9)		* (11)	* (13)	* (10)	* (10)
Cinnamic acid	*																								*			*		
Chlorocresol	*								*	*	"	*	*	*	*	*	*	*	*		*			*	*	*		*	*	
Chloroform	*					*					"				*			*							*	*				
Cresol	*			*	*	*				*	*	*	*	*	*	*		*	*	*	*		*	*	*	*			*	
Dehydroacetic acid	*	*		*							*																		*	
Dodecyl gallate																														
Ethyl gallate																														
Ethyl hydroxybenzoate	*			*		*	*			*	*	*	*	*			*		*	*	*	*	*	*	*	*	*		*	*
Methyl hydroxybenzoate																														
Monothioglycerol																														
Nordihydroguaiaretic acid																														
Octyl gallate																														
Phenethyl alcohol			*	*																*	*						*		*	*
Phenol	*		*	*		*	*			*	*	*	*				*		*	*	*	*		*	*		*		*	*
Phenoxyethanol																														
Phenylmercuric acetate		*		*																									*	*
Phenylmercuric borate (14)		*		*																	*						*		*	*
Phenylmercuric nitrate (15)				*		*												*		*			*						*	*
Potassium benzoate																														
Potassium metabisulphite																*														
Potassium sorbate (16)				*																									*	
Propyl gallate	*	*		*		*				*	*	*	*					*		*	*	*	*	*	*	*	*		*	*
Propyl hydroxybenzoate		*		*						*	*																		*	*
Sodium benzoate	*	*										*	*									*	*		*		*		*	
Sodium butyl hydroxybenzoate																														
Sodium dehydroacetate																							*							
Sodium formaldehyde sulphoxylate																														
Sodium metabisulphite		*		*													* (17)				*	*	* (18)		* (18)			*	*	*
Sodium methyl hydroxybenzoate				*																										*
Sodium propyl hydroxybenzoate				*																										*
Anhydrous sodium sulphite																							* (19)							*

National and international pharmacopoeias

	(20)
Sorbic acid	
Sulphur dioxide	
Thiomersal	
Thymol	

Key:

Arg — Argentinian Pharmacopoeia 1966
Aus — Austrian Pharmacopoeia 1981
Bel — Belgian Pharmacopoeia 1982
BP — British Pharmacopoeia 1988
BP Vet — British Pharmacopoeia (Veterinary) 1985
Braz — Brazilian Pharmacopoeia 1977
Chi — Chinese Pharmacopoeia 1985
Cz — Czechoslovak Pharmacopoeia 1987
Eur — European Pharmacopoeia, 2nd edn 1988, Fascicules 1–11
Egy — Egyptian Pharmacopoeia, 3rd edn 1984
Fr — French Pharmacopoeia 1982 and supplements 1–3
Ger — West German Pharmacopoeia 1986
Hun — VIth Hungarian Pharmacopoeia 1967
Ind — Pharmacopoeia of India, 3rd edn 1985
Int — International Pharmacopoeia 1967 (Specifications for the Quality Control of Pharmaceutical Preparations, 2nd edn 1967 and 3rd edn 1981 Vol.1)
It — Italian Pharmacopoeia 1985
Jap — The Pharmacopoeia of Japan, 11th edn 1986
Jug — Jugoslav Pharmacopoeia 1984
Mex — Mexican Pharmacopoeia 1952
Neth — Netherlands Pharmacopoeia 1983 and supplements to 1985
Nord — Nordic Pharmacopoeia 1963 including all addenda published up to 1976
Pol — Polish Pharmacopoeia 1965
Port — Portuguese Pharmacopoeia and Supplements 1961 and 1967
Rou — Romanian Pharmacopoeia 1976
Rus — Russian Pharmacopoeia (State Pharmacopoeia of the USSR 10th edn)
Span — Spanish Pharmacopoeia 1954
Sw — Swiss Pharmacopoeia 1987
Turk — Turkish Pharmacopoeia 1974
USNF — The United States National Formulary XVII 1990
USP — The United States Pharmacopeia XXII 1990

(1) BP specifies, under ethanol (96%), not less than 96% and not more than 96.6% v/v; 93.8 to 94.7% w/w of C_2H_5OH.
(2) USP specifies, under alcohol, not less than 94.9% and not more than 96.0% v/v; 92.3–93.8% w/w of C_2H_5OH.
(3) A mixture of alkylbenzyldimethylammonium chlorides of the general formula $(C_6H_5.CH_2N(CH_3)_2.R)Cl$, in which R represents a mixture of the alkyls from C_8H_{17} to $C_{18}H_{37}$.
(4) BP specifies that it contains 95–104% of alkylbenzyldimethylammonium chlorides, calculated as $C_{22}H_{40}ClN$ with reference to the anhydrous substance.
(5) Benzalkonium bromide in the Chinese Pharmacopoeia.
(6) Egypt specifies R from C_6H_{13} to $C_{18}H_{37}$ (see 3 above).
(7) USNF specifies not less than 40% of the $C_{12}H_{25}$ compound, calculated on the dried substance, not less than 20% of the $C_{14}H_{29}$ compound, and not less than 70% of these two compounds.
(8) It contains a variable proportion of 3-*tert*-butyl-4-methoxyphenol.
(9) With 1/2 H_2O (Bel Chi Cz Egy Hun Ind Jug Nord Pol Spa).
(10) Anhydrous or with 1/2 H_2O (Arg Braz Int Mex Port USNF).
(11) Have separate monographs for anhydrous and hemihydrate (Aus BP Eur Fr Ger It Neth Sw).
(12) Jap permits up to 6% of water.
(13) Turk has anhydrous.
(14) A compound consisting of equimolecular proportions of phenylmercuric orthoborate and phenylmercuric hydroxide or of the dehydrated form or a mixture of the two compounds.
(15) A mixture of phenylmercuric nitrate and phenylmercuric hydroxide.
(16) Some pharmacopoeias specify the (*E,E*)-hexa-2,4-dienoate.
(17) Jap also includes sodium bisulphite ($NaHSO_3=104.1$), a mixture of sodium bisulphite and sodium metabisulphite.
(18) Port and Spa have monographs for sodium bisulphite (probably metabisulphite, or mixture of the bisulphite and the metabisulphite).
(19) Port includes the heptahydrate.
(20) Some pharmacopoeias specify the (*E,E*)-hexa-2,4-dienoic acid.

Table 2 — Permitted preservatives abstracted from UK Statutory Instrument SI 1989 No. 533 Food Consumption and Labelling, The Preservatives in Food Regulations 1989, Schedule 1, Part 1

Permitted preservative	Serial number	Alternative form in which the permitted preservative may be used (to be calculated as the permitted preservative)	Serial number
Sorbic acid	E200	Sodium sorbate	E201
		Potassium sorbate	E202
		Calcium sorbate	E203
Benzoic acid	E210	Sodium benzoate	E211
		Potassium benzoate	E212
		Calcium benzoate	E213
Ethyl 4-hydroxybenzoate	E214	Ethyl 4-hydroxybenzoate, sodium salt	E215
Propyl 4-hydroxybenzoate	E216	Propyl 4-hydroxybenzoate, sodium salt	E217
Methyl 4-hydroxybenzoate	E218	Methyl 4-hydroxybenzoate, sodium salt	E219
Sulphur dioxide	E220	Sodium sulphite	E221
		Sodium hydrogen sulphite	E222
		Sodium metabisulphite	E223
		Potassium metabisulphite	E224
		Calcium sulphite	E226
		Calcium hydrogen sulphite	E227
Potassium bisulphite	E228		
Biphenyl	E230		
2-Hydroxybiphenyl	E231	Sodium biphenyl-2-yl-oxide	E232
2-(Thiazol-4-yl) benzimidazole	E233		
Nisin	E234		
Hexamine	E239		
Sodium nitrite	E250	Potassium nitrite	E249
Sodium nitrate	E251	Potassium nitrate	E252
Propionic acid	E280	Sodium propionate	E281
		Calcium propionate	E282
		Potassium propionate	E283

Other sections of the application form may well indicate the subject is of interest and will need to be reviewed. For instance, sections referring to formulation declarations, stability reports and labelling declarations would probably reveal that a preservative is present or a system of preservation is in use. Consequently, the authorities will have their attention drawn to the need to check the preservatives and systems employed.

Regulatory research should ascertain whether or not a specific authority is likely to allow or object to a particular preservative or system. For example, alcohol in certain Muslim countries may not be acceptable as part of the formulation (Ministry of Health Circulars 1985 and 1988).

Table 3 — EEC list of preservatives which cosmetic products may contain. This table lists preservatives allowed (A) and provisionally allowed (B) under the European Communities Eighth Commission Directive (Anon. 1986d). The table does not include substances which may have antimicrobial properties but are not included in the formulation for that primary purpose. Substances marked with (*) may, for specific purposes, e.g. as deodorants in soaps or as antidandruff agents in shampoos, be included in concentrations other than that indicated. For a full account of special considerations applying to this list the reader must consult the latest Directive.

(A) List of preservatives allowed

Substance	Maximum authorized concentration	Limitations and requirements
Benzoic acid, its salts and esters (*)	0.5% (acid)	
Propionic acid and its salts (*)	2% (acid)	
Salicylic acid and its salts (*)	0.5% (acid)	Not to be used in preparations for children under 3 years of age, except for shampoos
Sorbic acid (hexa-2,4-dienoic acid) and its salts (*)	0.6% (acid)	
Formaldehyde paraformaldehyde	0.2% (except for products for oral hygiene) 0.1% (products for oral hygiene) expressed as free formaldehyde	Prohibited in aerosol dispensers (sprays)
Biphenyl-2-ol (o-phenylphenol) and its salts (*)	0.2% expressed as the phenol	
Pyrithione zinc (INN) (*)	0.5%	Authorized in products rinsed off Forbidden in products for oral hygiene
Inorganic sulphites and hydrogen sulphites (*)	0.2% expressed as free SO_2	
Sodium iodate	0.1%	Rinse-off products only
Chlorobutanol (INN)	0.5%	Prohibited in aerosol dispensers (sprays)
4-Hydroxybenzoic acid and its salts and esters (*)	0.4% (acid) for one ester 0.8% (acid) for mixtures of esters	
3-Acetyl-6-methylpyran-2,4(3H)-dione (dehydroacetic acid) and its salts	0.6% (acid)	Prohibited in aerosol dispensers (sprays)
Formic acid (*)	0.5% (acid)	
3,3'-Dibromo-4,4'-hexamethylene-dioxydibenzamide (dibromohexamidine) and its salts (including isethionate)	0.1%	
Thiomersal (INN)	0.007% (of Hg) If mixed with other mercurial compounds authorized by this Directive, the maximum concentration of Hg remains fixed at 0.007%	For eye make-up and eye make-up remover only

Substance	Maximum authorized concentration	Limitations and requirements
Phenylmercuric salts (including borate)	0.007% (of Hg). If mixed with other mercurial compounds authorized by this Directive, the maximum concentration of Hg remains fixed at 0.007%	For eye make-up and eye make-up remover only
Undec-10-enoic acid and salts (*)	0.2% (acid)	
Hexetidine (INN) (*)	0.1%	
5-Bromo-5-nitro-1,3-dioxane	0.1%	Rinse-off products only. Avoid formation of nitrosamines
Bronopol (INN) (*)	0.1%	Avoid formation of nitrosamines
2,4-Dichlorobenzyl alcohol (*)	0.15%	
Triclocarban (INN) (*)	0.2%	Purity criteria: 3,3',4,4'-Tetrachloroazobenzene <1 p.p.m. 3,3',4,4'-Tetrachloroazoxybenzene <1 p.p.m.
4-Chloro-m-cresol (*)	0.2%	Prohibited in the products intended to come into contact with mucous membranes
Triclosan (INN) (*)	0.3%	
4-Chloro-3,5-xylenol (*)	0.5%	
3,3'-Bis(1-hydroxymethyl-2,5-dioxoimidazolidin-4-yl)-1,1'-methylenediurea ('imidazolidinyl urea') (*)	0.6%	
Poly(1-hexamethylenebiguanide) hydrochloride (*)	0.3%	
2-Phenoxyethanol (*)	1%	
Hexamethylenetetramine (*) (methenamine) (INN)	0.15%	
Methenamine 3-chloroallylochloride (INN)	0.2%	
1-(4-Chlorophenoxy)-1-(imidazol-1-yl)-3,3-dimethylbutan-2-one (*)	0.5%	
1,3-Bis(hydroxymethyl)-5,5-dimethylimidazolidine-2,4-dione (*)	0.6%	
Benzyl alcohol (*)	1%	
1-Hydroxy-4-methyl-6(2,4,4-trimethylpentyl)2-pyridon and its monoethanolamine salt (*)	1.0%	Products rinsed off
1,2-Dibromo-2,4-dicyanobutane	0.5%	For other products
6,6-Dibromo-4,4-dichloro 2,2'-methylene-diphenol (bromochlorophen) (*)	0.1%	
4-isopropyl-m-cresol	0.1%	
Mixture of 5-choro-2-methyl-isothiazol-3(2H)-one and 2-methyl-isothiazol-3(2H)-one with magnesium chloride and magnesium nitrate	0.0015% (of a mixture in the ratio 3:1 of 5-chloro-2-me-hylisothiazol-3(2H)-one and 2-methylisothiazol-3(2H)-one	
4-Benzyl-4-chlorophenol (chlorophene)	0.2%	
2-Chloroacetamide	0.3%	
Chlorhexidine (INN) and its digluconate diacetate and dihydrochloride (+)	0.3% expressed as chlorhexidine	
1-Phenoxypropan-2-ol	1.0%	1.0% only for rinse-off products

(B) List of preservatives provisionally allowed

Substance	Maximum authorized concentration	Limitations and requirements
Alkyl (C12–C22) trimethyl-ammonium bromide and chloride (including cetrimonium bromide (INN) (*))	0.1%	
4,4-Dimethyl-1,3-oxazolidine	0.1%	Rinse-off products only. The pH of the finished product shall not be lower than 6
Benzethonium chloride (INN) (*)	0.1%	Prohibited in the products intended to come into contact with mucous membranes
Benzalkonium chloride (INN), bromide and saccharinate (*)	0.25%	
1-(1,3-Bis(hydroxymethyl)-2,5-dioxoimidazolidin-1-yl)-1,3-bis(hydroxymethyl) urea	0.5%	
Hexamidine (INN) and its salts (including isethionate and 4-hydroxybenzoate) (*)	0.1%	
Benzylformal (a 1:1 mixture of benzyloxymethanol and (benzyloxymethoxy) methanol)	0.2%	
Glutaraldehyde	0.1%	Prohibited in aerosols (sprays)

* Solely for products which might be used for children under three years of age and which remain in prolonged contact with the skin.

5.3   Regulatory authorities that indirectly address attention to preservatives

Table 4 is the product of regulatory research into the registration requirements of 70 authorities, 66 of whom make indirect references implying that the preservatives will be noted and, therefore, they may require proof that the system is satisfactory. The following can be inferred from this registration research.

5.3.1   Marketing authorization period

Marketing authorization indicates the period granted for the licence by the authority after they have found the application acceptable. This is important because it shows how often renewal of the product licence may cause the registration data to come under scrutiny. Questions regarding stability or possible improvements in scientific techniques over the period prior to renewal can make earlier data obsolete. Each time this occurs there is a chance the authorities will demand further information to a modern standard before renewing the licence, thereby permitting the product to remain on the market. It therefore pays to consider whether or not the experimental studies being planned or the literature being provided will withstand the test of time. For instance, stability studies which earlier relied upon non-stability indicating assay methods, even though they appear to provide a true reflection of the stability of the preservative system, will no longer be acceptable to the authorities for modern-day studies. Some authorities may demand a full and repeated stability study to modern standards before agreeing to a renewed licence. Some interim agreement may be reached allowing the product to remain on the market whilst the new study is carried out, but there is always the danger this will not be permitted.

5.3.2   Registration data specifically required

Table 4 identifies those registration authorities which specifically demand details about the formulation and its stability and so they will undoubtedly expect preservatives, if present, to be mentioned. Once it is revealed that preservative materials are present, then a statement about the preservative system and its efficacy will also be needed. Similarly, Table 4 also lists those countries where label and leaflet declarations are required and these too may reveal the presence of preservatives, thus prompting the authorities to examine data concerning the preservative system in the product. Any submission to these authorities which omits a proper and full reference to the preservative system risks rejection.

5.3.3   Authorities who rely upon approved lists of preservatives

Where an authority issues lists of chemicals with approved permitted levels, for example antioxidants, colourants, flavours and sweeteners, they are also likely to favour approved and accepted preservatives. The final column in Table 4 provides information about such approved lists. Where the authorities have not issued a list of their own they are likely to refer to a list if there is one, issued by the national authority of the exporting country.

Table 4 — Regulatory authorities that indirectly address attention to preservatives

Country	Marketing authorization period granted	Registration data specifically required	Label declaration required (Quantitative QT) (Qualitative QL)	Leaflet declaration required	Approved list for Colourants C Antioxidants A Preservatives P Flavours F Sweeteners S
Algeria	Not specified	Formulation Stability	Pre-clearance	Pre-clearance	–
Argentina	5 years	Formulation	Actives (QT) Ingredients (QL)	Full formula (QL and QT)	C
Australia	Indefinitely	Formulation Stability	Actives (QT)	–	C
Austria	Indefinitely	Formulation Stability	Pre-clearance Actives (QL) and constituents if strongly active	Pre-clearance According to detailed guidelines	Additives C (in foods)
Belgium	5 years	Composition Stability	See EEC	See EEC	C
Brazil	5 years	Formulation Stability	Complete formula (QT)	–	C A (cosmetics)
Canada	Indefinitely	Formulation Stability	Parenterals (QL)	–	C None A S P Some items restricted if unsafe (e.g. saccharin)
Central America: (a) Costa Rica (b) Guatemala (c) Honduras (d) Nicaragua (e) Panama (f) El Salvador	5 years: (a) (b) (e) 1 year: (c) (d) (f)	Formulation Stability	Formulation (QL) (QT)	Pre-clearance (all countries)	C (all countries)
Chile	Indefinitely	Formulation Stability	Formula Pre-clearance	–	C None A F S P
China	4 years	Formulation Stability	–	Composition	–
Colombia	10 years	Formulation Stability	Actives	–	C
Czechoslovakia	5 years	Formulation Stability	–	–	None A F S P

Country					
Denmark	5 years	Composition Stability	Formula Preservative agent (where required)	Pre-clearance	Food Act: C A F S P and other excipients EEC directives
Ecuador	7 years	Formulation Stability	–	–	–
EEC	5 years	Composition Stability	Actives (QL) (QT)	Actives (QL) (QT)	None A F S P C 78/25/EEC 12/12/77 as amended
Egypt	10 years	Formulation Stability	Actives (QT)	Composition	C F S
Finland	1 year	Composition Stability	Formula	–	C for foodstuffs
France	5 years	Composition Stability	Actives (QL) (QT) Preservative (QL) (QT)	Composition Active Preservative	C A P
West Germany (FRG)	5 years	Composition stability	Actives (QT)	Actives (QT)	C
East Germany (GDR)	Indefinite	Formulation Stability	See detailed regulations prior to submission	See detailed regulations –	EEC directive
Greece	5 years	Composition Stability	Actives (QL) (QT)	Formula	C (those accepted by United States Food and Drug Administration)
Hong Kong	5 years	Formulation Stability	Composition	–	C A S (Food regulations)
Hungary	Indefinitely	Formulation Stability	Pre-clearance	Pre-clearance	C A F S P Other excipients
Iceland	5 years	Composition Stability	Formula Pre-clearance	–	Food additive regulations
India	Indefinitely	Formulation Stability	Pre-clearance	Pre-clearance	C A F P
Indonesia	4 years	Formulation Stability	Composition	–	C
Iran	3 years	Formulation Stability	Formula	Pre-clearance	C A F S P
Iraq	Indefinitely	Formulation Stability	–	–	C F A S P
Ireland	5 years	Composition Stability	Actives (QT)	Composition (QT)	C
Israel	5 years	Composition Stability	Actives	Actives	C S None A F P
Italy	5 years	Composition Stability	Actives (QT) (QL) Excipients (QT) (QL)	Pre-clearance	C A F S P

Country			Contents (QL) (QT)	Composition	Standards for ingredients not in Japanese Pharmacopoeia
Japan	Indefinitely	Formulation; Stability			C
Kenya	5 years	Stability	Excipients; Actives (QL) (QT); Bactericidal (%); Bacteriostatic (%)	—	—
Korea (South)	Indefinitely	Formulation; Stability	Composition	Composition	A C F S
Malaysia	Indefinitely	Formulation; Stability	—	—	—
Mexico	Indefinitely	Formulation; Stability	Actives; Pre-clearance	—	C A F S P
Morocco	5 years	Formulation; Stability	Pre-clearance	—	—
Netherlands	5 years	Composition; Stability	Actives (QL) (QT); Pre-clearance	Actives (QL) (QT); Pre-clearance	C F
New Zealand	Indefinitely	Actives; Ingredients	Special use labelling; Composition; Active/preservative/antiseptic (pre-clearance required); % and name preservative	—	Special use of C
Nigeria	Indefinitely	Actives (QT) and inactives; Stability	—	Composition (including preservative)	—
Norway	5 years	Stability	—	—	C (foods)
Pakistan	5 years	Formulation; Stability	—	—	—
Paraguay	5 years	Formulation; Stability	—	—	C
Peru	5 years	Formulation; Stability	Formula	—	C F S P
Philippines	3 years	Formulation; Stability	Formula	—	—
Poland	Indefinitely	Formulation; Stability	Actives	Actives	—
Portugal	10 years	Formulation; Stability	Pre-clearance	—	C (food) (pharmaceutical)
Saudi Arabia	Indefinitely	Actives C F P and excipients	Actives	Composition	C P F; Other excipients pre-clearance
Singapore	5 years	Formulation	Actives (QT); Pre-clearance	Actives (QT)	

Country	Stability period	Formulation / Stability	Active preservation and storage required / Preservative information	Composition (QT)	Other excipients
South Africa	1 year	Formulation Stability	Composition (QT)	Composition (QT)	C F P Other excipients
Spain	5 years (domestic) 3 years (imported)	Composition Stability	Actives (QT)	–	C A S P (food) (see EEC Regulations)
Sri Lanka	5 years	Composition (QL) Stability			–
Sweden	Indefinitely	Stability	Formula	–	–
Switzerland	5 years	Formulation Stability	Actives	Composition	C Additives (food) (see EEC Regulations)
Taiwan	5 years	Stability	Actives (QT) Pre-clearance	Formula	–
Thailand	Indefinitely	Formulation	Composition Actives (QT)		C F Other additives Food Act
Tunisia	5 years	Formulation Stability	Pre-clearance	Pre-clearance	–
Turkey	5 years	Formulation Stability	Actives (QT)	Actives (QT)	C
UK	5 years	Composition Stability	Actives (QT) Preservatives (QT) Formula (QT) (QL)	Composition (QT)	C F P excipients (Medicines Act)
Uruguay	5 years	Formulation Stability		Formula Pre-clearance	None C A F S P
USA	Indefinitely	Formulation Stability	Actives (QT) Inactives (QT) Pre-clearance	–	C A (food additives) S other excipients
USSR	10 years	Formulation Stability			–
Venezuela	Indefinitely	Formulation Stability	Formula		C
Yugoslavia	5 years	Formulation Stability	Actives (QT)	Actives (QT)	C A F P S
Zimbabwe	1 year	Formulation	Actives (QT) Inactives	–	–

Pre-clearance indicates approval by the authorities before use.
— indicates no information to suggest these authorities have any list or requirement.

6 SCIENTIFIC DATA FOR THE REGISTRATION PROCESS

From the formulator's point of view, the bulk of laboratory work in support of registration will mainly address matters of safety, efficacy and quality of the finished product, rather than the preservatives. For a product being sold in many markets, the way in which experimental work is tackled will depend upon the various authorities' scientific interests as well as any political or religious attitudes which are peculiar to that market. For example, the Delaney Clause of the Food Additives Amendment (1958) makes it illegal in the USA to approve any food additive if it is found to induce cancer when ingested by man or animal. As a result, the shipment of any drug or cosmetic containing, for example, chloroform as an active or inactive ingredient, has been banned in the USA since 1976 (Anon. 1976).

Following adverse public comment in the UK the authorities decided to remove 'as far as possible' 'artificial' preservatives from medicine. The proposal to remove sugar from certain liquid medicines because of the potential damage to teeth has also added to the formulator's difficulty (Anon. 1986e). Religious attitudes could well prohibit the use of certain alcohol- or animal-based materials.

Regulatory research should provide the basis for the choice of experiments confirming that both the formulation and the preservative system are completely satisfactory. A work programme should be devised between the scientific and regulatory staff which will satisfy the requirements of both parties. Frequently they will be synchronous, but occasionally the formulator will be frustrated by demands for laboratory work which addresses specific regulatory needs. For example, the need for the product to be stable at 45°C for at least six months is needed for registration in the Middle East (Girgis 1986). Some compromises in favour of the formulator may be appropriate, but if too many are attempted they may be the cause of costly delays in gaining the licence to market in a particular territory.

Finally, having completed desk research and set out the strategy for the research and development programme, there may be specific experimental points, which require clarification, possibly involving contact with the authorities. However, authorities should not be encouraged to spell out a development programme. Firstly, many do not wish to give, or take responsibility for, that sort of advice. Secondly, any opinion canvassed in a limited time will be less informed than that of staff involved with the work itself. It is the formulator, together with the regulatory advisor, and not the authorities who must decide what work is necessary to convince all parties that the product is satisfactory. Thirdly, different authorities may make conflicting proposals, adding to the cost of research. Furthermore, it is not practical to visist all the authorities; one must therefore rely upon expert registration advice nearer home when clarification for a definitive programme is needed.

6.1 Established preservatives

As often as not, official registration application forms and guidelines direct most attention to 'active principles' in the formulation rather than 'preservative systems'. For most applications the preservatives will probably be well known and their safety and efficacy well documented and understood. It merely remains for the formulator to show that, when combined with the ingredients of their particular product, nothing untoward occurs and that the preservative system works entirely as expected. The attention of the authorities will then focus mainly upon the product; registration problems will be minimized if the materials and systems used are already well known to the authorities.

6.2   Novel preservative systems

Occasionally the choice of preservative system will not be known to the authorities. The more novel the concept, the more extensive the laboratory work will have to be in support of its registration. At the extreme, the preservative may be treated as a new chemical entity. In such cases an authority's demands may be as stringent as those for the registration of a completely new 'active' drug substance. Tests for a new preservative will have to be provided in the same detail and possibly at a similar cost to that for a new 'active' pharmaceutical. Until the authorities involved are convinced that all tests for safety, efficacy and quality, both for the new raw material *per se* and in the formulated product, are satisfactory, the product will not be permitted a licence for sale or supply to the public. Under these circumstances a critical path programme for the whole development project will probably be worthwhile.

6.3   Typical problem areas for registration

It is not practical to consider all the potential regulatory problems which might arise when attempting to register a product containing either a well-known or a new preservative system. Table 5 lists some of the pharmaceutical parameters likely to be relevant to preservation and to require investigation or scientific comment for inclusion in the registration application. These are considered below and in further detail in Chapter 11.

Table 5 — Typical pharmaceutical parameters relevant to preservation which require attention for the registration application

Type of product
Toxicity
Type of container
Solubility
Volatility
Spectrum of activities
pH
Colour
Odour
Taste
Preservative ability and efficacy
Interaction with ingredients
Scale-up and production
Raw materials
Analytical methods
Results of tests and interpretation
Validation of methods

The British and EC guidelines (Anon. 1965, 1975a, 1975b, 1983a, 1983b, 1985, 1986a, 1986b, 1986c) also list registration parameters such as administration, pharmacology, pharmacokinetics, mutagenicity and others which are beyond the normal scope of the pharmaceutical development laboratory. For those items expert advice has to be sought elsewhere and appropriate studies conducted and collated into the submission. Care has to be exercised to see that pharmaceutical work is consistent with that in other sections of the application. Again a regulatory professional should make sure such inconsistencies do not occur.

6.3.1   Type of product
The type of product indicates the kind of preservative system to be chosen. The authorities will seek reassurance that the choice of preservative is appropriate for the purposes for which the product will be used. This is usually taken to mean that the degree of preservative activity should be related to the intended use and frequency of use of the product.

6.3.2   Toxic potential of preservatives
In formulating a medicine for administration to patients, it should not be forgotten that preservatives themselves may be a source of toxicity for the patient. Adverse drug reactions are constantly under scrutiny by regulatory authorities. It is reported in the UK that preservatives attract attention as a cause of adverse reactions and the authorities welcome the increasing trend towards the development of unit dose, preservative-free packaging for suitable products (Adams 1987).

6.3.3   Type of container
The container may be ideal for the use of the product but it may also be incompatible with the preservative system to be used (see Chapter 15). The registration submission will need to address these details of incompatibility when referring to the containers in which the product is stored. If the containers used in stability tests differ from those proposed for the marketed product, the significance of the differences should be discussed. The UK authorities would consider the following parameters and how they might influence stability of the product (Anon. 1985):

(a) *Fabric of the container:* i.e. the type of glass, plastic, composition of strip packaging, etc.
(b) *Nature of closures:* i.e. details of liners, caps, etc.
(c) *Dosage measurement:* i.e. where the container or component is designed as a dose-measuring device, this should be described in detail and information will be required on the accuracy of measurement.

Large packs intended for dispensing purposes may require more stringent tests to allow for the fact they will be opened and reopened and, over a period of time, the increasing ullage and ingression of possible contaminants will have an effect upon the contents and the preservative system (Anon. 1985).

6.3.4   Solubility
Preservatives are usually required to be dissolved in the product; to be effective they must be present at appropriate concentrations in the various phases of the product.

Reassurance is needed that preferential solubility of the preservative in one or other of the phases does not detract from its efficacy throughout all of the product (see Chapter 11).

It is usually appropriate to dissolve a preservative in a small portion of the aqueous phase (with the aid of heat if required); the solution should then be inspected visually before it is added to the bulk. It is necessary to demonstrate that preservatives do not precipitate from solution when added to the bulk.

6.3.5 Stability
A full stability programme for the finished product with a minimum of two batches studied over a three- to five-year period under elevated, reduced and temperate climatic conditions is essential information. EC advisors have proposed 25°C as normal room temperature, being the average for Europe as a whole (Anon. 1987b). The stability programme is primarily aimed at the finished product but during development and stability testing it will be necessary to demonstrate, using suitable antimicrobial challenge tests, the efficacy of the preservative system used. Products containing a preservative system should also be assayed for levels of preservative during the storage tests. An assurance should be provided (where necessary) that ongoing data will be generated to show that the product, at the end of the shelf-life, is satisfactorily preserved (Anon. 1985).

6.3.6 Volatility
For preservative action to be sustained it is essential that the preservative remains available at the correct strength within the product throughout the shelf-life. Volatility might be relevant to its action but it can also mean that the preservative is lost from the product due to evaporation. If this occurs at ambient temperature, it is likely to be even more pronounced at elevated temperatures. Consequently, the authorities will consider what effect hot climatic conditions or elevated temperature during manufacture might have upon the product. Particularly, they will wish to see evidence that the formulator is aware of the problem and has taken steps to overcome loss of ingredients. Most regulatory bodies will require evidence showing that the ingredient is not escaping from a poorly sealed container. Loss of a volatile preservative degradation product, a particular problem when using plastic containers, can shift the equilibrium to further degradation of the preservative, as happens with Thiomersal for example (Hepburn 1987). Under user conditions, once the pack is opened volatility is likely to result in a loss of preservative action, making user challenge tests an item for close scrutiny.

6.3.7 Spectrum of activities
A variety of pathogenic and non-pathogenic bacteria, moulds and yeasts may contaminate and spoil a product. The capability of the chosen preservative system to meet all eventualities throughout the shelf-life is a very important regulatory consideration. Practical laboratory studies demonstrating that the system works when challenged by a variety of organisms must be provided to the authorities (Hepburn 1987; Matthews 1987), particularly if the system is new. If the product is liable to attack by a specific organism peculiar to the conditions in a particular

market, then this aspect is likely to be scrutinized by the authority in that area. They would expect to see laboratory work demonstrating effective resistance to such contamination included in the application.

6.3.8 pH
Clearly the chosen preservative should be appropriate for the pH of the product or a reasoned argument should be given for its selection. For most ionizable preservatives the antimicrobial activity and the degree of dissociation are closely linked and both are, therefore, likely to be influenced by pH. If antimicrobial activity operates best at a specific pH, departure from that optimum will produce a less effective system. This clearly must be addressed during laboratory work on the proposed formulation. The formulator must show the authorities that the chosen formulation will not impair the preservative system either by being unfavourable for the stability of the preservatives or by changes within the basic formulation over time.

6.3.9 Colour
Most preservative systems create no colour problems for the formulator. Naturally, the appearance of colour during the lifetime of the product would call for close scrutiny as it might indicate a loss of preservative efficacy. The authorities would require to be convinced there was no problem. Any new preservative system which sought to provide a change in colour, for example, when preservative levels became ineffective would require substantial experimental data demonstrating its reliability.

6.3.10 Odour
Any preservative system which imparts an odour to a formulation but which is acceptable to the patient is not likely in itself to cause a registration failure. However, if the odour is distinctive it may create problems for the blinding of clinical trials if placebos or competitor products are noticeably different. An offensive odour could lead to questions by the authorities about potential patient non-compliance and possible dose evasion.

6.3.11 Taste
Most of the population have very sensitive palates and taste will be an important consideration for the formulator of an oral product. Preservatives, although present in small quantities, often impart an aftertaste which some patients may find unacceptable. From a regulatory point of view, taste is unlikely to be a contentious issue unless, like odour, it invalidates test results, for example in a double-blind clinical study, or leads to patient non-compliance during administration. The formulator who can provide matching placebos or with more difficulty matching competitor product for the clinical study will probably have no problems.

6.3.12 Preservative ability and efficacy
In designing a preservative efficacy test, consideration should be given to the proposed use of the product (Hepburn 1987). Factors such as reconstitution, dilution before use, duration of treatment and frequency of opening the pack in use may be relevant. Large packs intended for dispensing purposes may require a more stringent test. Both antibacterial and antifungal efficacy should be demonstrated and the tests

should include suitable positive and negative controls. The British Pharmacopoeia (1988) gives guidance on test methods and design and further details can be found in Chapter 13A. However, reliance cannot be placed upon any pharmacopoeial method as being definitive in terms of safety and efficacy testing of a particular product (Matthews 1987). For the purposes of registration one must always consider whether or not a test reflects the state of the art in this regard. Registration authorities have a duty when considering safety to apply the latest standards. This makes reliance upon pharmacopoeial and other published texts always a matter for circumspection on the part of the formulator.

6.3.13   Interactions with ingredients
Martindale (1989) offers ample evidence that preservatives interact with other chemicals, and this is covered in detail in Chapter 12. The formulator must consider and then demonstrate to the regulatory authority that ingredients in the formulation are compatible with both the pack and with the preservative system chosen. Literature references will give some guidance, but physical tests and ultimately chemical and biological tests must be conducted. The results must be interpreted in terms of compatibility as well as confirmation that the formulation is satisfactory.

6.3.14   Scale-up and production
The difference between laboratory preparation and full-scale manufacture can be marked. For example, in a liquid preparation containing hydrocortisone or aluminium hydroxide in suspension, an homogeneous mixture can be maintained in a beaker prior to dispensing into bottles by using a simple paddle stirrer. In a 1000-litre tank piped to the bottling machine, keeping the bulk homogeneous is not so easy. Settling in pipes and corners can become a problem. Continuous circulation between the bottling machine and the bulk may overcome the problem, but the introduction of flexible plastic tubing to achieve this may result in the preservative system being extracted by adsorption. Soaking the tubing in preservatives prior to use may slow or suitably change the rate of uptake. It may also result in preservative leaching from the tube into the product. The authorities will look for evidence that all the variables have been checked and considered.

In processes which use heat, the influence of temperature on stability is important. As batch size increases, the time for which preservatives are subjected to elevated temperature increases (unless forced cooling is used) and this can lead to greater degradation.

6.3.15   Raw materials
Preservatives, like any ingredient in a product, must be subject to the full rigour of a raw material specification and classification procedure. Where conventional supplies of European Pharmacopoeia or British Pharmacopoeia materials are used, it is likely there will be a full and complete specification for the preservative. However, if less conventional sources are used, for whatever reason, then a full characterization of the material will be needed. If a proprietary system is used, then the manufacturer must be prepared to release a full characterization and specification for the raw material which will satisfy the authorities that the material will be consistent and

remain within the stated limits on all occasions (Anon. 1985). Typically, the specification might include:

(a) *Characteristics:* odour, appearance, colour.
(b) *Identity tests:* melting point, boiling point, spectrophotometric and chromatographic characterization against a pure reference sample.
(c) *Physicochemical tests:* solubility in a variety of solvents.
(d) *Purity tests:* thin-layer chromatography, high-pressure liquid chromatography, ultraviolet spectroscopy, loss on drying, incineration, heavy metals.
(e) *Assay:* against a pure reference sample.

The authorities will seek reassurances that the material is not intrinsically toxic at the levels intended for use. Some authorities, for example Egyptian, still require an LD50 test on each batch as proof that raw materials are of consistent quality with time (Girgis 1986).

6.3.16   Analytical methods
The experimental studies employed must take account of the latest thinking and if the published method, in the light of scientific advance, has been found wanting then a more reliable method will have to be created.

Details are required of the analytical methods used to monitor stability during the studies. Where these methods are the same as those described under the finished product specification, cross-reference can be made. Where other methods are used they must be described in full. It is important that analytical assay methods used in the stability trials should be sufficiently specific and sensitive to detect deterioration. Reporting results obtained using non-specific methods without supporting data on levels of degradation products will not be sufficient. Similarly, if the method is not sufficiently precise, the early results of the long-term stability study will be of limited reliability as an indication of long-term stability (Anon. 1985).

6.3.17   Results of tests and interpretation
6.3.17.1   Results

Details of the actual results obtained when the samples were tested should be given in a tabulated form. In some instances a graphical presentation may also be helpful.

Initial assay results should be expressed in the same way as on the product label. Assay results for subsequent check-points should be given in the same way (Anon. 1985).

6.3.17.2   Discussion of results
Reference should be made to any special precautions, including storage conditions and user instructions required for the product. Comment should be made on any assay or other test results which are near to or outside the check assay limits (Anon. 1985). From a regulatory point of view the analysis of preservatives is of critical importance to the authorities. They need to see a clear demonstration of the correct level of preservatives over the shelf-life of the product, as well as evidence of effectiveness of preservatives using preservative efficacy tests.

6.3.18   *Validation of the methods used*

Data should be presented to show precision, accuracy and sensitivity of the methods used.

The analytical methods and assay procedures selected for routine control of the formulation should be discussed. This should include evidence to show the validity of the methods used, e.g. standard error of assay methods.

Copies of spectra or gas–liquid chromatography traces should be provided where these are used for assay or identification purposes. The emphasis here should be on demonstrating that the proposed specifications and methods are adequate to ensure batch-to-batch uniformity of the product (Anon. 1985).

7   OVERVIEW

Three cardinal points are critical to a successful registration and must be remembered at all times.

Firstly, one's paperwork is the shopfront of one's science. No matter how good the scientific work done, if it is not collected, collated and presented both clearly and concisely it will jeopardize the chance of gaining registration for the product. Poorly presented or incomplete data simply bring a lack of confidence to bear upon all work, inviting rejection of the whole registration application.

Secondly, regulations are the key to the marketplace. Any failure to understand the rules of the game simply invites disqualification regardless of the quality of the science.

Thirdly, at the time of the application one should ensure that both the regulatory and scientific aspects of the submission coincide and are comprehensive. Bearing in mind that both regulations and science are continuously changing, and not always in unison, early monitoring of both is a vital part of the success of any project.

8   REFERENCES

Adams, P. N. (1987) Clinical issues in the regulation of eye care products: a view from Market Towers. *BIRA J.* **6** 10–11.

Anon. (1965) *Official Journal of the European Communities,* Council Directive (65/65/EEC) Chapter II, Article 3.

Anon. (1968) Medicines Act, Ch. 67.

Anon. (1975a) *Official Journal of the European Communities,* (75/318/EEC).

Anon. (1975b) *Official Journal of the European Communities,* Second Council Directive (75/319/EEC).

Anon. (1976) Chloroform as an ingredient of human drug and cosmetic products. Federal Register, 41, No. 126, 26842.

Anon. (1982) Amendment of labelling requirements for over-the-counter human drugs, *Federal Register* **47,** No. 233, 54756.

Anon. (1983a) *Official Journal of the European Communities,* (83/570/EEC).

Anon. (1983b) *Official Journal of the European Communities,* (83/571/EEC).

Anon. (1984) Hearings and Representations Part II (MAL 59) Medicines Act 1968.

Anon. (1985) Guidance Notes on Applications for Product Licences (MAL 2) Medicines Act 1968.

Anon. (1986a) *Official Journal of the European Communities*, (87/19/EEC).

Anon. (1986b) *Official Journal of the European Communities*, (87/21/EEC).

Anon. (1986c) *Official Journal of the European Communities*, (87/22/EEC).

Anon. (1986d) *Official Journal of the European Communities*, Eighth Commission Directive (86/199/EEC).

Anon. (1986e) Sugar in oral liquid medicines. *MAIL* **47** 5–6.

Anon. (1987a) Supplement to Guidance Notes on Applications for Product Licences (MAL 2).

Anon. (1987b) Commission of European Communities, Annex to Directive 75/318/EEC.

Anon. (1989) Gross times taken to grant product licences (human medicines) 12 months ended 31 March 1989. *MAIL* **60** Appendix 4.

Begg, D. I. R. (1981) Production and GMP. *Proceedings of Third Annual Symposium of BIRA* 82–92.

Blanchfield, J. R. (1984) The Food and Drugs Act 1955. Non Medicines Act: Legislation which influences the regulatory process. *Proceedings of Sixth Annual Symposium of BIRA* 24–35.

British Pharmacopoeia (1988) HMSO, London.

Broad, R. D. (1981) Involvement of regulatory control with regard to safety studies and GLP. *Proceedings of Third Annual Symposium of BIRA* 19–25.

Christodoulou, H. M. (1984) Regulatory developments in export markets. *BIRA J.* **2** 65–67.

Dale, J. R. and Appelbe, G. E. (1989) *Pharmacy law and ethics*, 4th edn. Pharmaceutical Press, London.

European Pharmacopoeia (1988) 2nd edn, General Notices IV. 1.

Farrell, F. G. (1982) Regulatory requirements for clinical research in the pharmaceutical industry. *Proceedings of Fourth Annual Symposium of BIRA* 57–66.

Girgis, A. N. (1986) Health registration in the Middle East and Africa: past, present and future. *BIRA J.* **5**, 13–15.

Goldberg, A. (1986) Development of drug registration: a global view. *BIRA J.* **5** 2–5.

Greenwood, R. K. (1985) Chairman's report. *BIRA J.* **4** 1–5.

Hepburn, D. (1987) Achieving the complete Part II. *BIRA J.* **6** 12–15.

Keyes, R. (1984) Trade marks and general names. Non Medicines Act: legislation which influences the regulatory process. *Proceedings of Sixth Anuual Symposium of BIRA* 13–23.

Lawson, R. G. (1984) Trade Descriptions Act. Non Medicines Act: legislation which influences the regulatory process. *Proceedings of Sixth Annual Symposium of BIRA* 71–79.

Logan, M. P. (1984) Regulations specific to cosmetic products. Non Medicines Act: legislation which influences the regulatory process. *Proceedings of Sixth Annual Symposium of BIRA* 36–43.

Lynd, M. A. (1984) Patents. Non-medicines Act: legislation which influences the regulatory process. *Proceedings of Sixth Annual Symposium of BIRA* 1–12.

Marshall, V. (1984) Regulatory overview. *BIRA J* . **4** 18.

Martindale (1989) *The Extra Pharmacopoeia*, 29th edn. Pharmaceutical Press, London.

Matthews, B. R. (1987) Regulation of eye care products: a view from Market Towers. Pharmaceutical Issues. *BIRA J.* **6** 8–9.

McIntosh, D. A. (1987) Risk assessment and protection against civil and criminal liability in the pharmaceutical industry. *Proceedings of the Ninth Annual Symposium of BIRA* 18–29.

Ministry of Health Circular (1985) Saudi Arabia 61/766/20.

Ministry of Health Circular (1988) Saudi Arabia 1214/20/M.

Murray, M. (1984) The notification of new substances. Non Medicines Act: legislation which influences the regulatory process. *Proceedings of Sixth Annual Symposium of BIRA* 94–101.

Penn, R. G. (1982) Adverse drug reactions reporting in the UK *Proceedings of Fourth Annual Symposium of BIRA* 27–33.

Spink, J. D. (1982) Product liability in a clinical trial situation. *Proceedings of Fourth Annual Symposium of BIRA* 44–56.

Statutory Instrument SI (1989) No. 533. Food composition and labelling, the preservatives in food regulations.

Troup, R. G. (1984) Borderline substances. Non Medicines Act: legislation which influences the regulatory process. *Proceedings of Sixth Annual Symposium of BIRA* 61–64.

United States Pharmacopeia (1990) 22nd Revision and National Formulary 17th Revision, United States Pharmaceopeial Convention Inc., Rockville, MD.

15

Package design and product integrity

M. C. Allwood
Medicines Research Unit, Derbyshire Royal Infirmary, London Road, Derby
DE1 2QY, UK

1. INTRODUCTION

The packaging of medicines has often, in the past, taken little account of the microbiological aspects of maintaining product integrity. This is especially the case with non-sterile products. For example, consider the popularity of wide-necked jars for ointments and creams, of large bottles for liquid medicines, or the inclusion of separate droppers for nasal drops. All such packaging takes little or no account of the microbiological integrity of the contents, especially during use by the patient. Similarly, lack of such considerations can also be applied to many traditional forms of packaging for sterile products. The glass eye-drop bottle with a rubber delivery teat offers a good example, a packaging system never designed to be autoclaved nor to avoid contamination during use. In this case, maintaining a microbiologically safe product in use depends entirely on the preservative system. Large-volume sterile fluids packed in glass bottles also pose problems in maintaining the integrity of the seal between glass rim and rubber closure. Various designs for these rubber closures were, until recently, available but none were either pre-tested or proven to offer seal maintenance during autoclaving, or post-sterilization storage. Consequently, witness the rapid change in recent years to all-plastic containers with integral sealing systems. This has occurred partly because of our greater awareness of the limitations of glass-based, traditional designs. It is certainly true that greater interest in packaging design, arising from applied research, has led to improvements in systems to maintain the microbiological safety of products. This is part of any overall quality improvement programme. Microbiological considerations are now an essential element of the product design brief. This is clearly evident in non-sterile and sterile pharmaceuticals. It will be the major aim of this review to examine these changes and the important microbiological aspects of the packaging design and function. The major aspects are summarized in Table 1.

2 NON-STERILE PRODUCT PACKAGING DESIGN

2.1 Packaging of liquids

In many areas, traditional packaging of pharmaceuticals in glass has been superseded by more appealing packages made from various plastics. Since many of these dosage forms are constantly in danger of microbial contamination, such packaging advances, designed to improve overall product quality or reduce costs, should also take account of microbiological aspects. In particular, liquid medicines containing some proportion of free water are always those in most danger from microbiological contamination. Here the traditional bottle design has several disadvantages, and offers few opportunities for improvement to reduce chance contamination during use. For instance, airborne organisms may still gain entry when the container is opened, and poor design of the lip allows accumulation of product around the pouring area with subsequent risks of colonization by micro-organisms. If a bottle

Table 1 — Design features of containers that influence microbiological integrity of the product

The container should:

— Provide resistance to contamination through good design (e.g. neck width, lip characteristics, cap seal efficiency)

— Allow sterilization by the optimum method (in the case of sterile products). This requires such features as thermal resistance, radiation resistance and the maintenance of hermetic seals under stress

— Not interact with the formulation by sorption of active components or excipients, especially preservatives.

— Not release materials into the product (e.g. alkali leach from glass, antioxidants from polyethylene, plasticizers from PVC) or alter product characteristics which may adversely affect preservative efficacy

— Provide ready access for microbiological testing

— Not offer opportunities for microbial adhesion

— Provide light protection for photo-sensitive preservatives

— Be size-limited to reduce in-use shelf-life and minimize evaporative head-space.

design is to be used, bottle lips should be developed to minimize back-flow and non-surface wetting plastic can be used to reduce the accumulation of material around the pouring lip of a container after repeated use.

2.2 Packaging of creams and semi-solid formulations
The wide use of aluminium-lined or, occasionally, plastic, collapsible tubes to package creams and ointments is, microbiologically, essential. The demise of the wide-necked jar is to be welcomed. The continued microbial challenge offered from the hands of the users by repeated removal of small amounts of a cream or ointment should be of real concern. Tubes essentially minimize this risk as the contact area between product and the users' skin is small. Since creams are especially difficult formulations to preserve adequately, the use of tubes has offered a substantial improvement in the maintenance of microbiological integrity in use.

2.3 Effect of container on antimicrobial preservative agents
The wider use of plastic containers, whilst offering flexibility in container design, does have potential disadvantages. In particular, some preservatives may migrate from the product into the matrix of the plastic (see Table 2). This sorption process will depend on the lipophilicity of the preservative, the type of formulation and the particular plastic used to fabricate the container (Dean 1978; Allwood and Shaw 1987).

For example, Kakemi et al. (1971) have shown that sorption of the paraben esters to various plastics (high-density polyethylene, polypropylene, polycarbonate, polymethacrylate and polystyrene) is in proportion to ester carbon chain length, and therefore lipophilicity. However, the scale of losses remains relatively small (< 10%). Fischer and Neufeld (1971) reported sorption of organic mercurials to

Table 2 — Some important examples of preservative sorption to plastics and rubber

Preservative	Material				
	Natural rubber	Low-density poly-ethylene	High-density poly-ethylene	Poly-propylene	PVC
Benzoic acid	−	+	−	−	−
Benzyl alcohol	+	+	+	+	−
Benzalkonium chloride	−	−	−	−	−
Chlorbutol	+ +	+ + +	+ +	−	−
Chlorhexidine	+	−	−	−	−
Mercurials	+ + +	+ + [a]	+	+	−
Paraben esters	+	−	−	−	−
Phenols	+ + +	+ +	+ +	+ +	+

− = no significant interaction.
+ = mild binding.
+ + = moderate.
+ + + = substantial losses expected.
[a] Variable, depends on vehicle.

various plastics; losses depended on the particular plastic, with the highest recorded from solutions stored in low-density polyethylene and polypropylene. It has also been indicated that plastic containers, fabricated from identical polymers but manufactured by different producers, may show variable patterns and degrees of preservative sorption (Neufeld and Scheel 1969; Dempsey 1988). In general, however, while the possibility of loss of preservative to plastic containers cannot be ignored, it is not considered a serious problem for oral or topical liquid medicines. It should also be noted that many studies have not distinguished between sorption and degradation. What may have been reported as binding to plastic may be due to chemical degradation.

A second preservative-related problem influenced by the choice of container for a particular medicine concerns the total size of the bottle, since this will determine the head-space (or ullage) of the container. If the preservative is volatile, for example chloroform, then losses into the airspace of the container can significantly reduce preservative efficacy (Lynch et al. 1977; Purkiss 1978; Allwood and Shaw 1987). While the ullage in a bottle containing the maximum nominal volume of liquid may be relatively small, removal of repeated doses will lead to significant increases in the head-space and consequent loss of active preservative. This is one reason why chloroform is now finding little favour with the formulator, although its value as part of an overall preservative system should not be entirely ignored, especially in products such as emulsions and alkaline mixtures, which are notoriously difficult to preserve. Cetain other preservatives are liable to loss due to their volatility and some are listed in Table 3.

Table 3 — Volatile preservatives

Preservative	Degree of volatility
Chloroform	+ + +
Alcohols	+ +
Phenolics	+
Chlorbutol	+ +

+   = slightly volatile.
+ +   = moderately volatile.
+ + + = highly volatile.

The container may exert other, perhaps unexpected effects on particular preservatives. For example, sorbic acid is more stable in products stored in polyethylene containers compared to storage in other materials. This is because the polyethylene polymer contains residues of antioxidants that leach into the contents, preventing oxidation of sorbic acid (McCarthy 1984). Aluminium released from caps may accelerate degradation of bronopol and mercurials. Rubber closures may also leach materials which can complex with organic mercurial and quaternary ammonium compounds. Finally, some container materials offer poor light protection and therefore photodegradation of some particularly light-sensitive preservatives will occur; there are many examples, particularly amongst the phenolics and bronopol.

Surface adhesion of micro-organisms to solid, apparently smooth, materials can cause failure of a preservative to control the microbial challenge. Hugo *et al.* (1986) reported that the survival of *Pseudomonas cepacia* in the presence of relatively concentrated solutions of chlorhexidine was enhanced, due to surface attachment of viable bacterial cells. There are, in fact, a number of reports of biofilms forming on solid surfaces which offer subsequent protection to the micro-colonies that arise. Adhesion to diverse surfaces including glass (Hugo *et al.* 1986) and many plastics (Costerton 1984) has been reported. While the major group of organisms implicated in this phenomenon are pseudomonads, other types, including *Serratia* spp. and *Staphylococcus epidermidis*, have been recognized.

2.4   Unit-dose packaging
The introduction of unit-dose packaging is an advance that will substantially improve the microbiological quality of all liquid non-sterile medicines. In unit-dose systems, microbiological quality depends on the cleanliness of the packaging and manufacturing process alone, and cannot be compromised by the user. It is interesting to observe that such unitizing of items is very widely applied in the food industry. Clearly, however, it raises questions regarding product stability when embarking on an entirely new packaging form for pharmaceuticals, and full stability

testing becomes necessary as a consequence of such a technological change. Looking to the future, a move towards unit-dose packaging of liquids and certain topical preparations is inevitable, especially for supply to hospitals, where the greater risks of contamination with pathogenic organisms exist (Anon. 1971; Baird *et al.* 1976; Baird and Petrie 1981; Baird 1985). Indeed, it can only be a matter of time before unitization of doses becomes universal in order to remove in-use contamination of products in ward use, thereby eliminating one mechanism of cross-infection in hospitals.

2.5 Solid-dose packaging
The microbiological risks of solid oral dosage forms is generally considered nowadays to be negligible. Cross-contamination by the person handling such doses directly (against the pharmacists' code of practice (Anon. 1989)) is essentially the only in-use risk. It should be remembered that tablets and capsules are transferred by the dispenser and by ward staff to the patient when administering the dose. The advent of strip/foil unit packaging clearly removes these minor risks. However, it is noteworthy that this improvement in the microbiological integrity of the product is a valuable spin-off from product packaging development, and not primarily stimulated by microbiological considerations.

3 STERILE PRODUCTS
3.1 Packaging developments
The design of packaging for injections, large- and small-volume sterile solutions and ophthalmic products has evolved rapidly in the last twenty years. Few products are now packed in large glass bottles and the use of plastics is widespread. Even amino acid infusions for total parenteral nutrition are now available in collapsible plastic bags. The plastic bag offers a number of advantages, many of which are microbiological, for large-volume parenterals (LVPs), when compared with rigid glass bottles. In particular, the risk of contamination both during sterilization and administration are substantially reduced. Plastics are also employed to package topical sterile solutions, bladder irrigations and eye-drops with integral dropper assemblies. Finally, semi-rigid ampoules are now becoming available using blow-moulding, form-fill technology (Sharpe 1988). This wider use of plastics has led to considerable improvements in the microbiological aspects of sterile product manufacture and administration.

3.2 Packaging of LVPs

3.2.1 *Type of material*
Sterilization by autoclaving is essential to achieve maximum sterility assurance in the final product (Chapter 8) and this must be recognized in the choice of container material. Infusions in glass bottles sealed with rubber closures have always been subject to high levels of moist-heat exposure, a 121°C/15-minute cycle being preferred, although the less stressing 115°C/30-minute cycle is also acceptable to most authorities. A change in packaging to a plastic-fabricated container, which provides a more convenient and microbiologically safer pack for administration, should not necessitate reducing the lethality of the autoclaving cycle. The minimum

standard should remain a cycle delivering a lethality equivalent to an F_0 value of 8 (approximately equivalent to the 115°C/30-minute cycle; see Chapter 8). Infusion containers fabricated with PVC can withstand such cycles, although not at operating temperatures approaching 121°C. In contrast, polyethylene suitable for LVP packaging has a melting temperature below 115°C. The maximum temperature commensurate with maintaining package integrity is therefore in the region of 112–113°C. Consequently, in order to achieve lethality levels equivalent to an F_0 of 8, cycle times approaching 60 minutes are required. It must be appreciated that, where autoclave cycles are employed which provide lethality below the F_0 of 8 equivalent, additional pre-autoclaving bioburden testing is required. It is especially important to examine for heat-resistant micro-organisms. This can be conducted by heat-stressing (at say 98–100°C) samples of pre-autoclaved product, followed by recovery of survivors. It is also important to test all isolates for spore formation and the heat resistance of such spores. In this context, spore-forming isolates should be encouraged and allowed to sporulate by using appropriate media and incubation conditions before heat stress tests are carried out.

3.2.2 Advantages of plastic containers

The use of plastic material to fabricate LVP containers offers a number of potential microbiological advantages, both to the product manufacturer and to the user when compared to traditional, and largely obsolete, glass bottles.

For the manufacturer, it is possible to produce a pre-formed container from lay-flat tubing (PVC) or blow-mould systems (polyethylene, polypropylene) which are microbiologically cleaner than glass bottles, thereby reducing the pre-sterilization bioburden. Plastic containers are hermetically sealed, unlike glass bottles which rely on a non-hermetic seal between bottle rim and/or neck and rubber wad or bung. It is possible for this seal to fail during autoclaving due to the combination of the heat and pressure stress on a closure system (Coles and Tredree 1972). Pressure differences in excess of 30 lb in^{-2} (207 kPa) will occur inside a bottle during a typical autoclave cycle. This is caused by a combination of air expansion in the bottle head-space and expansion of the liquid, as well as other less important contributions (Allwood *et al.* 1975; Hambleton and Allwood 1976). If seal failure occurs during autoclaving, the rubber closure is forced off the bottle rim and air escapes. On cooling, the rubber closure is forced back onto the rim, leaving an unintentional vacuum in the bottle. Ingress of contaminated spray-cooling water, drawn in under the vacuum, is then a major threat. Further, this vacuum may fail during transport or storage, leading to the ingress of contaminated air. A major difficulty thus arises over the lack of control over this problem since it is governed by a number of variables, including design of rubber closure, the surface quality of the bottle rim, the tension applied by the metal closure and the ullage of the filled bottle. The removal of air from the bottle ullage prior to autoclaving eliminates these stresses on the closure. Most LVPs packed in glass containers (such as amino acid infusions and fat emulsions) are filled under vacuum and therefore this problem is controlled.

In contrast, the plastic container can be sealed as a single unit prior to autoclaving. Any seal failure due to inefficient seam welding is immediately obvious after autoclave-processing, especially if the LVP is overwrapped in a pouch before sterilization. This can be achieved with PVC packs, and, provided a small amount of moisture is present between the LVP pack and the pouch, the outer surfaces of the infusion container will be sterile. This has microbiological benefits in critical areas such as clean rooms and operating theatres, where good aseptic handling methods are employed to reduce risks of contamination or cross-infection. Polyethylene containers, however, cannot be overwrapped before autoclaving and an outer pouch is applied after sterilization. Therefore, the outer surface of these LVP containers will not, necessarily, be sterile.

Plastics for LVP packaging offer benefits in use and have led to substantial reductions in the risks of microbial contamination during administration (Maki 1976). As plastic is flexible, containers will collapse naturally as the contents flow out. Airways are therefore unnecessary, and there is no possibility of airborne contaminants entering the containers. It is also possible to design additive and administration set entry ports in PVC packs such that the possibility of touch contamination is either reduced or eliminated.

3.2.3 Disadvantages of plastic containers
The major difficulty associated with autoclaving LVPs in plastic containers concerns the need for air-ballasting in the autoclave chamber during sterilization to prevent permanent distortion or total failure of the packaging under the heat stresses imposed. If the pressure differences between the inside of the pack (due to residual air in the container and heat expansion of the contents) is not balanced by an approximately equal pressure in the autoclave chamber, plastic bags will distort and burst. Therefore, the chamber must contain a mixture of steam and air. In order to ensure even heat distribution throughout the cycle, an efficient means of continuous mixing of the air and steam must be assured. It is also important to replace steam with air at the commencement of the cooling cycle to maintain package integrity.

In summary, major advances have been made in the design of LVP packaging using plastics, especially plasticized PVC, which have effectively eliminated many of the microbiological weaknesses associated with glass bottles. This has been achieved without significantly altering the total safety profile of LVP packaging.

3.3 Packaging of small-volume parenterals
3.3.1 Glass ampoules and vials
Standard packaging for small-volume injections include glass ampoules or glass vials. While ampoules are all-glass, hermetically sealed units, vials comprise a glass body with a rubber plug held in place using a crimped aluminium ring. Vials are generally employed for drugs that are either manufactured by an aseptic fill process without terminal sterilization, for freeze-dried products when the drug is freeze-dried *in situ*, or for multidose presentations. For heat-stable (e.g. autoclavable) injections, ampoules are the preferred packaging mode although most glass vials will withstand autoclaving. For drugs in powder form (because of poor aqueous solution stability), vials are the most suitable form of packaging to permit dissolving of the drug in the container immediately prior to administration.

Multidose injections are now actively discouraged by regulatory authorities, because of the risks of in-use contamination and the poor efficacy of preservative systems that are available for parenterals (Allwood 1978). There is also mounting evidence that the toxicity of parenterally administered preservatives cannot be ignored (Allwood 1990). Thus, multidose injections are now largely confined to vaccines (for use in one session), insulin preparations (for use by one patient) and high-cost, variable-dose drugs. Preservatives are essential components of such formulations, and are also occasionally employed in single-dose injections prepared by aseptic processes as an added safeguard against adventitious contamination during manufacture. However, with the increasingly secure aseptic facilities now available, the case for such inclusions is becoming weaker. Sterility assurance levels, particularly in modern automated aseptic fill facilities, are approaching those of terminal heat or gamma radiation sterilization.

3.3.2 Plastic ampoules

A number of important developments in the packaging of small-volume parenteral products are emerging. The simplest, but probably the most significant in practice, is the introduction of plastic ampoules. These are blow-moulded units, using polyethylene granules, filled and sealed under aseptic conditions using the Rommelag technology (Sharpe 1988). It is also possible to autoclave the product but only at suboptimum temperatures. However, the combination of this with the high assurance levels of freedom from micro-organisms achieved in the Rommelag process offers a system achieving satisfactory levels of sterility assurance. This technology overcomes a major concern relating to glass ampoules which is the possibility of inadequate sealing leaving small channels through the seal of the ampoule. Incidences of seal failure have been reported (Brizell and Shatwell 1973). These authors pointed out the failings of many ampoule leak tests and recommended pressurized dye ingress testing, suggesting that pressures as high as $100\,\mathrm{lb\,in^{-2}}$ ($690\,\mathrm{kPa}$) were necessary to detect all unsealed ampoules. Plastic ampoules do not pose this risk and they also offer potential microbiological and safety benefits for the user. The seal can be broken by simple tear-off procedures, the horrors of opening glass ampoules are avoided, thus reducing the risks of touch contamination. Finally, the nozzle of the ampoule can be designed to fit exactly the luer end-fitting of a syringe so that the contents can be removed while the opening is effectively sealed by the syringe luer fit.

3.3.3 Novel designs for single-dose injections

Some major developments are emerging in the design of packaging which, in addition to other advantages, reduce the possibility of product contamination by the user. The aim of these designs is to provide the user with a ready-to-administer pack.

3.3.3.1 Single-compartment syringes

The simplest development is to present the drug in a pre-filled syringe. This is possible only if the drug is stable in the vehicle. Unfortunately, the syringe was not designed as a storage system (Mitrano *et al.* 1986). Consequently only specially modified glass-based syringes are currently suitable; at the present time, only a few products are available in syringes.

3.3.3.2 Dual-compartment syringes
There are now available syringe-based packages which can be used for drugs in powder form. These consist of double-chamber systems where the drug powder is contained in one chamber, which is separated by a rubber or breakable plastic septum from the second chamber containing the vehicle. The drug is dissolved in the vehicle after breaking the barrier between the chambers. This is achieved without exposing the contents to the environment, thus maintaining sterility of the injection. This system is applicable to small-volume injections, but is limited by the size of packs available.

3.3.3.3 Add-Vantage^{TM} system
A recent development in container systems allows a powdered drug to be dissolved in a relatively large volume of diluent. The Add-Vantage^{TM} system (Abbott Laboratories Ltd) incorporates a vial containing the drug in powder form and a plastic infusion container holding the diluent. The seal between the two units is broken by a twisting action to the outside of the packaging, allowing the vehicle to enter the vial. The plug removed from the vial remains inside the infusion bag. The drug can be reconstituted and then administered without exposing the contents to the environment. This double-chamber approach can be applied to heat-labile drugs prepared by freeze-drying in vials. However, such relatively complex designs can create microbiological problems associated with the sterilization of the total system. This aspect is discussed in a later section (4.1).

3.4 Packaging of ophthalmic preparations

3.4.1 Glass eye-drop bottles
Eye-drops are available as single- or multiple-dose solutions. The traditional glass hexagonal bottle with the screw cap incorporating a glass dropper/rubber teat assembly is rapidly being replaced by semi-rigid plastic bottles with integral dropper fitments. The glass eye-drop bottle/teat package was not designed to be used for sterilized products, and is essentially unsuitable for terminal sterilization of the product by autoclaving. The bakelite screw cap is clearly not able to withstand the heat and pressure stresses under autoclave conditions. It will not maintain a hermetic seal between the glass rim and rubber teat ring. Backing-off of the rubber seal during sterilization is commonly observed, resulting from air loss which in turn leads to a vacuum inside the container on cooling (compare with LVPs in section 3.2.2). Any seal failure during storage would then lead to ingress of contaminated air. Reliance on the preservative system of the formulation is then the only protection against multiplication of microbial contaminants in the eye-drop solution.

3.4.2 Plastic dropper bottles
The use of an integrated plastic container for multidose eye-drop products has had a substantial impact on the manufacture of ophthalmic preparations. These containers cannot, however, withstand autoclaving and sterilization is by filtration and aseptic filling into sterile containers (treated by γ-irradiation or ethylene oxide). The dropper device is attached under aseptic conditions. This system is safer than the glass bottle/rubber teat assembly during use, since the dropper is an inherent component of the container and is not removed from the bottle for application.

3.4.3   Single-dose eye-drops

Eye-drops are also available as single-dose disposable units. These small triangular pouches, with removable protective cap, contain 0.2–0.3 ml solution for direct administration to the eye. Although manufactured from flexible plastics, usually polycarbonate, they are autoclavable (115–117°C; with air ballasting) and no preservative is necessary.

3.4.4   Preservative sorption

A major problem associated with preservative control of microbial integrity in eye-drops during use is loss of preservative agent by migration into packaging components (Aspinall *et al.* 1980). It has been recognized for many years that some preservatives are absorbed into rubber, such as that used for eye-drop teats (see Table 2). In order to minimize such losses, it is normal practice to pre-saturate rubber components with preservative before use. Preservatives may also migrate into plastic bottles and this will depend on the type of preservative, the nature of the plastic and container size. For example, polyethylene containers will sorb organic mercurials (Aspinall *et al.* 1980) and phenylethanol (Miezitis *et al.* 1979). More polar preservatives (such as benzalkonium chloride and chlorhexidine) are not absorbed.

3.4.5   Eye ointments

Eye ointments continue to be packed in semi-rigid aluminium or plastic tubes with a narrow nozzle for the delivery of small amounts of ointment to an affected eye. Since these products are unlikely to support microbial growth and the packaging is unlikely to allow significant ingress of micro-organisms, it is difficult to envisage what improvements could be made to contribute to significantly greater microbiological safety. The pack size if usually restricted to less than 5 g.

3.5   Nebulizer solutions

Nebulizer solutions usually consist of aqueous steroid or bronchodilator drugs for the treatment and prophylaxis of asthmatic crises. A small volume, typically 1–2 ml, is placed in the reservoir of a nebulizer, and nebulized into small droplets which are swept into the lungs by inhaled air. Multidose solutions in glass bottles require a preservative (usually benzalkonium chloride) and the in-use life is restricted. Furthermore, owing to a number of clinical reports of paradoxical bronchoconstriction when using these multidose products, which has been attributed to excipients including preservatives, manufacturers are now generally obliged to pack nebulizer solutions as single-dose, preservative-free solutions. Blow-moulded polyethylene ampoules (Rommelag) or glass vials are used for this purpose. Each unit contains only sufficient solution for one treatment period. Polyethylene nebules are moulded in strips and each unit is designed for easy opening by tearing off the cap and transferring the contents without contact with contaminated surfaces. This represents an important packaging advance for a high-risk type of product.

3.6   Aerosol sprays

Aerosol sprays are employed in some areas of medication delivery, especially to topical sites. They include topical skin sprays and local anaesthetics and antimicrobials, spray dressings and oral hygiene products. When applied to unbroken skin, the need for assured sterility is unnecessary. Application to broken skin, however, such as wounds or burns, inflamed skin or surgical sites, requires such sprays to be sterile. Most sprays are based on dispersal of the drug in organic propellants which do not support microbial growth but the propellants are not necessarily self-sterilizing. Indeed, bacterial spores in particular may survive. The packaging is designed for one-way delivery of the contents and ingress of micro-organisms through the valve is extremely unlikely. It is important to ensure that the ingredients of the formulation, and the packaging components, are microbiologically clean.

4. INFLUENCE OF PACKAGING DESIGN ON MICROBIOLOGICAL QUALITY ASSURANCE

There is a growing interest in packaging design and its influence on the safe use of medicines, some examples having been given in earlier sections. While primarily designed to offer significant safety advantages, this is often accomplished through increased complexity in the pack design, especially for injectables. This may introduce hidden microbiological risks. In particular, dead-spaces may be introduced into packs in which product may become trapped allowing microbial survival and proliferation. Further, unit-dose packs may require delivery devices, such as aerosol generators, which may become a reservoir for contamination and are difficult to clean adequately; moisture-traps in nebulizer delivery equipment and non-cleanable dead-ends in delivery pumps for liquids must be avoided. The problems introduced by novel packaging design for parenterals require special thought. A major reason for introducing such packs is to reduce or eliminate chances of extrinsic contamination during reconstitution or administration. This is a laudable aim, but it is imperative to ensure that the pack itself does not compromise sterility by the presence of compartments not accessible to the sterilizing agent. Examples of packs which require such careful consideration are the pre-filled syringe and double-chamber infusion system.

Careful scrutiny of novel packaging by the microbiologist and pharmacist is very necessary to ensure that potential microbial risks are identified and overcome.

4.1 Validation of packaging for sterile products
The microbiologist must be involved at all stages of new packaging development, and should conduct studies to confirm that all product contact areas in a pack can be reached by the sterilant. To do this adequate validation studies must be performed to show that acceptable levels of sterility assurance are achieved at all points within a pack during the manufacturing processes. This will normally require biological, in addition to physical, validation. The methods applied often require considerable thought and ingenuity on the part of the microbiologist. A number of points must be borne in mind when designing such tests. Of crucial importance is the choice and nature of the biological model. Since our concern is with sterility assurance, a spore population of defined resistance to the sterilizing agent (chemical or physical) must be employed. An adequately large population must be applied to the test area in a complete standard pack. It is also important to use a dry microbial suspension; the presence of even minute amounts of moisture may confound the results and invalidate the test, since water is crucial to most sterilization processes used for these

products. Water used to prepare aqueous spore suspensions would clearly distort the lethality of the sterilization process. Spores should be suspended in a non-aqueous solvent, such as alcohol, and applied to surfaces or introduced into the test area using inoculated paper strips (previously dried or dried after application). Clearly, any method of biological testing should avoid introducing external factors not normally found in the user pack. Post-treatment removal of the spore population also requires careful consideration. The addition of a small amount of non-toxic detergent such as Polysorbate 80 to the diluent will aid removal of spores from solid surfaces. This again should be validated.

4.2 Microbiological testing and quality control
The testing of many items of packaging for the presence of micro-organisms, as part of a routine packaging quality-control procedure or during validation testing, requires careful thought. The removal of micro-organisms from solid surfaces requires the use of protective media able to maintain cell viability, with added surfactants or wetting agents. Such procedures should also be validated using specific organisms.

4.3 Integrity testing
Integrity testing of a new packaging should form part of any product development programme. Tests to ensure maintenance of a micro-organism-tight seal under practical stress conditions, and the penetrability of disinfecting agents used in cleaning procedures, may need biological validation. It is often considered important to use organisms of a minimum size for such tests such as *Pseudomonas diminuta*. However, in practice, size may be less important than survival of strains under test conditions and test organisms should also be selected based on their resistance to treatment procedures. For example, many of the smallest species of bacteria are Gram-negative, but their ability to survive under dry conditions is poor.

5 OVERVIEW
This review has attempted to describe the benefits of developments in packaging design, material and application in pharmaceuticals and cosmetics. Changes to achieve safer products through the elimination of microbiological risks have been numerous. However, as with all attempts to improve systems, those responsible must not unintentionally introduce alternative risks and all developments require careful evaluation, thorough validation and appropriate quality-control tests.

6 REFERENCES
Allwood, M. C. (1978) Antimicrobial agents in single- and multi-dose injections. *J. Appl. Bacteriol.* **44** Svii–Sxvii.

Allwood, M. C. (1990) Adverse reactions to parenterals. In: Florence, A. T. and Salole, E. G. (eds.), *Topics in pharmacy 1: formulation factors in adverse reactions.* Wright, London pp. 56–74.

Allwood, M. C. and Shaw, R. J. S. (1987) Preservation in mixtures, suspensions and syrups. In: Board, R. J., Allwood, M. C. and Banks, J. G. (eds), *Preservation in the food, pharmaceutical and environmental industries.* Blackwell Scientific, Oxford, pp. 197–210.

Allwood, M. C., Hambleton, R. H. and Beverley, S. (1975) Pressure changes in bottles during sterilisation by autoclaving. *J. Pharm. Sci.* **64** 333–334.

Anon. (1971) Report of Public Health Laboratory Service working party: microbial contamination of medicines administered to hospital patients. *Pharm. J.* **207** 96–103.

Anon. (1989) *Medicines, ethics and practice: a guide for pharmacists.* Royal Pharmaceutical Society of Great Britain, London.

Aspinall, J. A., Duffy, T. D., Saunders, M. B. and Taylor, C. G. (1980) The effect of low density polyethylene containers on some hospital-manufactured eye drop formulations. 1. Sorption of phenylmercuric acetate. *J. Clin. Hosp. Pharm.* **5** 21–29.

Baird, R. M. (1985) Microbial contamination of pharmaceutical products made in a hospital pharmacy: a nine year survey. *Pharm. J.* **235** 54–55.

Baird, R. M. and Petrie, P. S. (1981) A study of microbiological contamination of oral medicaments. *Pharm. J.* **226** 10–11.

Baird, R. M., Brown, W. R. L. and Shooter, R. A. (1976) *Pseudomonas aeruginosa* in hospital pharmacies. *Br. Med. J.* **1** 511–512.

Brizell, G. and Shatwell, J. (1973) Methods of detecting leaks in glass ampoules. *Pharm. J.* **211** 73–74.

Coles, J. and Tredree, R. L. (1972) Contamination of autoclaved fluids with cooling water. *Pharm. J.* **209** 193–195.

Costerton, J. W. (1984) The formulation of biocide-resistant biofilms in industrial, natural and medical systems. *Dev. Indust. Microbiol.* **25** 363–372.

Dean, D. A. (1978) Some recent advances in the packaging of pharmaceuticals. *Drug Dev. Ind. Pharm.* **4** v–vi.

Dempsey, G. (1988) The effect of container materials and multiple phase formulation components on the activity of antimicrobial agents. In: Bloomfield, S. F., Baird, R. M., Leak, R. E. and Leech, R. (eds), *Microbiological quality assurance in pharmaceuticals, cosmetics and toiletries.* Ellis Horwood, Chichester, pp. 94–103.

Fischer, H. and Neufeld, F. (1971) Sorption of mercury organic preservatives through plastic containers. *Pharm. Int.* **4** 11–15.

Hambleton, R. H. and Allwood, M. C. (1976) Evaluation of a new design of bottle closure for non-injectable water. *J. Appl. Bacteriol.* **41** 109–118.

Hugo, W. B., Pattent, L. J., Grant, D. J. W., Denyer, S. P. and Davies, A. (1986) Factors contributing to the survival of a strain of *Pseudomonas cepacia* in chlorhexidine solutions. *Lett. Appl. Microbiol.* **2** 37–42.

Kakemi, K., Sezaki, H., Arakawa, E., Kimura, K. and Ikeda, K. (1971) Interaction of parabens and other pharmaceutical adjuncts with plastic containers. *Chem. Pharm. Bull.* **19** 2523–2529.

Lynch, M., Lund, W. and Wilson, D. A. (1977) Chloroform as a preservative in aqueous systems. *Pharm. J.* **219** 507–510.

Maki, D. G. (1976) Sepsis arising from extrinsic contamination of the infusion and measures for control. In: Phillips. I., Meers, P. D. and D'Arcy, P. F. (eds), *Microbiological hazards of infusion therapy.* MTP Ltd, Lancaster, pp. 99–144.

McCarthy, T. J. (1984). Formulated factors affecting the activity of preservatives. In: Kabara, J. J. (ed.), *Cosmetic and drug preservation: principles and practice.* Marcel Dekker, New York, pp. 359–388.

Miezitis, E. O., Polack, A. E. and Roberts, M. S. (1979) Concentration changes during autoclaving of aqueous solutions in polyethylene containers: an examination of some methods for reduction of solute loss. *Aust. J. Pharm. Sci.* **8** 72–76.

Mitrano, F. P., Baptista, R. J., Newton, D. W. and Augustini, S. C. (1986) Microbial contamination potential of solutions in pre-filled disposable syringes used with a syringe pump. *Am. J. Pharm. Sci.* **43** 78–80.

Neufeld, F. and Scheel, D. (1969) The problems of packaging medicines in plastic containers. *Pharm. Int.* **2** 51–54.

Purkiss, R. (1978) Loss of chloroform from magnesium trisilicate mixture under simulated in-use conditions. *J. Clin. Pharm.* **2** 163–170.

Sharpe, J. (1988) Validation of a new form–fill–seal installation. *Manuf. Chem.* **59** 22, 23, 27, 55.

16

Microbial standards for pharmaceuticals

A. L. Davison
NETRHA Pharmaceutical Microbiology Laboratory, St. Bartholomew's Hospital,
48 Bartholomew Close, London EC1A 7HP, UK

1 Introduction 356
2 Microbiological standards 357
  2.1 Purified water 357
  2.2 Sterile pharmaceuticals 357
  2.3 Non-sterile pharmaceuticals 358
  2.4 Overall microbial quality 364
3 References 364

1 INTRODUCTION

It has been appreciated for many years that pharmaceutical products may become
vectors of microbial contamination during their manufacture, storage and subsequent use. Hence authorities control the microbial purity of pharmaceuticals by use
of official and licensing requirements, inspection of manufacturing facilities and the
production process, and examination of samples for conformity with pharmacopoeial specifications, where available. Techniques used in microbiological testing are
discussed in Chapter 6A.

The role of the microbiological specification is to provide a standard, or
guideline, for a pharmaceutical preparation to ensure its safety for use; this will
require freedom from contaminants which may pose a potential health hazard
relative to the product's intended mode and circumstance of use. Appropriate
microbial specifications designed to ensure quality throughout manufacture, storage
and use are difficult to predict, and only evolve following appreciation and identification of specific health, manufacturing and storage problems; these may not be
apparent until the preparation has been extensively manufactured and used in
different locations. No single microbiological criterion is universally applicable to
the wide range of pharmaceutical preparations available, hence specifications of

differing severity have developed relative to the potential risk posed by sterile and non-sterile categories of pharmaceutical preparation, and the raw materials (including water) used in the manufacture. These are subdivided into mandatory pharmacopoeial standards and non-mandatory guidelines indicative of the purity attainable with correctly validated manufacturing and control procedures.

2 MICROBIOLOGICAL STANDARDS

2.1 Purified water

The microbial quality of purified water produced for the manufacture of pharmaceuticals is dependent primarily on its age and method of storage, since proliferation of pseudomonads and the presence of endotoxin can arise under suitable conditions. Limits for potable water requiring absence of coliform bacilli in 100 ml are insufficient (Anon. 1982). Water for Injection, which is suitable for the manufacture of sterile products, has a pharmacopoeial limit of <0.25 endotoxin units (EU) per millilitre, when determined by the *Limulus* amoebocyte lysate test of the European Pharmacopoeia (EP 1986) and an accepted microbial limit of <10 c.f.u. per 100 ml with the absence of pseudomonads. Limits have yet to be resolved for purified water used for non-sterile manufacture due to the diversity of quailty available; suggested values are dependent on intended use and range from <10 to <100 c.f.u. per 100 ml, with a requirement for absence of pseudomonads.

2.2 Sterile pharmaceuticals

The criterion of sterility is a mandatory requirement for parenteral products, ophthalmic preparations, including contact lens solutions, and products applied to broken skin or used for the irrigation of body cavities, all of which are required to be manufactured as sterile products. Furthermore, if tested they must pass a test for sterility. The conditions for manufacture are laid down in both UK and EEC guidelines for good pharmaceutical manufacturing practice (GMP) (Anon. 1983, 1989a). The current test for sterility in the British Pharmacopoeia (BP 1988), which is identical to that of the European Pharmacopoeia (EP 1986), has undergone major modification since it first appeared in the BP over fifty years ago, in particular with the introduction of membrane filtration as the preferred method of test instead of direct transfer into broth. Assessment of sterility is based on the absence of growth following culture in fluid thioglycollate and soya bean casein digest broths, designed primarily for culture of anaerobic bacteria and aerobic bacteria/fungi, respectively. The media are incubated at 30–35°C and 20–25°C for bacteria and fungi respectively for a period of either 7 days duration with membrane filtration, or 14 days with direct transfer.

The test protocol of the United States Pharmacopeia (USP 1990) is similar although the requirements for minimum weights and volumes sampled differ from those of the BP. The fundamental distinction is in the rationale on retesting, with the USP only permitting a single retest (with twice the number of samples) and no second retest, for distinguishable contamination, as is allowed with the BP. This is the main obstacle to international harmonization of requirements, as membrane filtration has now largely eliminated the necessity for minimum weights and volumes to prevent inhibition of growth due to an excess of product. A simple compromise which permitted one retest only on the original number of samples, in order to confirm the absence or presence of contamination (irrespective of its identity) would resolve those problems of interpretation associated with skin contaminants originating from production or control personnel.

The inability of the sterility test to detect a significant level of contamination of 1 in 1000 (Anon. 1973; see also Chapter 9) has highlighted the importance of minimal bioburdens and verification of the terminal sterilization and aseptic filling operations for assurance of sterility. The BP (1988) has included both the overkill and F_0 method of sterilization (see Chapters 7 and 9). The Federation of Industrial Pharmacists (FIP) has also published guidelines (Anon. 1989b, 1990) to achieve the recommended sterility assurance levels of 10^{-6} and 10^{-3} for terminal sterilization and aseptic filling, respectively. Specifications for monitoring of bioburden, where limits are process and product dependent, are outside the scope of the pharmacopoeiae and are, instead, a matter for agreement between the manufacturer and the licensing authority for registration as in-house limits. In practice, a minimum heat lethality of F_0 8 will achieve a level of 10^{-6} (<1 contaminated unit per million) with a normally thermosensitive bioburden, and the overkill obtained with a standard reference cycle of 121°C for 15 minutes will provide a wide margin of safety with a thermoresistant bioburden. Specifications for aseptic filling under clean-room manufacturing conditions, as described in GMP guidelines and using broth filling in place of product followed by incubation, are dependent on the degree of operator intervention. The 0.3% guideline set by the World Health Organization (Anon. 1973) is applicable to manual operations, whereas the <0.1% guideline of the FIP which is similar to that of the Parenteral Drug Association (PDA) in the USA (Anon. 1980) is more likely to be achievable only with automated processing (see Chapters 4 and 17).

2.3 Non-sterile pharmaceuticals
There is no single mandatory standard, analogous to the criterion of sterility, for non-sterile oral and topical formulations, and their constituent materials; here the degree of microbial purity needs to reflect the absence of microbial flora capable of eliciting biodegradation and medication-borne infection. The rationale of guidelines and criteria are based on established and potential risks from contaminated materials of plant, animal and tellural origin and from aqueous formulations; these have been identified as possible vectors of opportunist pathogens, in surveys by Nobel and Savin (1966), Kallings *et al.* (1966), Schiller *et al.* (1968) the Public Health Laboratory Service (Anon. 1971a), the Royal Pharmaceutical Society of Great Britain (Anon. 1971b) and Baird (1985).

This realization of risk has led to the introduction of EP microbial limits on total viable count (TVC), and absence of enteric pathogens in raw materials of natural origin. These are non-mandatory specifications for implementation at the discretion of the national control authority. The EP limits shown in Table 1 differ, in part, from those in the BP (1988), as limits on TVC are not applicable in the UK, where reliance is placed instead on the absence of pathogens. This contrasts with the Scandinavian philosophy for a TVC limit of 10^2 for raw materials and products, with requirements for absence of pathogens only where the TVC limit is exceeded (Anon. 1967).

The BP and EP raw material requirements for absence of *Escherichia coli* in 1 g, *Salmonella* in 10 g, and on occasion Enterobacteriaceae and pseudomonads, differ from those of the United States Pharmacopeia and National Formulary (USP 1990),

Table 1 — Microbial limits for raw materials (BP and EP)

Raw material	TVC (per g or ml)	E. coli (per g or ml)	Salmonella (per 10 g or 10 ml)	Enterobacteriaceae pseudomonads[a]
Acacia	10^4	+		
Agar	10^3	+		
Aluminium hydroxide	10^3	+		+
Aluminium phosphate				+
Bentonite	10^2			
Charcoal, activated	10^2			
Calcium glutonate	10^3			
Digitalis powder		+	+	
Ferrous gluconate	10^2			
Gelatin	10^3	+	+	
Kaolin, heavy	10^2			
Lactose	10^3	+		
Pancreatin	10^4	+	+	
Maize starch ⎫	10^3	+		
Potato starch ⎬	(bacteria)			
Rice starch ⎪	10^2			
Wheat starch ⎭	(fungi)			
Sterculia		+		
Talc	10^2			
Tragacanth	10^4	+	+	

[a]See monograph.
+, absence required.
NB: TVC applicable to EP only.

which contain variable requirements for absence of *E. coli, Salmonella, Pseudomonas aeruginosa* and *Staphylococcus aureus* (all in 10 g) and TVC (Table 2). Furthermore, the USP has extended these requirements to 34 oral and 66 topical formulations, mainly for the absence of *E. coli* and/or *Salmonella* in oral preparations and *Staph. aureus* and *Ps. aeruginosa* in topical products (Tables 3 and 4). The rationale is unclear, as these requirements exclude some aqueous creams, gels and lotions, but include some non-aqueous ointments, which normally are not subject to microbial contamination. Furthermore, in two topical preparations (haloprogin cream and benzocaine otic solution), TVC and absence of *E. coli* and *Salmonella* are also included.

These pharmacopoeial requirements, however, are insufficient to cater for the wide range of opportunist pathogens, which include many species of Gram-negative bacilli regarded as either occasionally or always objectionable by Bruch (1972) (see Chapter 10). Limits requiring identification of a range of Gram-negative species, where differentiation of species may prove difficult, are unrealistic and can be circumvented by adoption of guidelines as proposed by FIP (Anon. 1976). Here a limit is set for Enterobacteriaceae and certain other Gram-negative bacteria (pseudomonads) as a group, with differing values for oral and topical formulations in addition to limits for TVC, *E. coli, Salmonella, Ps. aeruginosa* and *Staph. aureus* (Table 5). The applicability of these limits for inclusion as non-mandatory

Table 2 — Microbial limits for raw materials (USP 1990)

Raw material	TVC (per g or ml)	E. coli (per 10 g or 10 ml)	Salmonella (per 10 g or 10 ml)
Acacia			+
Activated attapulgite		+	
Agar			+
Alginic acid	<200	+	+
Bentonite		+	
Bentonite, purified	<1000	+	
Calamine[a]			
Caramel		+	+
Carrageenan	<200	+	+
Charcoal, activated		+	+
Chymotrypsin[a]			+
Colloidal activated attapulgite		+	
Dehydrocholic acid			+
Digitalis powder			+
Gelatin	<1000	+	+
Insulin	<300		
Insulin, human	<300		
Inulin[a]	<1000	+	+
Kaolin		+	
Lactose	<100	+	+
Magnesium carbonate		+	
Magnesium hydroxide		+	
Magnesium phosphate		+	
Magnesium aluminium silicate	<1000	+	
Magnesium stearate	<1000	+	
Magaldrate		+	
Pancreatin			+
Pancrelipase		+	+
Pectin			+
Propylene glycol alginate	<200	+	+
Psyllium husk	<1000 fungi	+	+
Purified water†			
Rauwolfia serpentina			+
Rauwolfia serpentina, powdered			+
Sodium alginate	<200	+	+
Sodium starch glycolate		+	+
Starch		+	+
Pregelatinized starch		+	+
Compressible sugar		+	+
Confectioner's sugar		+	+
Sugar spheres[a]	<100	+	+
Topical starch	<500 (<50 fungi)		
Talc	<500		
Thryoglobulin		+	+
Thyroid		+	+
Tragacanth		+	+
Trypsin, crystallized[a]			+
Xanthan gum		+	+
Zein	<1000	+	+

[a]Denotes requirements for absence of *Staph. aureus* and *Ps. aeruginosa* in 10 g or 10 ml.
+, absence required.
† See monograph.

Table 3 — Microbial limits for oral preparations (USP 1990)

Product	TVC (per g or ml)	E. coli (per 10 g or 10 ml)	Salmonella (per 10 g or 10 ml)
Alumina and magnesia oral suspension	<100	+	
Alumina, magnesia and calcium carbonate oral suspension[a]	<100	+	
Alulmina, magnesia and simethicone oral suspension	<100	+	
Alumina and magnesium carbonate oral suspension[b]	<100	+	+
Basic aluminium carbonate gel	<100	+	
Aluminium hydroxide gel	<100	+	
Bentonite magma		+	
Calcium carbonate oral suspension[a]	<100	+	
Carboxymethylcellulose sodium paste	<1000	+	+
Chlorpromazine hydrochloride oral concentrate		+	
Dehydrocholic acid tablets			+
Digitalis capsules			+
Digitalis tablets			+
Dihydroxyaluminium aminoacetate magma	<100	+	
Ipecac syrup		+	
Lactulose syrup	<100	+	+
Magaldrate oral suspension	<100	+	
Magaldrate tablets		+	
Magaldrate and simethicone oral suspension	<100	+	
Magaldrate and simethicone tablets		+	
Magnesium hydroxide paste	<400	+	
Milk of magnesia	<100	+	
Milk of bismuth	<100	+	
Methycellulose oral solution	<100	+	
Pancreatin capsules			+
Pancreatin tablets			+
Pancrelipase capsules		+	+
Pancrelipase tablets		+	+
Psyllium hydrophilic mucilloid for oral suspension		+	+
Rauwolfia serpentina tablets			+
Simethicone emulsion	<100		
Sodium polystyrene sulphonate suspension[a]	<100 (<100 fungi)		
Thyroid tablets		+	+
Thyroglobulin tablets		+	+

[a]Denotes additional requirement for absence of *Ps. aeruginosa* in 10 g or 10 ml.
[b]Denotes additional requirement for absence of *Staph. aureus* and *Ps aeruginosa* in 10 g or 10 ml.
+, absence required.

pharmacopoeial recommendations remain under discussion. The methodology which utilizes differing enrichment procedures for individual tests is too complex; often the same can be achieved by a non-selective enrichment in tryptone soya broth to establish presumptive contamination, invariably by a single species, with diagnostic tests to confirm identity.

This approach has been developed in the UK by some hospital authorities and pharmaceutical manufacturers for 'in-house' monitoring of microbial purity, by

Table 4 — Microbial limits for topicals (USP 1990)

Product	Staph. aureus Ps. aeruginosa (per 10 g or 10 ml)	Product	Staph. aureus Ps. aeruginosa (per 10 g or 10 ml)
Alclometasone diproprionate cream	+	Flurandrenolide tape	+
Alclometasone diproprionate ointment	+	Halcinonide cream	+
		Halcinonide ointment	+
Amcinonide cream	+	Halcinonide topical solution	+
Amcinonide ointment	+	Haloprogin cream[a]	+
Benzalkonium chloride solution (≤5%)	(+)	Hexachlorophane cleansing emulsion	+
Benzocaine cream	+	Hexachlorophane liquid soap	+
Benzocaine ointment	+	Hydrocortisone cream	+
Benzocaine otic solution[a]	+	Hydrocortisone lotion	+
Benzocaine topical solution	+	Hydrocortisone ointment	+
Betamethasone cream	+	Hydrocortisone acetate cream	+
Betamethasone benzoate gel	+	Hydrocortisone acetate ointment	+
Betamethasone valerate cream	+		
Betamethasone valerate lotion	+	Hydrocortisone butyrate cream	+
		Isoproterenol sulphate inhalation aerosol	+
Betamethasone valerate ointment	+	Lidocaine topical aerosol	+
Calamine lotion	+	Lidocaine ointment	+
Clotrimazole lotion	+	Neomycin sulphate and fluradrenolide lotion	+
Clotrimazole and betamethasone diproprionate cream	+	Papain tablets for topical solution	+
Dexamethasone topical aerosol	+	Polymyxin B sulphate and bacitracin zinc topical aerosol[b]	+
Dexamethasone sodium phosphate cream	+	Polymyxin B sulphate and bacitracin zinc topical powder[b]	+
Dibucaine cream	+		
Dibucaine ointment	+	Pramoxine hydrochloride cream	+
Diflorasone diacetate cream	+	Pramoxine hydrochloride jelly	+
Diflorasone diacetate ointment	+	Tetracaine ointment	+
		Tetracaine hydrochloride cream	+
Ephedrine sulphate nasal solution	+	Tetrahydrozoline hydrochloride nasal solution	+
Estradiol vaginal cream	+		
Flumethasone pivalate cream	+	Ticonazole cream	+
Fluocinolone acetonide cream	+	Triamcinolone acetonide topical aerosol	+
Fluocinolone acetonide ointment	+		
Fluocinolone acetonide topical solution	+	Triamcinolone acetonide cream	+
Fluocinonide cream	+	Triamcinolone acetonide lotion	+
Fluoromethalone cream	+	Triamcinolone acetonide ointment	+
Fluorouracil cream	+		
Fluorouracil topical solution	+	Triamcinolone acetonide dental paste	+
Flurandrenolide cream	+		
Flurandrenolide lotion	+		
Flurandrenolide ointment	+		

[a] Denotes an additional requirement for TVC<100 per g or ml, and absence of *E. coli* and *Salmonella* in 10 g or 10 ml.
[b] Denotes an additional requirement for TVC (see monograph).
+, Absence required; (+), absence for *Ps. aeruginosa* only required.

Table 5 — Microbial limit guidelines for non-sterile categories of pharmaceuticals
(Anon. 1976)

Criteria	Topical preparations	Oral preparations
Limit of TVC g^{-1}		
Bacteria	10^2	10^3–10^4
Fungi	10^2	10^2
Limit of Enterobacteriaceae	Absent in 1 g or 1 ml	$<10^2$ in 1 g or 1 ml
Absence in 1 g	*Ps. aeruginosa* *Staph. aureus*	*E. coli* *Salmonella*

means of low TVC values and absence of opportunist pathogens, over the shelf-life of the product. The data require skilled interpretation for the evolution of flexible in-house guidelines which are indicative of microbial purity. These guidelines are increasingly required for product licensing, registration and review, since an absolute criterion, analogous to sterility, is inapplicable. The hospital authority guidelines, derived a decade ago for use by Regional Quality Controllers and updated in 1989 (Table 6), contain acceptable levels and upper limits to provide flexibility in the

Table 6 — Microbial limit for raw materials and non-sterile categories of pharmaceuticals for hospital use

Criteria	Raw materials	Topical preparations	Oral preparations
TVC per g or ml			
Acceptable	10^2	10^1	10^2
Maximum	10^3	10^2	10^3
Absence in 1 g or 1 ml	*Staph. aureus* Enterobacteriaceae Pseudomonads Clostridia	*Staph. aureus* Enterobacteriaceae Pseudomonads	*E. coli* Enterobacteriaceae[a] Pseudomonads[a]
Absence in 10 g or 10 ml	*Salmonella*		*Salmonella*

[a]Denotes upper limit of 10 per ml or g.

interpretation of non-critical viable count criteria but not for critical criteria; in the latter case absence of Gram-negative opportunist pathogens associated with hospital infection is essential when preparations are to be used by debilitated hospital patients.

2.4   Overall microbial quality

The microbial quality of raw materials and manufactured products has improved with awareness of the necessity for microbiological quality assurance and the implementation of 'in-house' monitoring programmes for assessment of microbial purity. However, without published data from control agencies on the incidence and causes of product recall attributable to microbial contamination, or reject data on industrially manufactured products, realistic assessment of the impact of preventive guidelines is impossible. It would appear that limits for TVC and consistent absence of *Ps. aeruginosa, Staph. aureus, E. coli,* and *Salmonella* are both attainable and demonstrable but specialized methodology and expertise is required to detect transient product-specific contamination by Gram-negative bacteria, in particular *Ps. cepacia* in marginally preserved formulations arising from deficiencies in GMP. Inclusion of *Ps. cepacia* in microbial limit requirements as a GMP indicator is long overdue in order to prevent it from becoming a cause of product recall since, in the author's experience, high levels of this preservative- and antibiotic-resistant opportunist pathogen may develop in products prior to use.

3   REFERENCES

Anon. (1967) *Production hygiene and bacteriological control in the manufacture of pharmaceuticals.* Swedish National Board of Health, Document No. 115, Stockholm.

Anon. (1971a) Microbial contamination of medicines administered to hospital patients. *Pharm. J.* **207** 96–99.

Anon. (1971b) Microbial contamination in pharmaceuticals for oral and topical use. *Pharm. J.* **207** 400–402.

Anon. (1973) *Sterility and sterility testing of pharmaceutical preparations and biological substances.* World Health Organization, Documents WHO/BS/73.1062 and WHO/PHARM/73.474.

Anon. (1976) Microbiological purity of non-compulsorily sterile pharmaceutical preparations. *Pharm. Acta Helv.* **51** 33–40.

Anon. (1980) *Validation of aseptic filling for drug products.* Technical Monograph No. 2, Parenteral Drug Association, Philadelphia.

Anon. (1982) *The bacteriological examination of drinking water supplies.* Report on public health and medical subjects, No. 71. HMSO, London.

Anon. (1983) *Guide to good pharmaceutical manufacturing practice.* HMSO, London.

Anon. (1989a) *The rules governing medicinal products in the European Community. Vol. IV. Guide to good manufacturing practice for medicinal products.* HMSO, London.

Anon. (1989b) Sterility assurance based on validation of the sterilisation process using steam under pressure. *J. Parenter. Sci. Technol.* **43** 226–230.

Anon. (1990) Validation and environmental monitoring of aseptic processing. *J. Parenter. Sci. Technol.* (in press).

Baird, R. M. (1985) Microbial contamination of pharmaceutical products made in a hospital pharmacy: a nine year survey. *Pharm. J.* **231** 54–55.

British Pharmacopoeia (1988) HMSO, London.

Bruch, C. W. (1972) Objectionable micro-organisms in non-sterile drugs and cosmetics. *Drug Cosmet. Ind.* **111** 51–54, 150–156.

European Pharmacopoeia (1986) 2nd edn. Maisonneuve SA, Sainte-Ruffine, France.

Kallings, L. O., Ringertz, O., Silverstolpe, L. and Ernerfeldt, F. (1966) Microbial contamination of medicinal preparations. *Acta Pharm. Suec.* **3** 219–228.

Nobel, W. C. and Savin, J. A. (1966) Steroid cream contaminated with *Pseudomonas aeruginosa. Lancet* **i** 347–349.

Schiller, I., Kuntscher, H., Wolff, A. and Nekola, M. (1968) Microbial content of non-sterile therapeutic agents containing natural or seminatural active ingredients. *Appl. Microbiol.* **16** 1924–1928.

United States Pharmacopeia (1990) 22nd revision and National Formulary 17th revision. United States Pharmacopeial Convention, Rockville, MD.

17

Risk assessment and microbiological auditing

David I. R. Begg
David Begg Associates, 10 High Market Place, Kirkbymoorside, York YO6 6AX, UK

1 INTRODUCTION

Potential contamination of a pharmaceutical product can be classified into biological, microbiological and physical (i.e. particles) and these aspects must be considered in relationship to each other. Chemical contamination, whilst not to be forgotten, can be treated as a separate subject and will not be considered in this chapter. In assessing the risks of microbial contamination in pharmaceutical products, a wide variety of factors before, during and after manufacturing must be considered.

One of the difficulties in risk assessment is the lack of official published microbiological standards, especially in relationship to bioburden and environmental monitoring levels. It is also extremely difficult to relate environmental standards to product quality — hence 'the edge of failure' remains elusive and consequently there is a tendency to 'over-engineer' facilities with attendant high costs.

Auditing is an essential element in the overall management of product quality. Auditing microbiological aspects within a quality system will require a skilled and experienced auditor armed with a proper audit plan, a systematic approach to the audit, and the ability to interpret audit findings. The auditor's primary objective is to ensure that hazardous situations are eliminated by follow-up action initiated by senior management.

2 RISK ASSESSMENT
2.1 Pharmaceutical considerations

Medicines are practically unique as items which can be applied to the body or introduced to the body system by insertion, ingestion, inhalation or injection. Sensible comparisons can be made with cosmetics and foodstuffs, which are also 'introduced' to the body system and consequently may, if not correctly manufactured and controlled, present a risk to the consumer. Assessing the risk of microbial contamination with medicines may be more properly viewed by asking the basic question 'what is the hazard to the patient?' Such an approach must take into consideration the following:

(a) the nature of the product, its use, and how it will be administered to the patient;
(b) specifications that should be set for the starting materials, the in-process controls and the finished product;
(c) the complexity and time-scale of the manufacturing process and the steps taken to reduce progressively and/or eliminate the risk of microbial contamination during all manufacturing and packaging stages;
(d) the sources of contamination.

Comparison of products may serve to illustrate a rational approach to assessing microbiological risk or hazard to the patient.

Example 1: large-volume sterile injectable product
Product: Large-volume sterile product manufactured by aseptic processing from a thermolabile raw material which, in its final form, acts as a good substrate for microbial growth; likely to be administered in large volumes over an extended period of time.
Comment: Risks of contamination during processing are high because of the nature of the raw materials and the vulnerability of the formulated product to contamination at any stage of processing and packing. Furthermore the patient's exposure to risk is enhanced because of the intravenous route and extended period of administration. Requirements for processing environment and microbiological monitoring and control are most stringent; assurance of pack integrity from factory to point of use is critical.

Example 2: Small-volume sterile injectable product
Product: Small-volume sterile product made from a chemical raw material known to have an inherent antimicrobial effect. Product is formulated into a solution, filled into vials under aseptic conditions and subsequently freeze-dried. Product is used in a limited time-span (e.g. anaesthetic agent).

Comment: Risks of contamination during processing cannot be ignored, but vulnerability of product to contamination is low because of the nature of the active material. Moreover, in its final form as a dry product it is unlikely to be easily contaminated or support growth. Product is administered in small volumes by intramuscular injection over a limited period of time, which again restricts the hazard. Requirements for processing environment and microbiological control and monitoring remain high.

Example 3: Multidose eye-drop preparation

Product: a multi-dose eye drop preparation made from synthetic organic and inorganic chemicals incorporating a known preservative system which complies with a pharmacopoeial challenge test and which is terminally sterilized in its final container.

Comment: Such a product is inherently less vulnerable to contamination, has the benefit of a validated preservative system and a known level of sterility assurance by application of a compendial sterilization process.

Other, equally valid, comparisons can be made with liquid oral products (e.g. some antacids which are administered long-term are poorly preserved and known to be vulnerable to microbial contamination when compared with well-preserved formulations which are also inherently less liable to contamination).

Even tablet products, especially those containing materials of natural origin, should not escape assessment of the risk of microbiological contamination. Contamination of thyroid tablets by *Salmonella* in Sweden (Kallings *et al.* 1966) illustrates this point, as does the known susceptibility of paracetamol tablets to mould growth.

Other oral products such as bulk laxatives prepared from natural materials have also shown themselves capable of being heavily contaminated with micro-organisms. Whilst no patient risk has been established, the regulatory authorities have put pressure on companies to set their own standards and reduce the microbial levels by additional processing.

Certain groups of patients, such as those on immunosuppressive therapy, will always be at risk. Barrett (1984) drew special attention to the need for microbiological monitoring of all pharmaceutical preparations used in hospitals where contamination can spread easily.

In recent years the nature and use of sterile medicines has slowly but perceptibly changed. These developments all affect the assessment of risk and some examples are given below:

(a) rapid increase in the use of large-volume parenteral nutrition products, some of which cannot be terminally sterilized and may also be vulnerable to microbial growth;

(b) reduction in the use of preservatives, particularly in small-volume injections;

(c) increased use of aseptic processing for many products, some of which will easily support microbial growth.

The suggestion that microbiological controls should be applied to inhalation products must again be viewed against the risk of contamination. In the case of metered-dose aerosol products, most of which are formulated using volatile organic solvents as propellants, the nature of the vehicle itself presents a hostile environment for micro-organisms and it follows that the risk of contamination is very small indeed.

2.2 Microbiological considerations
Microbiological risk assessment must never forget the nature of the 'enemy', which is summarized in Table 1.

Table 1 — Nature of the microbial contaminant

Size	Hard to see and identify
Variety and adaptability	Many different organisms, many of which are specifically adapted to live in almost any environment
Activity	Can grow very rapidly, causing spoilage and infection
Ubiquity	Can live in almost any environment
Undemanding	Can use many and varied substances as a source of nutrition
Hardy	Can survive long periods under adverse conditions
Mobility	Easily transmitted by air, water or by direct contact

Whilst sources of contamination have been well documented (Clegg 1988), it is vital that whoever is involved in risk assessment is properly armed with such knowledge and examines the steps by which contamination is minimized.

2.3 Standards
Microbiological standards and limits for a number of raw materials and finished products are published in the United States, British and European pharmacopoeias (see Chapter 16). The manufacturer generally has no problem in complying with such standards, although the British Pharmacopoeia challenge test for preservative efficiency has aroused considerable controversy. What is less helpful for the manufacturer, however, is the lack of unambiguous guidelines and official standards which can be applied as in-process controls and limits, for example to water supply and distribution systems; bioburden levels for raw materials and products prior to sterilization processes; and microbiological limits for environmental monitoring during the operational phase.

In practice the risk of contamination is assessed on an individual basis, and in-house limits are set by the manufacturer according to the circumstances. Such in-house limits can, however, vary considerably from one manufacturer to another. There is a good case for generalized guidelines for manufacturers that will more readily assist in risk assessment during each of the process and packaging stages. Nevertheless it has to be admitted that attempts at setting microbial standards have always proved difficult. The authorities have been slow in publishing standards and have fought shy of quoting numerical limits for micro-organisms because of the debate which would inevitably ensue. In view of the inherent errors in microbiological counting techniques, it would probably be better to express limits as orders of magnitude which more adequately reflect the ability of current microbiological control methods.

The Food and Drug Administration (FDA) of America published explicit proposals for regulating good manufacturing practice (GMP) for large-volume parenterals (LVP; Anon. 1976). Although these regulations were never approved, they have had a significant effect on manufacturers who tend, still, to treat them as official. The microbiological quality limits and sample sizes for water are given in Table 2.

Table 2 — FDA proposed microbial quality limits for water used in LVPs (Anon. 1976)

Water type	Sample size	Microbial limit
Water for cleansing and initial rinsing	Three consecutive samples of 100 ml	No more than 50 microorganisms per 100 ml
Manufacturing or final rinsing of equipment and containers	Three consecutive samples of 250 ml or more from same site	No more than 10 microorganisms per 100 ml
Water[a] used for cooling the product after sterilization	Three consecutive samples of 1 litre or more from same site	No more than 1 viable organism per 100 ml

[a] Water is treated by chlorination or other appropriate method to reduce microbial population.

Most GMP guides also propose that water for use in sterile products is stored and circulated at elevated temperatures to prevent microbial growth, but it is curious that requirements can differ, as shown in Table 3.

Table 3 — GMP requirements for water storage temperature

Country	Storage temperature
UK (Orange Guide; Anon. 1973)	above 65°C
EC Guide to GMP (Anon. 1989a)	above 70°C
FDA (proposed GMP regulations; Anon. 1976)	at least 80°C[a]

[a]If stored at ambient temperature or lower, water should be dumped to drain every 24 hours.

Despite the fact that neither the most recent British Standard (BS 5295, 1989) nor the US Federal Standard 209D (1988) for Controlled Environments quote microbiological limits, American and European GMP Guidelines now provide some microbial environmental limits which are compared in Table 4 (see also Chapter 5). FDA guidelines specifically refer to a 1967 publication from NASA where those responsible for the space programme were more concerned about contamination of outer space than the production of pharmaceuticals!

Table 4 — Comparison of microbial environmental standards for sterile products

Nearest equivalent air classification system		Maximum number of viable organisms (expressed as c.f.u. m^{-3})	
US Federal Standard 209D	EC Guide to GMP (Anon. 1989a)	FDA guideline for sterile products (Anon. 1987)	EC Guide to GMP for sterile products (Anon. 1989a)
100	A (LAF work station)	No more than 3.5	Less than 1
100	B	—	5
10 000	C	—	100
100 000	D	No more than 87.5	500

It is interesting to note that these standards are not based upon any accurate scientific evidence which relates product quality to the quoted environmental standards. Additionally, no guidance is given concerning the sample size (volume of air) to be taken in relationship to the quoted limit.

2.4 Appropriateness of standards
In 1977 the second edition of the UK 'Orange Guide' to *Good pharmaceutical manufacturing practice* (Anon. 1977) referred to the application of the then new BS 5295 (1976) for the manufacture of sterile products. Whyte (1983) challenged the need for such standards and concluded that, in relationship to terminally sterilized products, 'airborne bacteria cannot be a practical problem in terms of the quality of the product' but conceded that such a conclusion would not apply to an aseptic area. Elsewhere these standards have been attacked as 'inappropriate', causing the diversion of a great deal of money from other NHS services which would have been of greater value to patients (Anon. 1981).

2.5 Quantifying risk
Evaluating the risks of bacterial contamination during aseptic manufacture of sterile products has been studied by Whyte and colleagues over a period of time and probably represents some of the most objective work carried out. In one study they related the risk of product contamination in vials to hand skin carriage rate and airborne contamination (Whyte *et al.* 1982). This is expressed as:

$$\log_{10} C = 0.42 \log_{10} A + 0.32 \log_{10} H - 0.91$$

where
C=contamination rate/1000 vials filled
A=airborne bacteria per cubic metre in filling environment
H=hand-wash bacterial concentration (c.f.u.)/hand.

Later, in another study with 'closed' ampoules, Whyte (1986) concluded that contamination rate (and hence the risk) was directly related to: the settle plate count per surface area per hour; the area of the ampoule neck; and exposure time of ampoules during filling. Further mathematical treatments of microbial deposition are given in Chapter 5.

Using the data from actual filling operations, it has been calculated that the chance of contamination with 'closed' ampoules is of the low order of 1 in 1.43×10^6. It can be said that this compares favourably with the statistical definition of sterility and is orders of magnitude better than the standards for media fills suggested by the Parenteral Drug Association (1980).

The risk of bacterial contamination is generally thought to be much higher in aseptic processing than with terminal sterilization. This is reflected in the attitude of the regulatory authorities who continue to accept the practical difficulties of operating so called 'aseptic' areas with people working in them and thereby spreading contamination throughout the environment in which the product is exposed.

It is curious indeed that such compromise should still be accepted in the light of new technology which has been developed over the last ten years (see Chapter 5). Application of technology such as the isolator (developed by La Calhene), robotics, total body exhaust suit (by Charnley Howorth) and form–fill–seal (by Rommelag and others) have all shown dramatic improvements in reducing such risks of contamination. This is done primarily by eliminating or minimizing human contact with processing and the product. Sharp (1988) reported on the validation of form–fill–seal technology using liquid nutrient media where, out of a total of 36 000 units filled during six runs, only two showed growth, both of which were later found to be leakers. Sharp commented that the aim should be to achieve no growth in any unit filled, although no more than 1 in 6000 (0.017%) may be acceptable. Other unpublished work using isolator and form–fill–seal technology corroborates Sharp's findings and proves, beyond doubt, that keeping people out of aseptic areas has a significant effect upon reducing contamination risks. It is noteworthy that the recently published EC guide to GMP (Anon. 1989a) states that 'the utilization of absolute barrier technology and automated systems to minimize human interventions in process areas can produce significant [sic] advantages in assurance of sterility of medicinal products'.

Further evidence of the need to look more closely at aseptic filling was given by Whyte *et al.* (1989), reporting on microbial growth in small-volume parenterals. Aseptically filled single-dose containers were also found to be at risk from contamination, suggesting that the deletion of a preservative from an aseptically formulated parenteral should not be lightly undertaken. In this instance we must therefore balance the risk:benefit ratio, where the recent move away from preservatives (because of their possible toxicity) has highlighted the need for increased vigilance and higher standards in aseptic processing. Furthermore the introduction of more biological products, many of which cannot be terminally sterilized or preserved and which may be more vulnerable to microbial contamination, can only heighten awareness to the risks of contamination during processing.

Risk assessment must be governed, not only by attempting to predict what might happen, but also by past experience, including some most unfortunate incidents involving death or injury to the patient. In contrast to what has been said about the inherently higher risks of microbial contamination during aseptic processing, history reminds us that serious events have occurred with terminally sterilized products (Phillips *et al.* 1972; Report 1976). In the words of the Clothier (1972) report 'The Committee considers that too many people believe that sterilization of fluids is easily achieved with simple plant operated by men of little skill under a minimum of supervision, a view of the task which is wrong in every respect.'

2.6 Risk management
Management of risk within the pharmaceutical industry is an activity which is not commonly in evidence on a formal basis. However, increasing pressures from costs, competition and potential liability are causing a reappraisal of the preventative measures taken to limit the risks of microbial contamination. A critical analysis of risk at every stage of the operation should be undertaken as part of the audit function referred to in the next section. What is more difficult is quantifying such risks in order to assist management to justify the preventative measures which need to be installed.

A recent publication by the Health and Safety Executive (Anon. 1989b) gives some useful guidance on quantified risk assessment (QRA) which has largely been developed from tolerability of risk from nuclear power-stations. In the pharmaceutical industry asking the simple question 'what are the potential hazards to the patient?' may go some way to answering questions about risk assessment. Russell (1985) has suggested that the potential risk to a patient by the administration of an injection is extremely small. The 'Orange Guide' (Anon. 1983) reminds us that 'the great majority of defective medicinal products reported result simply from human error or carelessness, not from failures in technology'.

3 MICROBIOLOGICAL AUDITING
3.1 Why audit?
The pharmaceutical industry has gone to considerable lengths to introduce systems of assuring quality and hence many companies accept that the audit is an essential part of managing quality and assessing compliance with the 'quality system'. Furthermore, auditing is recommended, in some cases required, by the various national and international regulatory authorities. Auditing has the benefits shown in Table 5.

In order to be successful, audits must display certain essential criteria. They must be:

(a) Formal; there is no such thing as an informal audit. Everyone (especially the auditor) must understand the nature, scope and purpose of the audit if its benefits are to be fully realized in the organization.

(b) Systematic; audits must be carefully planned, skilfully executed and competently (and promptly) reported. Structure is an essential feature of any well-planned and systematic audit.

(c) Objective; the purpose and justification for any audit must be clearly stated from the outset. The audit must also be carried out against known standards or reference points. As far as possible it should be quantitative, and must be carried out by skilled and well-trained auditors.

Table 5 — Benefits of auditing

Assists management to comply with GMP, and provides it with evidence that obligations to its customers and the community are being fulfilled

Builds confidence in the quality system, and ensures that it continues to be complete, effective and relevant

When carried out properly, the audit builds trust, understanding and good communications between various departments, disciplines and individuals who are part of the same team

Provides an independent survey of performance, use of resource and also, by challenging established practices, it can act as a stimulus for change

Promotes education and training

Establishes good relationships between the company and its suppliers

Helps to implement corporate quality policies

3.2 The auditor

In essence the auditor is an extension of the quality system whose prime task is to limit the risk to the patient through prevention of errors. Therefore the job of the auditor is in three parts:

(a) The surveyor who observes things that are wrong or capable of going wrong, and who oversees the entire system of microbiological quality assurance.

(b) The colleague who collaborates with those involved in all the microbiological aspects of manufacture and control of medicines.

(c) The counsellor who as a valuable team member can advise, and contribute towards problem solving and maintenance of microbiological standards. Providing continued technical support enhances the role and credibility of the auditor.

The auditor should never be viewed as a policeman trying to catch people out and subsequently applying punitive measures to those responsible!

A major challenge facing the auditor is to gain widespread acceptance from people within the company that not only is the audit job necessary, but also that it fulfils a valuable function in maintaining standards, questioning established practices, and proposing changes where necessary, thereby enabling the company and its people to use their resources in the most effective and economic manner. The auditor has a golden opportunity to provide feedback and communication which can cross managerial and reporting boundaries. He or she can, therefore, become a focus for new ideas and attitudes which might otherwise become lost or diluted by the system or the organization.

A primary objective is to establish mutual confidence between the auditor and auditee. If both parties respect each other's position, and are willing to learn from each other, the audits can be very instructive and rewarding exercises.

3.3 Training the auditor

Auditors must be properly trained to undertake the tasks which are assigned to them. Unfortunately, in many organizations, auditing is regarded as a part-time activity which can be undertaken by anyone who happens to be available! Such an approach will at best be regarded by the auditee with scepticism, and can be a costly waste of time and resource for everyone involved. Careful assessment of the attributes of the microbiological auditor will help to avoid such pitfalls and assist in planning an effective auditor training programme. These attributes are:

(a) *Appropriate qualifications.* Ideally the auditor should be either a qualified microbiologist or, alternatively, well trained in pharmaceutical microbiology and conversant with the relevant standards and tests which must be applied. In either case interpretation of standards in a practical sense is an essential prerequisite.

(b) *Wide experience.* The microbiological auditor should have wide knowledge and experience of all microbiological quality and GMP aspects of manufacture, packaging and control of both sterile and non-sterile medicines. Background knowledge of engineering aspects such as water systems, sterilizers, air supplies, equipment, building standards and materials of construction is also important. Direct experience of hygiene practices, cleaning procedures and disinfection routines is vital if the role of the microbiological auditor is to be fully exploited within the company.

(c) *Well informed.* The auditor should have a clear understanding of the company's organization, the general business objectives and the products produced. Making contacts with people at all levels in the company will become part of an auditor's routine task and it is essential that he or she is fully conversant with company policies and procedures.

(d) *Trained in auditing.* As mentioned earlier, being systematic and objective is vital to the auditor. The auditor therefore needs to possess planning skills, understand the various types and techniques of auditing which may be applied and generally know how to conduct the audit from start to finish. He or she must acquire the ability to report audit findings in a structured, fair and unbiased manner. One of the main tasks will be to ensure follow-up action on critical issues.

(e) *Personal skills.* It is essential that the auditor establishes a good rapport with all people with whom he or she comes into contact. Above all, auditing is concerned with human relationships and attitudes. A constructive, fair and balanced approach will always yield results and establish the auditor's credibility in human terms. Conversely an officious and aggressive audit full of destructive criticisms may satisfy the auditor's personal ego but may demoralize company personnel and achieve nothing for the organization in its attempts to maintain or improve product quality.

A good auditor with the right interpersonal skills will quickly remove any doubts or fears that individuals may have about being subjected to independent scrutiny. He or she will also know to give praise when it is warranted, thus giving a balanced judgement. Regular audits can also help to build confidence in the organization's ability to deal easily with external (regulatory) audits when they occur. The main features of a training programme for auditors are given in Table 6.

Table 6 — Principal elements of a training programme for auditors

---

Analysis of the trainees' gaps in knowledge and experience and planning of the background technical training accordingly

Carrying out additional induction training where required (e.g. company products, organization, policy, procedures and the 'quality system')

Gaining practical experience in auditing (ideally with an experienced auditor)

Continuous training of a general or specialist nature (particularly applicable to the microbiological auditor) in order to keep up to date with standards

General management training — especially with regard to interpersonal skills

---

3.4 Importance of microbiological auditing

The manufacture and control of both sterile and non-sterile medicines requires very careful microbiological consideration throughout every stage of manufacture. Microbiological auditing demands close involvement with the production, engineering and quality assurance departments and all people who work in them. Hence microbiological auditing must never be seen simply as an examination of a testing service which may be removed from the day-to-day operational activities. Nevertheless the microbiology laboratory itself will be an integral part of any audit, and this aspect is covered in Chapter 6A. Microbiological auditing involves assessment of various criteria as shown in Table 7.

Table 7 — Criteria to be assessed in microbiological audits

Specifications for materials and products

Effectiveness of sampling programmes

Suitability of chosen test methods and testing environment

Reaction to trends in results (e.g. communicating out-of-limit results and monitoring response and feedback from production)

Monitoring the starting materials and components

Monitoring and control of the water supply, treatment, storage and distribution systems throughout the factory

Monitoring of the environment (people, air, fluids)

Hygiene and housekeeping practices

Effectiveness of cleaning and disinfection routines

Control of bioburdens

The use (and misuse) of biological indicators

Sterilization processes (validation, control, maintenance)

General in-process control limits, their application and interpretation of results

Staff training in basic microbiology

Hence the auditor is totally involved, through a logical progression, in the sampling, testing, checking and monitoring of all phases of the manufacturing and packing processes. Furthermore, a well-trained and experienced microbiological auditor has a fundamental part to play in:

(a) staff training and education;
(b) advising (during process design, facility design, control procedures, documentation, sampling and testing);
(c) problem solving (especially interpretation of unusual results);
(d) risk assessment (with a specially clear view of maintaining realistic and achieveable levels of sterility assurance);
(e) ensuring that the philosophy of 'prevention rather than cure' pervades the entire operation. This is particularly important in the manufacture of sterile products where end-product testing is of very limited value and hence validation and in-process controls assume a singular importance. Nevertheless, once the final product has been made, samples will be required for certain tests, as required by the authorities. The auditor needs to be fully conversant with official requirements in order to satisfy licensing or compendial requirements. These may include, for example, the test for sterility, tests for pyrogens, and package integrity tests.

Official compendial tests for sterility, pyrogens and particulates have all evoked widespread controversy regarding their reliability, sensitivity and applicability. In particular the test of sterility is no longer regarded as a good indicator of quality, and yet many of the regulatory bodies still insist that it is performed routinely as an end-product test. The auditor must understand the background and limitations of the test for sterility and other tests.

Whilst impressive technological advances have been made in the production of parenteral and other pharmaceutical products, resulting in higher levels of assurance and lower levels of potential contamination in the product, the testing for the quality of these products still involves relatively unsophisticated procedures.

The challenge facing the microbiologist is a hard one — essentially proving a negative! Furthermore microbiological testing is fraught with problems. The testing is time-consuming, inaccurate, prone to operator error, very demanding of human skills and expertise, and even when the results become available they often require expert interpretation. The microbiological auditor must bear this in mind when considering sampling plans where some of the currently suggested limits are of an extremely low order, and yet conversely the sample size must be increased considerably if it is to be statistically significant. A good example of this is the EC quoted limit (Anon. 1989a) of less than one organism per cubic metre of air in a grade A sterile products manufacturing facility, and yet, commonly, sample sizes rarely exceed 160 litres!

The same situation can also be found in sampling distilled water systems where sample volumes fail to reflect the extremely stringent limits which have been imposed. The Parenteral Society has responded to members' request for more specific guidance on environmental control practice with a technical monograph (Parenteral Society 1989) which attempts to provide a comprehensive list of target levels for limiting contamination. The microbiological auditor may find the additional guidance of value, but care will still need to be exercised when comparing actual results with the suggested standards.

In the final analysis there can be no substitute for a well-planned microbiological audit which embraces all the considerations mentioned above. However, whilst it is vital that the auditor understands the role that microbiology plays in the overall assurance of quality, he or she must always remember that auditing the microbiological aspects is only one part of a company's complete audit strategy. The results of any microbiological audit will have to be carefully integrated into the complete assessment of a quality system.

4   OVERVIEW

Risk assessment and auditing go hand in hand in assisting companies towards a realistic and practical application of quality systems in the manufacture of pharmaceutical products. This chapter has concerned itself with some of the microbiological aspects of quality in the manufacture and control of medicines, and the reader will forgive a timely reminder that many other factors enter into the full assessment of quality systems within the pharmaceutical industry. The industry bears a heavy responsibility for producing medicines of the right quality, but becoming increasingly apparent are the economic realities where the world relies upon the industry for a plentiful supply of medicines at an affordable price. There are undoubtedly some instances where unnecessarily high standards, possibly borne out of creative pessimism, play their part in forcing up production costs instead of adding value. Finding the right balance in terms of standards is not an easy task, but it is one which the microbiological auditor must constantly bear in mind. Objective risk assessment and auditing both have an important part to play in striking this balance.

5   REFERENCES

Anon. (1976) Proposed rules. Current good manufacturing practice in the manufacture, processing, packing, or holding of large volume parenterals. *Federal Register* **41** No. 106.

Anon. (1977) *Guide to good pharmaceutical manufacturing practice*, 2nd edn. HMSO, London.

Anon. (1981) Inappropriate environmental standards for sterile manufacture: can we afford them? *J. Soc. Comm. Med.* **95** 304–306.

Anon. (1983) *Guide to good pharmaceutical manufacturing practice*, 3rd edn. HMSO, London.

Anon. (1987) Guideline on sterile drug products produced by aseptic processing. US Food and Drug Administration.

Anon (1989a) *The rules governing medicinal products in the European Community,*

Vol. IV. Guide to good manufacturing practice for medicinal products. HMSO, London.

Anon. (1989b) *Quantified risk assessment: its input to decision making.* HMSO, London.

Barrett, C. W. (1984) The effects of microbiological monitoring on the presentation of pharmaceuticals for use in hospitals. *Correspondence Journal*, September, pp. 9–15. College of Pharmacy Practice, London.

British Pharmacopoeia (1988) HMSO, London.

British Standard 5295 (1976) *Environmental cleanliness in enclosed spaces.* British Standards Institution, London.

British Standard 5295 (1989) *Environmental cleanliness in enclosed spaces.* British Standards Institution, London.

Clegg, A. (1988) Control of microbial contamination during manufacture. In: Bloomfield, S. F., Baird, R., Leek, R. E. and Leach, R. (eds), *Microbial quality assurance in pharmaceuticals, cosmetics and toiletries.* Ellis Horwood, Chichester, pp. 49–60.

Clothier (1972) *Report of the Committee appointed to enquire into the circumstances, including the production, which led to the use of contaminated infusion fluids in the Devonport Section of Plymouth General Hospital.* HMSO, London.

Kallings, L. O., Ringertz, O., Silverstolpe, L. and Ernerfeldt, F. (1966) Microbiological contamination of medicinal preparations. *Acta Pharm. Suec.* **3** 219–228.

NASA standard for clean room and work stations for microbially controlled environment (1967). Publication NHB 5340.2.

Parenteral Drug Association (1980) *Validation of aseptic filling for solution drug products,* Technical Monograph No. 2. Parenteral Drug Association, Philadelphia.

Parenteral Society (1989) *Environmental contamination control practice,* Technical Monograph No. 2. Parenteral Society, Swindon.

Phillips, I., Eykyn, S. and Laker, M. (1972) Outbreak of hospital infections caused by contaminated autoclaved fluids. *Lancet* **i** 1258–1260.

Report (1976) Report of the Comptroller General of the United States: Recalls of Large-Volume Parenterals (MSD-76-67) March 12.

Russell, M. P. (1985) *Bacteriology of the manufacture of sterile products.* PhD thesis, London.

Sharp, J. R. (1988) Validation of a new form–fill–seal installation. *Manufact. Chem.* February 22, 23, 27, 55.

United States Federal Standard 209 D (1988) Cleanroom and workstation requirements, controlled environment. Washington, DC.

Whyte, W. (1983) A multicentered investigation of clean air requirements for terminally sterilised pharmaceuticals. *J. Parenter. Sci. Technol.* **37** 138–144.

Whyte, W. (1986) Sterility assurance and models for assessing airborne bacterial contamination. *J. Parenter. Sci. Technol.* **40** 188–197.

Whyte, W., Bailey, P. V., Tinkler, J., McCubbin, I., Young, L. and Jess, J. (1982) An evaluation of the routes of bacterial contamination occurring during aseptic pharmaceutical manufacturing. *J. Parenter. Sci. Technol.* **36** 102–107.

Whyte, W., Niven, L. and Bell, N. D. S. (1989) Microbial growth in small-volume pharmaceuticals. *J. Parenter. Sci. Technol.* **43** 208–212.

Index